POLYNUCLEOTIDES

SOLE DISTRIBUTORS FOR THE UNITED STATES OF NORTH AMERICA:

D. VAN NOSTRAND COMPANY, INC.

120 Alexander Street, Princeton, N. J. (Principal office)

24 West 40th Street, New York 18, N.Y.

SOLE DISTRIBUTORS FOR CANADA:

D. VAN NOSTRAND COMPANY (CANADA), LTD.

25 Hollinger Road, Toronto 16

SOLE DISTRIBUTORS FOR THE BRITISH COMMONWEALTH EXCLUDING CANADA:

D. VAN NOSTRAND COMPANY, LTD.

358 Kensington High Street, London, W. 14

POLYNUCLEOTIDES

NATURAL AND SYNTHETIC NUCLEIC ACIDS

by

ROBERT F. STEINER

Naval Medical Research Institute,
National Naval Medical Center,
Bethesda, Md. (U.S.A.)

and

ROLAND F. BEERS Jr.

Director of Research, Bowles Memorial Laboratory,
Children's Hospital School, Baltimore, Md.(U.S.A.)

ELSEVIER PUBLISHING COMPANY

AMSTERDAM · LONDON · NEW YORK · PRINCETON

1961

Library of Congress Catalog Card Number 60-12359

With 121 illustrations and 38 tables

PRINTED IN THE NETHERLANDS BY
A. SIJTHOFF N.V., THE HAGUE

Preface

The present book is a systematic account of the properties of natural and synthetic polynucleotides, including most aspects of their structure, synthesis, physical properties, and biological function. It is intended for the active worker in this field, or, a related one. A particular emphasis has been placed upon developments since 1955.

The opening chapters deal with the properties and chemical synthesis of the nucleotide subunits and the manner in which they are linked to form the primary sugar-phosphate backbones of the natural and synthetic polynucleotides. An account of the recent developments as to the purely chemical synthesis of the phosphodiester linkage is included.

This section is followed by chapters dealing with the preparation and properties of the various nucleotide-polymerizing enzymes which have been isolated by Ochoa, Kornberg, and others. Among the topics discussed are the kinetics of polymerization and the technique of enzyme assay.

Next comes a group of chapters devoted to the macromolecular configuration of the known polynucleotides and the manner in which this is reflected by their solution properties. Among the topics discussed are the various helical forms which polynucleotides can assume, the interaction of polynucleotides in solution and a descriptive treatment of several order–disorder transitions which have been observed. This section concludes with a detailed discussion of the helical fine structure of several polynucleotide systems, as revealed by X-ray diffraction.

This is followed by a theoretical chapter dealing with the helix-coil transition for polynucleotide systems. The various statistical-mechanical treatments which have been proposed are discussed.

The next chapter discusses the binding properties of polynucleotides. The interpretation of adsorption isotherms is stressed. The topics dealt with include the binding of divalent cations and the phenomenon of metachromasy.

The book concludes with a discussion of the biological role of nucleic acids. The currently prevalent theories as to the genetic function of DNA and the role of RNA in protein synthesis are cited and discussed, as are the attempts at developing a coding scheme.

The appendix is concerned with the practical aspects of experimental procedures in this field. Methods for the isolation of natural DNA and RNA and the various nucleotide-polymerizing enzymes are cited. The various enzyme assay procedures are also given in detail.

Bethesda/Baltimore, Md.   ROBERT F. STEINER.

October 1960   ROLAND F. BEERS JR.

Contents

Chapter 1

Introduction

The rapid growth of the field of nucleic acids into its present position of central importance in the biological sciences has been largely a post-World War II phenomenon. Indeed, until 1947 the subject of nucleic acids was considered for review only every two or three years in the *Annual Review of Biochemistry*. In the 1947 volume of the annual index of *Chemical Abstracts* only 67 entries were listed under the general classification of nucleic acids. The entries listed under proteins numbered over 700, or ten times as many. However, ten years later, in 1957, the annual index listed 875 entries under nucleic acids, an eleven-fold increase from 1947. The protein entries now numbered 2,150 or only $2\frac{1}{2}$ times as many as the nucleic acid entries.

From 1947 until 1957 the growth of entries in the field of proteins increased logarithmically with a doubling of the number every 5.3 years. From 1947 until 1954 a similar logarithmic growth in the nucleic acid entries occurred with a doubling of the number every 2.7 years. For some inexplicable reason there was a stationary period between 1954 and 1956, followed by a resumption of the logarithmic growth of nucleic acid entries. If we extrapolate the two curves for proteins and nucleic acids it appears that in 1963 the number of nucleic acid entries will be equal to, or will exceed, those of proteins. A major reason for the large number of protein entries is the impact this field has had on clinical and experimental medicine. A similar impact can be expected ultimately from the field of nucleic acids.

By early 1950 it had become apparent that the subject of nucleic acids was of importance both because of its own intrinsic interest and because of the influence this science has had on such disciplines as biochemistry, physiology, genetics, microbiology, virology, etc. For the investigator working in any of these fields today it is imperative that he have a fairly good understanding of the fundamentals of nucleic acid structure and chemistry. By 1950 the early treatises on nucleic acids by Jones[1], Feulgen[2], and Levene and Bass[3] had become obsolete, and the need for a comprehensive text in the field of nucleic acids became a pressing one. Under the editorship of Chargaff and Davidson the two-volume classic, *The Nucleic Acids*[4], was published in 1954. This text has accomplished the difficult task of compiling and correlating selectively the bulk of the information known about nucleic acids up to the year 1954. Since the publication of this text, however, the field of nucleic acids has expanded to such an extent that any future comprehensive text would have to be encyclopedic in character.

From the foregoing we see that the field of nucleic acids has reached a stage of development in which, because of its size, major subdivisions are appearing. This segmentation of a major science results in part from the unwieldiness of its own size and, more importantly, from the interactions of this science with active marginal fields. Thus, to name a few, chemical genetics, biochemistry of viruses, polynucleotide synthesis, protein synthesis, and the physical chemistry of poly-nucleotides have developed into major disciplines having their origins in nucleic acids. The extensive developments in the fields of polynucleotide synthesis and the physical chemistry of polynucleotides during the past five years have, in the opinion of the authors, reached the stage in which the publication of a monograph dealing with this area of polynucleotides would fulfil a very useful function today.

It is probably no exaggeration to state that today the heart of biochemistry lies in the field of nucleic acids and nucleic acid derivatives. In view of the importance of nucleic acids in the living cell it is somewhat surprising that the science of nucleic acids did not display any accelerated rate of development until after World War II. Certainly, on the basis of the age of this field, progress should have been much faster during the early part of this century. Nucleic acids were recognized as cellular components almost 100 years ago by Miescher[5]. However, the reasons for the slow growth during the last century and the rapid growth since the last war reside primarily in the historical development of techniques applicable to this particular field.

The historical evolution of the field of nucleic acids can be divided into three major eras. The first, which began in the middle of the last century with the dis-covery by Miescher of nucleic acid containing material, called nuclein, in cells[5], reached a state of advanced development in recent times with the discovery of techniques suitable for the isolation of nucleic acids from biological sources with-out extensive destruction or degradation of the molecules. Originally, nucleic acids were extracted from cell nuclei with the use of alkali. They were early recognized to be acidic in character and to contain a large quantity of phosphorus[6], later identified as phosphoric acid. During the latter part of the 19th century purine and pyrimidine bases were also recognized as constituents of nucleic acids[7-10].

During the first quarter of the present century two types of nucleic acid were distinguished. One was obtained first from yeast. Acid hydrolysis under drastic conditions yielded the nitrogenous bases adenine, guanine, cytosine and uracil; phosphoric acid; and a pentose identified as ribose[11]. The other nucleic acid was isolated from animal thymus and yielded after exhaustive acid hydrolysis the bases adenine, guanine, cytosine and thymine; phosphoric acid; and a pentose identified as deoxyribose[12]. The two nucleic acids were called ribonucleic acid* and deoxyri-bonucleic acid, respectively. The former is found primarily in the cytoplasm of the cell[13], the latter in the nucleus[14]. Table 1 lists the components of the two types

---

* The term, pentose nucleic acid, is used in the text edited by Chargaff and Davidson[4]. However, since the term, polyribonucleotide, has become the accepted name for polynucleotides containing ribose we prefer to use the form given above for nucleic acids of this type.

TABLE 1

CONSTITUENTS OF THE NUCLEIC ACIDS

Type	Major base constituents	Minor base constituents	Sugar
Ribonucleic	adenine		ribose
	uracil		
	cytosine		
	guanine		
Deoxyribonucleic	adenine	5-methylcytosine	deoxyribose
	thymine	5-hydroxymethyl-	
	cytosine	cytosine	
	guanine	6-N-methyladenine	

of nucleic acids. In addition to the original five bases, several derivatives have been found in lesser proportions.

Much of the early information about nucleic acids led to faulty conclusions regarding their structure and size because of the drastic methods used for their extraction and purification and the inadequate procedures employed for determining their molecular weights[15]. The procedures originally developed usually included alkaline extraction from the tissues. This process extensively depolymerized the ribonucleic acids and "denatured" the deoxyribonucleic acids. Diffusion studies by Myrback and Jorpes indicated an apparent molecular weight of about $1.3 \cdot 10^3$ for a preparation of ribonucleic acid, which was consistent with a tetranucleotide structure[15]. It was primarily on the basis of these studies that the tetranucleotide hypothesis for the structure of ribonucleic acid became firmly entrenched. Indeed, the tetranucleotide hypothesis for nucleic acid structure was still to be found in texts published in the early 1940's[16,17]. The fact that it went unchallenged for so long can probably be attributed to the inactive nature of the field at that time.

It soon became apparent to some investigators who determined the molecular weights and compositions of a variety of ribonucleic acid preparations[18-20] that the tetranucleotide hypothesis might not be valid. During the latter part of the 1940's and early part of the 1950's much of the major work in this field was devoted to the development of isolation techniques for nucleic acids without degradation during the process. The reader is referred to the two chapters in *Nucleic Acids*[4] which describe in considerable detail the various techniques developed for the isolation of ribonucleic acids (B. Magasanik, p. 373, Vol. 1) and of deoxyribonucleic acids (E. Chargaff, p. 307, Vol. 1). The alkaline extraction procedure has now been completely abandoned in favor of milder procedures utilizing extraction with salt solutions[21–24], anionic detergents[25], phenol[26,27], and other agents[28,29]. It is now well established that both ribonucleic acid and deoxyribonucleic acid are generally highly polymerized molecules in the native state, with molecular weights ranging up to $2 \cdot 10^6$ for tobacco mosaic virus ribonucleic acid[19] and $8 \cdot 10^6$ for thymus deoxyribonucleic acid[30].

Nucleic acids are believed to exist in the cell primarily as complexes with basic proteins forming enormous macromolecules, nucleoproteins, which may represent the biological form of nucleic acid. The separation of the protein component from the nucleoprotein macromolecule was originally accomplished by preferential denaturation and precipitation of the protein by the action of heat or a protein denaturant such as chloroform[21]. However, the technique of separating proteins from nucleic acids has in many cases reached the point where it is possible to remove the protein without its destruction. Thus, tobacco mosaic virus can be fractionated by selective salt precipitation procedures into protein and nucleic acid components which, when mixed under appropriate conditions, can reconstitute the viable virus particle[31,32].

The second major development in the field of nucleic acids might be called the analytical phase, that is, the period devoted to the determination of the chemical structure of the polynucleotides and the physico-chemical properties of these large molecules. Indispensable to any success in this field has been the development of paper chromatographic and electrophoretic methods and ion exchange chromatography. By the application of these procedures it has been possible to isolate and identify the products of nucleic acid degradation. Only by means of these techniques was it possible, for example, to detect isomeric forms of the various nucleotides obtained from nucleic acids* by alkaline or enzymatic hydrolysis.

For example, alkaline degradation of yeast nucleic acid yields two isomeric forms of adenylic acid, which were found to be different from adenylic acid isolated from the acid soluble fraction of the yeast cell[33,34]. Similar isomers have been found for the other nucleotides.

Once the existence and structure of the various isomeric forms of the nucleotides had been recognized, the problem of determining how they were produced by the degradation of nucleic acids and of identifying the particular type of inter-nucleotide linkage present in nucleic acids became more readily susceptible to experimental attack.

The general primary structure of the nucleic acids had been proposed by Levene and Simms[35] to contain a diesterified sugar-phosphate backbone with the purine and pyrimidine bases attached to the sugars. Thus, schematically:

---

* For a review of the analytical methods the reader is referred to the chapters on ion-exchange chromatography (W. E. Cohn, p. 211), paper chromatography (G. R. Wyatt, p. 243) and electrophoresis (J. D. Smith, p. 267) to be found in Vol. 1 of *The Nucleic Acids*[4].

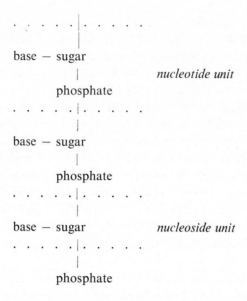

The nucleoside residues were visualized as linked together through phosphodiester bonds. The major problem remaining was to determine which carbons of adjacent sugars were linked by phosphodiester bridges and the position of the third glycosidic linkage to the base.

Ultimately, it was established that the base is attached to the $C_{1'}$ atom of the sugar and that the phosphodiester linkage is between the $C_{3'}$ and $C_{5'}$ atoms of linked sugars. Details leading to this conclusion are given in Chapter 3 of this text. The primary structures of polydeoxyribonucleotides and polyribonucleotides are identical except for the absence of the hydroxyl group on $C_{2'}$ of deoxyribose.

In order to determine unequivocally the type of diester linkage in polynucleotides it was necessary to take advantage of a variety of techniques, of which the most important were chemical and enzymatic synthesis and degradation processes. Consequently, the organic chemist and the enzymologist have contributed immeasurably to the present understanding of the chemical structure of natural and synthetic polynucleotides.

The final stages of the classical investigations which resulted in the clarification of the primary structure of natural nucleic acids were paralled by equally dramatic progress toward an understanding of their spatial conformation. This latter development, which is still in progress, achieved its first major success with the proposal by Watson and Crick[36], of a helical duplex structure for deoxyribonucleic acid. Subsequent work has consistently confirmed and reinforced their postulated model, which has required only minor modification and refinement.

The kind of secondary structure found for native deoxyribonucleic acid reoccurs for a whole class of polynucleotides of high helical content. Indeed, the helical duplex, stabilized by inter-base hydrogen bonding, occupies the same central position in the polynucleotide field as does the α-helix in the polypeptide field.

There is, however, a basic difference between the two cases. The α-helix is stabilized by hydrogen bonding of the "vertical" type, for which the hydrogen bonds link groups of the peptide backbone itself and are parallel to the fiber axis. The hydrogen bonding of the polynucleotide helical duplex does not usually involve the sugar-phosphate backbone. Furthermore, the bonding is of the "horizontal" type, with the hydrogen bonds roughly perpendicular to the fiber axis.

Native deoxyribonucleic acid approaches the extreme case of a completely helical conformation. The biosynthetic polynucleotides, which will be dealt with in detail in subsequent chapters, have been found to include all gradations of secondary structure, from the completely amorphous to the highly helical. For example, polyribouridylic acid has been found to show all the properties typical of unorganized polyelectrolytes. In contrast, the equimolar complexes formed by polyriboadenylic acid with polyribouridylic acid and with polyriboinosinic acid appear to have doubly stranded helical structures quite similar to that of native deoxyribonucleic acid.

Helical forms other than the duplex have also been found to occur for the biosynthetic polymers. Thus the doubly stranded polyriboadenylic-polyribouridylic complex can, under appropriate conditions, add a second strand of polyribouridylic acid to form a triply stranded helix.

Many polynucleotides are currently believed to have structures intermediate to the helical and amorphous extremes. Into this category fall the alkaline form of polyriboadenylic acid and the co-polymers of adenylic and uridylic acids.

A third, very important, example of an incompletely organized polynucleotide is furnished by natural ribonucleic acid. While progress in this area has been relatively slow, it has recently come to be recognized that the physical properties of ribonucleic acid are consistent with, and suggest, a configuration which is intermittently helical in character and probably consists of fairly short helical regions separated by unorganized, random sequences. In many respects, this kind of structure has a definite similarity to that of the globular proteins.

Several instances have emerged of polynucleotides which can exist in either a highly ordered or a largely amorphous form. The transition between the two can result from variations in pH, ionic strength, or temperature, and often assumes a dramatically sharp character, having some resemblance to a phase transition. The statistical mechanical theory of such one-dimensional transitions has recently undergone a very rapid development and will be the subject of a subsequent chapter.

The achievements in this area have been made possible only by calling upon all of the conventional physico-chemical techniques for establishing the gross size and shape of macromolecules in solution. These include light scattering, ultra-centrifugation, viscometry, and streaming birefringence. To probe the detailed fine structure of the polynucleotides, the use of such techniques as X-ray diffraction, infra-red spectroscopy, and optical rotation has been crucial.

In general, it can probably be stated without undue optimism that the establishment of the nature of the secondary structures of most polynucleotide systems is approaching completion. In the opinion of the authors, further progress in this area will take the form of a refinement of current concepts, without any major revisions being required in most cases.

Indeed, our knowledge of the structure of the natural nucleic acids can be said to have obtained a plateau. The next phase of this problem is, of course, the determination of the linear sequence of nucleotides. Barely a start has been made so far in this direction. The problem appears formidable indeed at present and will in all probability require more powerful techniques than are now available.

A third major development in the field of nucleic acids has been in the area of enzymatic and chemical syntheses of these compounds. The classical evolution of many areas of biochemistry from a descriptive to an analytical and finally a synthetic phase finds its parallel in nucleic acids. Although considerable progress had been made in gaining an understanding of the biosynthetic mechanisms leading to the synthesis of the sugar and bases of the nucleotides and of the corresponding nucleosides and nucleotides, the information obtained by 1954 about the synthesis of polynucleotides was inadequate to suggest a universal biosynthetic mechanism, if, indeed, one does exist. Until 1954 the majority of studies directed toward the elucidation of the biological mechanism for phosphodiester synthesis was carried out with animals, micro-organisms, and viruses. In the case of ribonucleic acid synthesis the accumulated evidence suggested strongly that the immediate precursors, or "active" derivatives, of nucleotides in ribonucleic acid were phosphorylated derivatives. However, much of the information obtained was conflicting and indicated that different mechanisms may be responsible for the synthesis of ribonucleic acid in different organisms.

For example, Roll et al.[37] injected ^{14}C, ^{15}N and ^{32}P labeled adenylic and guanylic acids a and b (the isomeric 2'- and 3'-phosphomonoesters obtained from alkaline hydrolysis of yeast nucleic acid) into rats. The nucleic acid isolated from rat tissue contained no ^{32}P, but 80% of the ribose of incorporated adenylic acid was labeled with ^{14}C. These results suggested that the precursor is at least a nucleoside. Earlier, Weinfeld and Roll[38] showed that the a and b forms of adenylic acid are incorporated into ribonucleic acid to an extent about two times that of adenosine-5'-phosphate. Balis et al.[39] showed a preferential utilization of adenosine 3'-phosphate (b isomer) by L. casei.

However, a major criticism against the use of ^{32}P labeled nucleotides for the identification of a phosphorylated derivative acting as an immediate precursor of ribonucleic acid synthesis is the extreme lability of the phosphate group in vivo. Thus, the difference between adenosine-5'-phosphate and adenylic acids a and b may be related to the fact that the metabolic turnover of adenosine-5'-phosphate in a variety of competing reactions is so much greater than that of the 2'- and 3'-isomers that the dilution effect reflecting this masks the true relationship between adenosine-5'-phosphate and ribonucleic acid synthesis[40].

More direct evidence for the importance of the 5'-isomers of the nucleotides was obtained by Schmitz, Hurlbert, and Potter[41] who identified in acid soluble extracts of rat tissue the 5'-monophosphate, -diphosphate and -triphosphate of the nucleosides of adenine, guanine, cytosine and uracil. Hurlbert and Potter[42] showed that orotic acid-6-^{14}C was converted to uridine - 5'-phosphates (UMP, UDP and UTP) and was incorporated into ribonucleic acid as uridylic acid. This suggested that the uridine - 5'-phosphates constituted a metabolic pool for the immediate precursor of ribonucleic acid synthesis. Similar results were obtained with pigeon and rat liver extracts[43] using orotic acid-2-^{14}C. The nucleoside uridine was not a precursor or intermediate in nucleic acid synthesis. These authors concluded that an immediate precursor of ribonucleic acid is a 5'-uridine nucleotide[44].

The biosynthesis of the 3', 5'-phosphodiester linkages of polyribonucleotides appeared, therefore, to involve the direct addition of nucleoside-5'-phosphates to the polynucleotide by means of a group transfer reaction. Studies by Merrifield and Dunn[45] and Merrifield and Wooley[46] with *L. helviticus* showed a marked growth response of the organism to the addition of partial hydrolysates of ribonucleic acid and of dinucleotides containing the terminal cytidine - 5'-phosphate. They concluded that the dinucleotides can act as carriers of specific groups which are transferred to polynucleotides. Brawerman and Chargaff[47] suggested that a nucleoside transferase provided a biosynthetic pathway for nucleic acid synthesis in which the nucleosides are intermediates. However, few other investigators appear to have given any serious consideration to the possibility of a nucleoside transferase.

The possible importance of phosphorylating and pyrophosphorylating reactions in the synthesis of nucleic acids had become apparent by 1955. Two general types of group transfer reactions are possible:

$$X - R - PP \; + Y \rightarrow X - R - P + Y - P \qquad\qquad (1a)$$

$$X - R - PPP + Y \rightarrow X - R - P + Y - PP \qquad\qquad (1b)$$

$$X - R - PP \; + Y \rightarrow P \qquad + X - R - P - Y \qquad\qquad (2a)$$

$$X - R - PPP + Y \rightarrow PP \qquad + X - R - P - Y \qquad\qquad (2b)$$

X is a purine or pyrimidine base, R is the sugar moiety, P orthophosphate, PP pyrophosphate, and Y an acceptor which has a suitable OH group such as HOH (hydrolysis), $-$COH or $-$POH. Reactions of the type (1a) and (1b) are phosphotransferase and pyrophosphotransferase catalyzed reactions, respectively[48], and cannot lead to the synthesis of a diester linkage between two nucleotides. Reactions of the type (2a) and (2b) are nucleotide transferase-catalyzed reactions and can lead to the synthesis of a phosphodiester linkage between two nucleotides, provided Y is a suitable nucleotide or polynucleotide. A few examples of (2b) have been observed.

Kornberg[49] demonstrated the reversible synthesis of diphosphopyridine nucleotide catalyzed by an enzyme obtained from yeast or pig liver:

nicotinamide mononucleotide + ATP → diphosphopyridine nucleotide + PP

For this reaction Mg^{++} is required; the equilibrium is approximately 0.45.

Schrecker and Kornberg[50] found a similar reaction for the synthesis of flavin-adenine dinucleotide:

flavin mononucleotide + ATP → flavin-adenine dinucleotide + PP

Reactions corresponding to (2a) had not been observed. Consequently, the major line of attack on nucleic acid synthesis was directed toward the demonstration of an enzyme system capable of exchanging nucleoside triphosphates with deoxyribonucleic or ribonucleic acids[51]. Subsequent events have shown that ribonucleic acid synthesis can occur by reaction (2a) and deoxyribonucleic acid synthesis by reaction (2b).

In the meantime, Heppel and Whitfield[52] showed that pancreatic ribonuclease and spleen phosphodiesterase catalyze the transfer of nucleotide residues from diester linkages to alkyl hydroxyls. One such reaction catalyzed by ribonuclease is as follows:

cytidine-2':3'-phosphate + MeOH → cytidine-3'-methyl phosphate + H$_2$O

The cyclic cytidine phosphate compound can be replaced by cytidine-3'-benzyl phosphate, and methanol can be replaced by ethanol. The reaction will also take place with the corresponding uracil derivatives, but not with purine nucleotides or the isomer, cytidine-2'-benzyl phosphate. This reflects the specificity of this enzyme towards pyrimidines and the 3'-isomers of the nucleotide derivatives[53]. Spleen phosphodiesterase differs from ribonuclease in that it is inactive toward the cyclic compounds, a fact which is consistent with the observation that this enzyme does not hydrolyze the cyclic phosphodiester linkage.

The authors suggest that the mechanism of transfer involves the formation of an intermediate activated nucleoside - 3'-phosphoryl group in which the energy of the phosphodiester linkage is conserved. This activated complex is believed to be formed by the enzyme from either nucleoside-3'-phosphate esters or from nucleoside-2':3'-phosphates. Thus, if a suitable acceptor molecule is present, the activated complex will react to give the corresponding ester. The reaction is competitive with respect to water and in the absence of a suitable acceptor other than water the nucleotide diesterase acts as a hydrolytic enzyme. This ability of other acceptors to compete with water finds its parallel in a variety of hydrolytic and oxidative reactions, e.g., phosphatase- and catalase-catalyzed reactions[54].

Heppel, Whitfield and Markham[55] found that, in addition to water, ethanol and methanol, ribonucleosides and cyclic nucleotides can also participate as acceptor molecules in the reactions catalyzed by ribonuclease. Thus, a net synthesis of a variety of polynucleotides was obtained. In order to depress the hydrolytic reaction with water, it is necessary that the concentrations of the reactants be quite high. At low concentrations cytidine-2' : 3'-phosphate is hydrolyzed by ribonucleave to cytidine-3'-phosphate. However, in the presence of the nucleoside, cytidine, the compound cytidylyl-cytidine is synthesized. At higher concentrations of cytidine-2' : 3'-phosphate, even in the absence of cytidine, the compounds cyclic dicytidylic and cyclic tricytidylic acid are formed as follows:

cytidine-2':3'-phosphate → cytidine-3'-phosphate +
cytidylyl-cytidine-2':3'phosphate +
cytidylyl-cytidylyl-cytidine-2':3'-phosphate

The addition of cytidine yields tricytidine diphosphate (cytidylyl-cytidylyl-cytidine). Longer chain polymers are also synthesized, but the degree of polymerization probably does not extend beyond 5 or 6.

The purine derivatives, adenosine and adenosine - 2' : 3'-phosphate also react with cytidine-2' : 3'-phosphate to give cytidylyl-adenosine and cytidylyl-adenylic acid, respectively.

The spleen phosphodiesterase, because of its inactivity toward the cyclic nucleotides, does not catalyze the polymerization of nucleotides from cyclic nucleotides. However, it does catalyze a transfer reaction of the type:

adenylyl-uridylic acid + cytidine → adenylyl-cytidine + uridylic acid

Markham and Strominger[56] have described similar reactions catalyzed by pea leaf ribonuclease. Hakim[57] has separated pancreatic ribonuclease into two major fractions and has found some specificity associated with each fraction. In each instance the phosphodiester linkage synthesized is the 3',5'-type.

The possible significance and biological importance of this type of polynucleotide synthesis is obscured by the fact that the cyclic nucleotides have not been observed in tissue extracts. In view of the fact, however, that the cycle nucleotides are products of ribonuclease action on ribonucleic acid, failure to demonstrate these compounds does not necessarily preclude their existence in and importance in ribonucleic acid synthesis or, at least, in nucleotide transferase reactions. It is apparent that the effects of tissue ribonuclease on ribonucleic acid during extraction procedures may involve both degradation and nucleotide transfer artifacts.

The similarities between the reactions catalyzed by ribonuclease and those developed chemically by Michelson[58], which involve the use of nucleoside-2':3'-phosphate derivatives, are discussed in Chapter 2.

A possible basic difference between the polymerization reactions catalyzed by ribonuclease and reactions of type (2a) is the probable location of the source of chemical energy driving the reaction. In the former case it is located in the cyclic nucleotide at the end of the polymer; in the latter it is located in the nucleoside pyrophosphate attacking the polymer. This may, in part, account for the failure of the polymerization by ribonuclease to extend beyond the oligonucleotide stage. A second explanation may be the decrease in reactivity of the longer polymers.

The second major development in the study of possible mechanisms of phosphodiester synthesis occurred in the laboratory of Dr. Severo Ochoa. During the
course of investigations of the mechanism of formation of adenosine triphosphate
in extracts of *Azotobacter agile (vinelandii)* Grunberg-Manago and Ochoa[59]
observed a rapid exchange of inorganic ^{32}P-labeled orthophosphate with the
terminal phosphate of nucleoside diphosphates, ADP, IDP, UDP, CDP and, to
a lesser extent, GDP. The reaction was specific for the nucleoside diphosphates
containing the 5'-pyrophosphate group and did not involve a reversible phosphorylation of nucleoside-5'-monophosphates. Subsequently, it was noted that there
was a net increase in orthophosphate and a decrease in nucleoside diphosphate[60].
The missing nucleotide was, in fact, incorporated into a water-soluble, non-
dialyzable, acid- and alcohol-insoluble material, which formed a highly viscous
solution in water and failed to migrate from the origin on paper chromatograms
with the solvent system of Krebs and Hems[61].

Hydrolysis of the material with alkali yielded a mixture of the 2'- and 3'-isomers
of the corresponding nucleotides. Treatment of the material with snake venom
phosphodiesterase, which splits the phosphodiester linkage of ribonucleic acid
between the 3'-carbon of ribose and the phosphate group, yielded the 5'-isomer
of the corresponding nucleotides. Careful enzymatic and chemical degradations
by Heppel's group[62] showed that the material had the same 3',5'-phosphodiester
linkage as ribonucleic acid. Thus, it was established that the *Azotobacter* extract
had brought about the synthesis of a polyribonucleotide structurally identical with
ribonucleic acid.

The reaction is reversible and requires Mg^{++}. The mechanism of orthophosphate
exchange with nucleoside diphosphates can be explained by the following simplified
scheme:

$$n \, X-R-PP \longleftrightarrow (X-R-P)_n + nP_i$$

where $X-R-PP$ is the nucleoside diphosphate; $(X-R-P)_n$, the polyribonucleotide with n nucleotide monomers; and P_i, the inorganic orthophospate. Because
of the obvious similarities of this reaction with that catalyzed by the muscle or the
potato phosphorylase discovered by Cori and Cori[63]:

$$n \, glucose\text{-}l\text{-}phosphate \longrightarrow (glucose)_n + nP_i$$

where $(glucose)_n$ is glycogen, Ochoa elected to name this enzyme polynucleotide
phosphorylase. The requirement for a primer suggested by the findings of Ochoa
with more extensively purified preparations of the enzyme emphasizes the similarities between the two enzyme systems.

A major difference between the two enzyme catalyzed reactions, as pointed
out by Cohn to Kornberg[51], is the fact that the phosphorolysis of glycogen results
in the formation of a $C-O-P-$ bond, whereas in the phosphorolysis of a polynucleotide a $P-O-P-$ bond is formed. A second difference is the cleavage of a
$C-O-C-$ bond in glycogen and a $X-O-P-$ bond in the polynucleotide.

Once the substrates for polyribonucleotide synthesis were identified, demonstrations of polynucleotide phosphorylase activity in other micro-organisms became a simple matter. Table 2 gives a list of the organisms in which polynucleotide phosphorylase activity has been observed. Extensive studies have been made with the enzyme prepared from *M. lysodeikticus* by Beers[64]. Other investigators have examined in detail the properties of polynucleotide phosphorylase from *E. coli* (Littauer[65] and Heppel *et al.*[66]). Until recently attempts to detect the enzyme in animal tissues were unsuccessful. However, Hilmoe and Heppel[67] were able to

TABLE 2

SOURCES OF POLYRIBONUCLEOTIDE PHOSPHORYLASE

A. vinelandii	*B. megatherium*	*C. kluyveri*
M. phlei	*S. hemolyticus*	*C. diphtheriae*
M. lysodeikticus	*S. faecalis*	*A. faecalis*
E. coli	*S. lactis R*	*H. facilis*
M. pyrogenes	*Pneumococcus*	sperm
B. subtilis	*B. cereus*	liver

show with liver nuclei the exchange of orthophosphate with ADP and phosphorolysis of polyadenylic acid to ADP. They were not able to demonstrate a net synthesis of polyribonucleotides, presumably because of the degradation of the polymer by nucleases in the liver preparation. Hakim has demonstrated polynucleotide phosphorylase activity in human sperm extracts and human urine, with a net synthesis of polymer[68]. It appears, therefore, that polynucleotide phosphorylase activity is a property of a large fraction of, if not of all, living species.

The discovery of this enzyme was of particular interest to the investigators of nucleic acid structure and properties. The polymers prepared by means of this enzyme could be restricted in their composition to one kind of nucleotide, *i.e.*, polyadenylic acid, polyuridylic acid, polyinosinic acid, polycytidylic acid, and polythymidylic acid. Or, two nucleotides could be incorporated into the polymer in any desired ratio, *i.e.*, polyuridylic-adenylic acid, polycytidylic–adenylic acid, *etc.* Finally, all four nucleotides could be incorporated to yield a polymer having the same base distribution as natural ribonucleic acid. Insofar as can be established, synthetic polyadenylic–cytidylic–guanylic–uridylic acid containing approximately equal ratios of the four bases has essentially the same chemical and physical properties as natural ribonucleic acid isolated from various sources. However, any biological activity reflecting the specific base sequence of the natural material, is of course, lacking.

Because of the selected distribution of bases in the synthetic polynucleotides, investigations of the physical properties of the polymers have produced a mass of information having a direct bearing on the structure of both ribonucleic acid and deoxyribonucleic acid. Thus, for example, it has been found that polyadenylic acid and polyuridylic acid will combine under appropriate conditions to form a double or triple stranded structure whose physical properties are remarkably similar to those of deoxyribonucleic acid, also a double stranded structure. Molecular weights of the synthetic polymers prepared from *M. lysodeikticus* polynucleotide phosphorylase have been as high as 2 to 4 million (weight average) for polyadenylic and polyinosinic acids. Thus, the quality of a high degree of polymerization, generally desired but often unattainable in ribonucleic acid isolated from biological sources, can be easily obtained with synthetic polymers. This has permitted a rapid advance into the understanding of the structure of ribonucleic acid.

A third mechanism for the transfer of nucleotides to polynucleotides has been discovered independently by several groups[69–71]. Mammalian and pigeon tissue extracts catalyze the incorporation of adenosine - 5′-triphosphate into a terminal cytidylic group of RNA as follows[69]:

$$ATP + cytidylic - RNA \rightarrow adenylic\text{-}cytidylic - RNA + PP$$

The reaction is, therefore, of type (2b). The phosphodiester linkage is 3′,5′-phosphate. The reaction shows a high degree of specificity and apparently does not extend beyond the addition of one monomer. In this respect it is similar to the co-enzyme synthesis reactions described by Kornberg[49]. Subsequent studies have shown that this particular reaction is associated with the activation of amino acids and the incorporation of amino acids into soluble ribonucleic acid[70]. It probably does not provide an *in vivo* method of ribonucleic acid synthesis.

A fourth enzyme system capable of catalyzing the synthesis of a phosphodiester linkage was found by Grunberg-Manago in yeast extracts[72]. Like the polynucleotide phosphorylase enzyme discovered by Grunberg-Manago and Ochoa, this preparation also used nucleoside diphosphates as substrates. In contrast, however, Mg^{++} is not required. The polymer obtained differs in several respects from that synthesized by polynucleotide phosphorylase, and from natural ribonucleic acid. The major difference is the presence of excess phosphate in the polymer, which alters the physico-chemical characteristics of the polymer.

Progress in the field of deoxyribonucleotide phosphodiester synthesis by *in vivo* systems more or less paralleled that of polyribonucleotides. Because of the low metabolic activity of deoxyribonucleic acid tracer studies have not been as fruitful. Studies on the synthesis of deoxyribonucleic acid in the phage of infected bacteria showed that 75% of the virus deoxyribonucleic acid phosphorus was derived from the media, while the remainder originated from the deoxyribonucleic acid phosphorus of the host cell[73]. Similar results have been obtained using ^{15}N-labeled whole cells and medium. In general, there appears to be a relatively greater transfer of bacterial nitrogen than of bacterial phosphorus to the virus deoxyribonucleic acid.

Hoff-Jorgensen[74] observed in the cytoplasm of the egg cells large amounts of deoxyribonucleotide derivatives. Thus, as in the case of ribonucleic acid synthesis, the evidence that phosphorylated derivatives of nucleotides are the precursors of deoxyribonucleic acid synthesis is circumstantial rather than conclusive.

It was not until Kornberg[51] and his associates began to attack the problem from the point of view that a pyrophosphorylase-catalyzed system may be responsible for the synthesis of polynucleotides that the ultimate solution to the enzymatic synthesis of polydeoxyribonucleotides was found. The enzymatic syntheses of diphosphopyridine nucleotide and flavin–adenine dinucleotide were considered analogous reactions. This consists of a displacement by a nucleophilic group of the pyrophosphate group of a nucleoside triphosphate. The polynucleotide chain would grow by virtue of an attack on the 5′-phosphoryl group of the nucleoside triphosphate by the oxygen of the alcohol group at the $C_{3'}$ position of the sugar. Two mechanisms were considered. In the first, mechanism A, the polynucleotide chain or acceptor group ends with a triphosphate. With the addition of a mononucleoside triphosphate to this end, pyrophosphate is displaced from the acceptor. In mechanism B, which was considered the more plausible, the nucleoside triphosphate adds

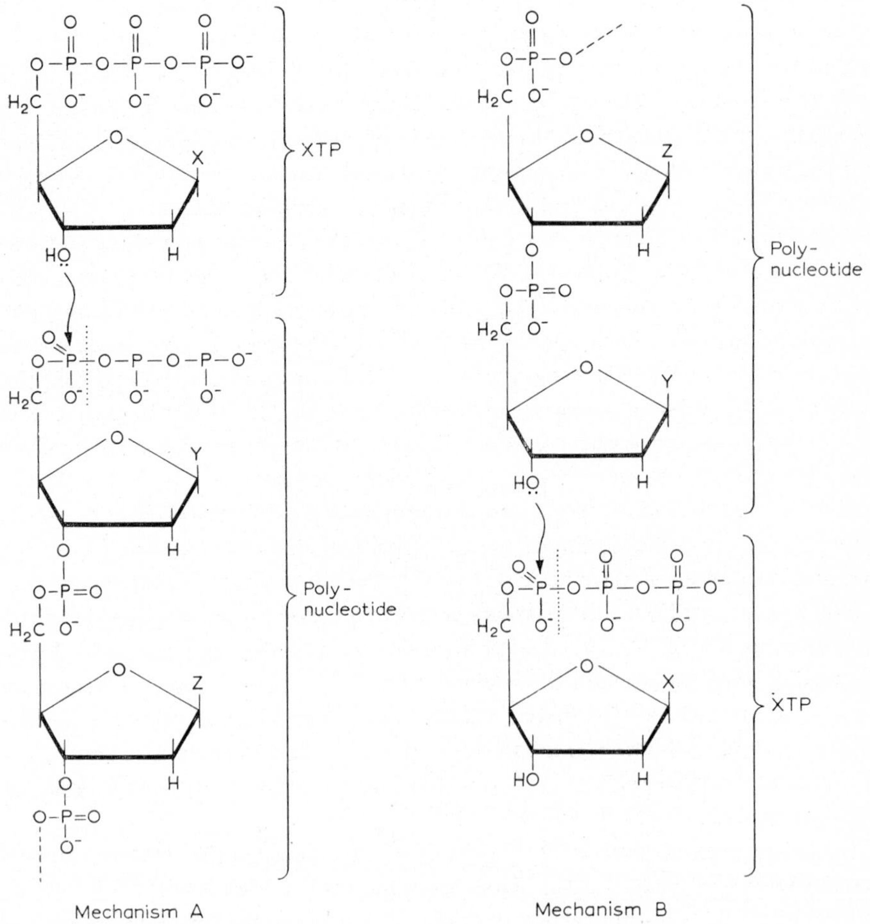

Fig. 1. Two alternative mechanisms for the enzymatic synthesis of polydeoxyribonucleotides[51].

to the sugar end of the acceptor ($C_{3'} - OH$) with the displacement of pyrophosphate from the donor. These mechanisms are illustrated in Fig. 1.

An enzyme system capable of carrying out the synthesis of polydeoxyribonucleotide was obtained from extracts of *E. coli*[75]. The reaction was detected by measuring the incorporation of isotopically labeled deoxyribonucleoside triphosphates into a deoxyribonucleic acid fraction of the bacteria. Of considerable importance was the observation that all four deoxynucleoside triphosphates (deoxythymidine, deoxycytidine, deoxyguanosine, and deoxyadenosine) are required for the extensive incorporation of any one into the deoxyribonucleic acid fraction. The reaction is specific for the deoxyribonucleotides and does not require the presence of any ribose nucleotide derivatives.

The stoichiometry of the reaction is as follows[75]:

$$n(dTPPP + dCPPP + dGPPP + dAPPP) \xrightarrow[\text{primer}]{\text{DNA}} DNA - (dTP - dCP - dGP - dAP)_n$$

$$+ 4(n)PP$$

Both Mg^{++} and a highly polymerized DNA primer are required for the net synthesis of polydeoxyribonucleotides. The reaction is catalyzed by a pyrophosphorylase, instead of a phosphorylase. Unlike all of the nucleotide transfer reactions described so far, the deoxyribonucleotide transferase-catalyzed reaction is largely irreversible, although one can barely detect the reverse reaction by suitable exchange studies[51]. Kornberg stresses the importance of the relative irreversibility of this reaction in relation to the metabolic role of deoxyribonucleic acid, which may act as a bearer of genetic information in the cell and which has considerable metabolic stability.

The chemical structure of the synthetic polydeoxyribonucleotides is identical with that of deoxyribonucleic acid and contains the 3′,5′-phosphodiester linkage. X-ray studies of the material indicate that it exists as a double helix. The molecular weight of the polymer approaches that of natural deoxyribonucleic acid. In most respects, therefore, the chemical and physical properties of the synthetic polymer are identical with those of native deoxyribonucleic acid.

Recently, Hurwitz obtained from *E. coli* an enzyme system capable of synthesizing a mixed polynucleotide containing both ribonucleotides and deoxyribonucleotides[76]. The reaction is of considerable interest because the polymer can be hydrolyzed by either ribonuclease or deoxyribonuclease, each to an extent corresponding to the amount of diester linkages specific for the hydrolyzing enzyme. A similar specificity relationship was observed with regard to the susceptibility of the polymer to alkaline hydrolysis. The enzyme is a pyrophosphorylase and uses the nucleoside triphosphates as substrates.

This rather remarkable polynucleotide hybrid may have no biological significance, but it is conceivable that it might have some bearing on the mechanism by which information from the deoxyribonucleic acid molecule is transferred to ribonucleic acid.

The chemical synthesis of the 3′,5′-phosphodiester linkage of polyribonucleotides has been attempted with little success and low yields and degrees of polymerization. Recently, Michelson[77] was able to synthesize oligonucleotides from the nucleoside-2′:3′-phosphate compounds in the presence of tetraphenylpyrophosphate and an anhydrous medium. The reaction is similar to that observed by Heppel and his associates[55] using ribonuclease as the catalyst. The product of the Michelson reaction contains roughly equal molar ratios of the 2′,5′- and 3′,5′-phosphodiester linkages. The distribution of the two kinds of linkages appears to be random throughout the polymer. Since the reaction must be carried out in the presence of an anhydrous medium, the molecular weight of these compounds is kept small by virtue of the insolubility of the larger polymers in the medium.

Smith and Khorana recently reported the specific synthesis of the 3′,5′-phosphodiester linkage in the dinucleotide, uridylyl-uridine[78]. The starting material is uridine-3′:5′-phosphate rather than uridine-2′:3′-phosphate.

The chemical synthesis of deoxyribonucleotide diester linkages has met with considerably more success than has that of ribonucleotides, chiefly because the deoxyribonucleotide does not contain a $C_{3'}$-OH group, which renders the phosphoester linkage extremely susceptible to hydrolysis. The details of the synthesis of both the ribonucleotide and deoxyribonucleotide phosphodiester linkages are considered in greater detail in Chapter 2.

This phase of the field of nucleic acids, or more properly, polynucleotides, which we have characterized as the synthetic phase, leads to a fourth as yet undeveloped but major phase, namely, the biological role of nucleic acids. Some aspects of this are considered briefly in the last Chapter of this text. At this point it is well to bear in mind some of the observations which have suggested the biological role of these compounds.

The central genetic role of deoxyribonucleic acid has been suspected ever since early histochemical studies demonstrated that it accounts for a large fraction of the chromosomal material of the cell nucleus[79], where it occurs as a nucleoprotein complex. As the chromosomes have been recognized as the carriers of genetic information since the classical investigations of Morgan[80], it is not surprising that considerable attention has been directed toward deoxyribonucleic acid as a system for the storage and transfer of information in the cell. The limited number of different kinds of nucleotides in the deoxyribonucleic acid molecule made it obvious that if it acts as a coding system it must do so by virtue of a particular specific sequence of bases or base pairs along the chain. Precisely how this specificity of base sequence is translated ultimately into the characteristic amino acid sequences of the enzymes and other protein components of the living cell remains uncertain. A number of ingenious theories have been proposed, which will be discussed in a subsequent chapter.

The widespread belief in the genetic importance of deoxyribonucleic acid was for a long time based entirely upon indirect evidence. However, in recent times, at least two instances have emerged in which its mediation has been demonstrated directly. One example is the transforming principle of pneumococcus and other micro-organisms[81]. The pneumococcus transforming principle, which has the ability of altering the serological properties of this organism, was identified almost two decades ago as deoxyribonucleic acid. Since then a number of bacterial transforming principles have been isolated and invariably found to be of a similar nature.

Another example is furnished by the bacterial viruses or bacteriophages. In the best-studied case of these, the coliphages, the infective process has been shown to involve the injection of the phage deoxyribonucleic acid into the host cell[82]. The injected nucleic acid subsequently assumes dictatorial powers over the metabolism of the host and compels the extensive synthesis of new phage deoxyribonucleic acid and ultimately of new infectious particles. The final phase of the process is the rupture of the bacterial cell wall and the release of phage into solution.

A considerable body of evidence has been accumulated which suggests that the participation of deoxyribonucleic acid in the guided synthesis of proteins is indirect. The prevalent view at present is that deoxyribonucleic acid serves to direct the synthesis of ribonucleic acid, which in turn mediates the actual formation of protein[83]. Ribonucleic acid thus acts as a secondary carrier of genetic information, according to this model.

There exist a number of instances where the role of deoxyribonucleic acid appears to be circumvented altogether. This is the case with several plant viruses, of which the best-studied example is tobacco mosaic virus, from which a protein-free ribonucleic acid has been isolated and shown to have infectious properties[84]. This example is all the more interesting in that it is believed that all of the ribonucleic acid of this virus occurs as a single molecule.

Thus the dim outlines of the intricate schemes which relate genetics and classical biochemistry are beginning to emerge. There is reason to believe that the near future may bring spectacular developments in this area.

The recent finding that the chemical energy in the phosphodiester linkage is similar in magnitude to that of the pyrophosphate linkage of the ribonucleoside diphosphates suggests that an alternate role for ribonucleic acid may be as a high energy source for the cell. It may serve in this capacity as a source of high-energy-containing co-enzymes for a variety of enzyme-catalyzed reactions[85, 86].

If this volume can be said to have a recurrent theme, this might well be the inter-relationship of the natural and synthetic polynucleotides. The development of chemical and enzymatic means for the synthesis of a variety of polynucleotides, which permits at present the control of the composition and which may ultimately permit the control of the nucleotide sequence, is rapidly making the synthetic polynucleotides a field in themselves. Indeed, an enormous amount of experimental data has been gathered within the short period of five years. The study of the biosynthetic polymers is providing us with valuable assistance in understanding the structure and properties of natural nucleic acids. In this volume we have devoted considerable attention to the synthesis and properties of polynucleotides. Whenever feasible, an attempt has been made to make a direct correlation with the available information for natural nucleic acids.

A few remarks as to nomenclature are probably desirable. We prefer in general to reserve the term *nucleic acid* for material which has been isolated from the living cell. To extend this term to the polyribonucleotides synthesized *in vitro* would tend to obscure the very real differences between the two, such as the specificity of nucleotide sequence of the natural ribonucleic acids, which is not paralleled by their synthetic analogs. The only case where the distinction may be artificial is the biosynthetic polydeoxyribonucleotides of Kornberg. Here there is real reason to believe that a specificity of base sequence does persist in the synthetic material. Accordingly we shall not hesitate to refer to this as *synthetic deoxyribonucleic acid*.

The term *polynucleotide* will be used in a generic sense for all polymers of nucleotides which are linked by phosphodiester bonds and which thus have a ribose-phosphate primary backbone, irrespective of their origin. A similar form of nomenclature exists in the field of polypeptides. All proteins are polypeptides, but not all polypeptides are proteins.

The chapters which follow are meant to take the reader in a logical sequence thru first the chemistry of the nucleotide sub-units, then the manner in which they are linked to form the primary structure of polynucleotides, next the spatial arrangement of the polymers into their characteristic secondary structures, and finally the current ideas as to the biological role of the nucleic acids. Attention has been centered upon results rather than methods, but some relevant experimental details about polymer synthesis and enzyme production are included in the appendix. It will be assumed that the reader has some knowledge of biochemistry, but that he does not possess an extensive specialized knowledge of nucleic acids.

Parts of the book unavoidably are fairly mathematical in character. In such cases an effort has been made to segregate the actual derivations so that they may be skipped by the more casual reader without interrupting the continuity.

REFERENCES

1 W. JONES, *Nucleic Acids: Their Chemical Properties and Physiological Conduct*, London, 1920.
2 R. FEULGEN, *Chemie und Physiologie der Nukleinstoffe*, Berlin, 1923.
3 P. LEVENE AND L. BASS, *Nucleic Acids*, New York, 1931.
4 E. CHARGAFF AND J. DAVIDSON, *The Nucleic Acids*, New York, 1954.
5 F. MIESCHER, *Hoppe-Seyler's Med. Chem. Unters.*, p. 441 (1871).
6 F. VOGEL, *Die histochemischen und physiologischen Arbeiten von Friedrich Miescher*, Leipzig, 1897.
7 J. PICCARD, *Ber.*, 7 (1874) 1714.
8 A. KOSSEL, *Z. physiol. Chem.*, 12 (1888) 241.
9 A. KOSSEL AND A. NEUMANN, *Ber.*, 27 (1894) 2215.
10 A. KOSSEL AND H. STEUDEL, *Z. physiol. Chem.*, 37 (1902) 177.
11 P. LEVENE AND W. JACOBS, *Ber.*, 42 (1909) 2102, 2469, 2474, 2703.
12 P. LEVENE, L. MIKESKA AND T. MORI, *J. Biol. Chem.*, 85 (1930) 785.
13 J. BRACHET, *Arch. biol. (Liège)*, 44 (1933) 519; 51 (1940) 151, 167; 48 (1937) 529.
14 R. FEULGEN AND H. ROSSENBECK, *Z. physiol. Chem.*, 135 (1924) 203.
15 K. MYRBACK AND E. JORPES, *Z. physiol. Chem.*, 237 (1935) 159.
16 M. BODANSKY, *Introduction to Physiological Chemistry*, New York, 1938.
17 P. HAWK, B. OSER AND W. SUMMERSON, *Practical Physiological Chemistry*, Philadelphia, 1947.
18 W. FLETCHER, *On the Structure of Nucleic Acids*, Doctoral thesis, London (Great Britain), 1948.
19 S. COHEN AND W. STANLEY, *J. Biol. Chem.*, 144 (1942) 589.
20 L. DELCAMBE AND V. DESREUX, *Bull. soc. chim. Belges*, 59 (1950) 521.
21 M. SEVAG, *Biochem. Z.*, 273 (1934) 419.
22 R. SIGNER AND H. SCHWANDER, *Helv. Chim. Acta*, 32 (1949) 853.
23 H. SCHWANDER AND R. SIGNER, *Helv. Chim. Acta*, 33 (1950) 1521.
24 E. CHARGAFF AND S. ZAMENHOF, *J. Biol. Chem.*, 173 (1948) 327.
25 E. KAY, N. SIMMONS AND A. DOUNCE, *J. Am. Chem. Soc.*, 74 (1952) 1724.
26 K. KIRBY, *Biochem. J.*, 66 (1957) 495.
27 K. KIRBY, *Biochem. J.*, 64 (1956) 405.
28 A. SASAKI, *Nippon Saikingaku Zasshi*, 11 (1956) 193; *Chem. Abstr.*, 51 (1957) 13959.
29 A. BENDICH, J. FRESCO, H. ROSENKRANZ AND S. BEISER, *J. Am. Chem. Soc.*, 77 (1955) 3671.
30 M. REICHMANN, R. VARIN AND P. DOTY, *J. Am. Chem. Soc.*, 74 (1952) 3203.
31 H. FRAENKEL-CONRAT AND R. WILLIAMS, *Proc. U. S. Natl. Acad. Sci.*, 41 (1955) 690.
32 J. LIPPINCOTT AND B. COMMONER, *Biochim. et Biophys. Acta*, 19 (1956) 198.
33 P. LEVENE AND S. HARRIS, *J. Biol. Chem.*, 101 (1933) 419.
34 S. THANNHAUSER, *Z. physiol. Chem.*, 107 (1919) 157.
35 P. LEVENE AND H. SIMMS, *J. Biol. Chem.*, 65 (1925) 519; 70 (1926) 327.
36 J. WATSON AND F. CRICK, *Nature*, 171 (1953) 737.
37 P. ROLL, H. WEINFELD AND G. BROWN, *Biochim. et Biophys. Acta*, 13 (1954) 141.
38 H. WEINFELD AND P. ROLL, *Fed. Proc.*, 12 (1953) 287.
39 M. BALIS, D. LEVIN, G. BROWN, G. ELION, H. VANDERWERFF AND G. HITCHINGS, *J. Biol. Chem.*, 200 (1953) 1.
40 K. LEIBMAN AND C. HEIDELBERGER, *J. Biol. Chem.*, 216 (1955) 823.
41 H. SCHMITZ, R. HURLBERT, V. POTTER, A. BRUMM AND D. WHITE, *J. Biol. Chem.*, 209 (1954) 41.
42 R. HURLBERT AND V. POTTER, *J. Biol. Chem.*, 209 (1954) 1.
43 R. HURLBERT AND P. REICHARD, *Acta Chem. Scand.*, 8 (1954) 701.
44 V. POTTER, E. HERBERT, L HECHT, Y. TAKAGI AND J. STONE, *Abstr. Am. Chem. Soc. 128th Meeting*, 12C (1955).
45 R. MERRIFIELD AND M. DUNN, *J. Biol. Chem.*, 186 (1950) 331.
46 R. MERRIFIELD AND D. WOOLEY, *J. Biol. Chem.*, 197 (1952) 521.
47 G. BRAWERMAN AND E. CHARGAFF, *Biochim. et Biophys. Acta*, 15 (1954) 549.
48 H. KALCKAR AND H. KLENOW, *Ann. Rev. Biochem.*, 23 (1954) 527.
49 A. KORNBERG, *J. Biol. Chem.*, 182 (1950) 779.
50 A. SCHRECKER AND A. KORNBERG, *J. Biol. Chem.*, 182 (1950) 795.
51 A. KORNBERG, *Adv. Enzymol.*, 18 (1957) 191.

52 L. Heppel and P. Whitfield, *Biochem. J.*, 60 (1955) 1.

53 L. Heppel and J. Rabinowitz, *Ann. Rev. Biochem.*, 27 (1958) 613.

54 D. Keilin and E. Hartree, *Proc. Roy. Soc. (London)*, 119B (1936) 114.

55 L. Heppel, P. Whitfield and R. Markham, *Biochem. J.*, 60 (1955) 8.

56 R. Markham and D. Strominger, *Biochem. J.*, 64 (1956) 46 P.

57 A. Hakim, *Arch. Biochem. Biophys.*, 70 (1957) 591.

58 A. Michelson, *J. Chem. Soc.*, (1959) 1371.

59 M. Grunberg-Manago and S. Ochoa, *Fed. Proc.*, 14 (1955) 221.

60 M. Grunberg-Manago and S. Ochoa, *J. Am. Chem. Soc.*, 77 (1955) 3165.

61 H. Krebs and R. Hems, *Biochim. et Biophys. Acta*, 12 (1953) 172.

62 L. Heppel, P. Ortiz and S. Ochoa, *J. Biol. Chem.*, 229 (1957) 679.

63 C. Cori and G. Cori, *Proc. Soc. Expt. Biol. Med.*, 34 (1936) 702.

64 R. Beers Jr., *Fed. Proc.*, 15 (1956) 13; *Nature*, 177 (1956) 790.

65 U. Littauer, *Fed. Proc.*, 15 (1956) 302; U. Littauer and A. Kornberg, *J. Biol. Chem.*, 226 (1957) 1077.

66 L. Heppel, M. Singer and R. Hilmoe, *Ann. N. Y. Acad. Sci.*, 81 (1959) 635.

67 R. Hilmoe and L. Heppel, *J. Am. Chem. Soc.*, 79 (1957) 4810.

68 A. Hakim, *Biochem. Z.*, 331 (1959) 229.

69 E. Canellakis, *Biochim. et Biophys. Acta*, 23 (1957) 217; 25 (1957) 217.

70 P. Zamecnik, M. Stephenson, J. Scott and M. Hoagland, *Fed. Proc.*, 16 (1957) 275.

71 E. Herbert, V. Potter and L. Hecht, *J. Biol. Chem.*, 225, (1957) 659.

72 M. Grunberg-Manago and J. Fresco, *Fed. Proc.*, 17 (1958) 235.

73 E. Evans, *Bacteriol. Revs.*, 14 (1950) 210.

74 E. Hoff-Jorgensen and E. Zeuthen, *Nature*, 169 (1952) 245.

75 A. Kornberg, I. Lehman and E. Simms, *Fed. Proc.*, 15 (1956) 291.

76 J. Hurwitz, *J. Biol. Chem.*, 234 (1959) 2351.

77 A. Michelson, *Nature*, 181 (1958) 303.

78 M. Smith and H. Khorana, *J. Am. Chem. Soc.*, 81 (1959) 2911.

79 B. Theorell, Chapter 20 in *The Nucleic Acids*[4].

80 T. Morgan, *J. Exptl. Zool.*, 11 (1911) 365.

81 O. Avery, C. MacLeod and M. McCarty, *J. Exptl. Med.*, 79 (1944) 137.

82 G. Stent, *Adv. Virus Research*, 5 (1958) 95.

83 A. Meister, *Rev. Mod. Phys.*, 31 (1959) 210.

84 B. Commoner, J. Lippincott, G. Shearer, E. Richmann and J. Wu, *Nature*, 178 (1956) 767.

85 E. Keller and P. Zamecnik, *J. Biol. Chem.*, 221 (1956) 45.

86 M. Hoagland, M. Stephenson, J. Scott, L. Hecht and P. Zamecnik, *J. Biol. Chem.*, 231 (1958) 241.

Chapter 2

The Chemistry of Nucleotides

This chapter will be devoted to the basic chemistry of the nucleotides, which are the sub-units of the natural and synthetic polynucleotides, and to the purely chemical methods which have been developed for their polymerization. Subsequent chapters will deal with the production of polynucleotides by enzymatic means and with the mode of internucleotide linkage of the natural and biosynthetic polynucleotides.

To anticipate, each mononucleotide is composed of a purine or pyrimidine base, a pentose sugar, and phosphoric acid. A glycosidic bond unites the pentose and the base at the C'_1 position of the former. The pentose carbons are conventionally designated as C'_1 through C'_5.

In the case of ribonucleotides, which are produced by alkaline or enzymatic hydrolysis of ribonucleic acid, the pentose is D-ribose. In the case of deoxyribonucleotides, which are obtained from deoxyribonucleic acid, the pentose is 2-deoxyribose.

The phosphate group may be attached, by means of an ester linkage, to the 2', 3', or 5' positions of ribonucleotides and to the 3' or 5' positions of deoxyribonucleotides. The trifunctional character of the phosphates makes both linear and branched polynucleotides potentially possible. However, all the natural and biosynthetic polynucleotides so far examined appear to consist of linear chains united by phosphodiester linkages which are exclusively of the 3'–5' type.

Structure I is that of a ribonucleotide, adenosine-5'-monophosphate.

PURINE AND PYRIMIDINE BASES

The bases are either purines or pyrimidines. Each type has the basic ring structure denoted by II for pyrimidines and by III for purines. The ring positions will be designated as is indicated. The R groups represent the usual positions of possible substituents. The points of attachment of the sugar are at the N_3 and N_9 positions for pyrimidine and purine mononucleotides, respectively.

The pyrimidines occurring in substantial quantities in deoxyribonucleic acids (DNA) include thymine (2,6-dihydroxy,5-methyl-pyrimidine), cytosine (2-hydroxy, 6-amino-pyrimidine), and, considerably less frequently), 5-methyl-cytosine, and 5-hydroxymethylcytosine*. The pyrimidines commonly found in ribonucleic acids (RNA) are cytosine and uracil (2,6-dihydroxy-pyrimidine)*. The purines frequently isolated from nucleic acids are adenine (6-amino purine) and guanine (2-amino,

---

* See footnote on p. 22.

6-hydroxypurine). An additional purine not normally found in nucleic acids but readily incorporated into synthetic polynucleotides is hypoxanthine (6-hydroxy-purine)*.

In addition to the above bases, trace quantities of 5-ribosyl uracil[1], 6-methyl-amino-purine[2-4], 6-hydroxy, 2-methylamino-purine[3], 6,6-dimethylamino-purine[4],

1-methyl guanine[3], and 2-methyl-adenine[4] have been reported in nucleic acid digests. In all probability the number of such derivatives detected in nucleic acids will increase. By growing bacteria or tissue cultures in media containing other purine derivatives, a variety of such bases has been incorporated into the nucleic acids isolated from such sources, including 5-fluorouracil[5, 6], 5-bromo-uracil[7, 8], 5-chloro-uracil[8], 5-iodouracil[7, 8], thiouracil[9], and 8-azaguanine[10].

The bases are isolated from the nucleic acids with varying degrees of difficulty, depending upon the base and the sugar. Acid hydrolysis by ethanolic HCl[11, 12] or 0.4 to 6 N HCl or H_2SO_4 at 100–120° for one to two hours[12-16] liberates the purine bases quantitatively. The pyrimidine nucleotides are relatively resistant to acid hydrolysis at the glycosidic linkage and require rather drastic procedures for their liberation, such as 2 hours at 175° in 25% H_2SO_4. Under these conditions cytosine is frequently extensively deaminated to uracil, yielding abnormally high uracil–cytosine ratios. The deamination is minimized if the hydrolysis is carried out in 20% HCl[12], in concentrated formic acid[12], and in 12 N perchloric acid[17]. However, liberation is generally incomplete under these milder conditions.

---

* The use of the term *hydroxy* for these derivatives is made primarily for the sake of convention and is not intended to prejudice the assignment of the prevalent tautomeric form. In actuality, as will be seen later, the evidence is strong that all of these exist predominantly in the keto form.

The liberated bases can be separated into their purified constituents by ion exchange chromatography with Dowex 50-H$^+$ eluted with 2 N HCl[18]. The order of evolution is: uracil, cytosine, guanine and adenine. They may also be separated by Dowex-1-Cl$^-$ with the elution system, 0.2 M NH$_4$OH and 0.025 M NH$_4$Cl[18]. The elution sequence is cytosine, uracil, thymine, guanine, and adenine. Paper chromatography is also used for the separation of the bases. The solvents, isopropanol–HCl (sp.gr. 1.19)–H$_2$O (170 ml : 41 ml : to make 250 ml)[19], and tertiary-butanol–HCl–H$_2$O (700 ml : 132 ml : to make 1000 ml)[15] are useful systems for the separation of the bases. A third method involves the use of paper electrophoresis at pH values in the vicinity of 3.5[20].

Structure and synthesis

The first valid evidence for the structure of adenine was obtained by Fischer[21] by the synthesis of adenine and hypoxanthine from uric acid (2,6,8-trihydroxy-purine). The steps involved treatment of uric acid with POCl$_3$ to yield 2,6,8-trichloropurine; substitution of the 6-chloro group with ammonia to give 6-amino, 2,8-dichloropurine; and removal of the remaining chloro groups with HI to yield adenine. Deamination of the 6-amino group by nitrous acid hydrolysis yielded hypoxanthine. Total synthesis of adenine from formamidine and phenylazomalononitrile was accomplished by Traube[22].

In a similar manner Fischer elucidated the structure of guanine[21]. Treatment of 2,6,8-trichloropurine with KOH replaced the 6-chloro group with a hydroxyl group to yield 6-hydroxy,2,8-dichloropurine. This compound, when treated with ammonia, lost the 2-chloro group to give 2-amino, 6-hydroxy, 8-chloropurine. Subsequent treatment with HI removed the 8-chloro group to give guanine. Deamination of guanine with nitrous acid yielded xanthine (2,6-dihydroxy-purine).

Both xanthine and hypoxanthine can be synthesized directly from 2,6,8-trichloropurine. Total syntheses of guanine and xanthine were first described by Traube[23].

The structure of uracil was determined by Fischer and Roeder[24]. Urea, (NH$_2$)$_2$C=O, treated with acrylic acid, CH$_2$CHCOOH, at high temperatures forms a hydrogenated derivative of uracil, hydrouracil, in which C$_4$ and C$_5$ are saturated. Bromination of this compound with bromine gas in acetic acid at 100°, followed by heating of the resulting product in pyridine at 100°, selectively removed one hydrogen from C$_4$ and C$_5$ each to yield the fully unsaturated uracil.

Thymine structure was first elucidated by Steudel[25]. The synthesis of the pyrimidine nucleus and of thymine has been accomplished by several methods. Wheeler and Merriam[26], starting with S-methylthiourea, CH$_3$SC(NH$_2$)=NH, and ethyl formyl propionate, C$_2$H$_5$OC(O)C(CH$_3$)=C(OH)H, synthesized 2-methylmercapto, 5-methyl, 6-hydroxypyrimidine. Refluxing with concentrated HCl removed the 2-methylmercapto group by hydrolysis to yield thymine.

Cytosine has been synthesized in a similar manner[27] starting with S-ethylthiourea and ethylformylacetate to yield 2-ethylmercapto, 6-hydroxy-pyrimidine. The 6-hydroxyl group was replaced by chlorine via PCl₅ treatment to give 2-ethyl-mercapto, 6-chloropyrimidine. Treatment with ammonia in ethanol removed the 6-chloro group to yield 2-ethylmercapto, 6-amino-pyrimidine. Hydrolysis of the 2-ethylmercapto group was accomplished by refluxing with HBr. The structures of 5-methyl cytosine[28] and 5-hydroxy-methylcytosine[29] have been shown recently to be homologs of cytosine. The latter derivative is present in place of cytosine in DNA of T-even coliphages[29].

The parent purine and pyrimidine bases are quite soluble in water. The solubili-ties of the derivatives depend upon the kind and number of substituents. The pK's of the bases may originate either from the ring nitrogens or the substituent groups. Until recently, it was not possible to assign the loci of proton binding with certainty because of the uncertainties introduced by enolization or lactim–lactam tautomerism. In Table 3 are compiled the measured pK's of the seven principal bases.

Because of the conjugated structure of the bases, these compounds absorb strongly in the ultraviolet region, the observed absorption spectrum depending upon the ring structure, the substituents, and the state of ionization. Variations of the absorption spectrum with pH have been used to detect ionizable groups difficult to measure by conventional titration methods. The addition of the glycosidic bond alters the ultraviolet absorption spectra of the bases slightly, but the presence of one or more phosphate groups on the sugar has no effect on the spectrum. In contrast, polymerization of the nucleotides to form a polynucleotide chain causes a marked hypochromatic change in the spectrum, frequently accompanied by a shift of the absorption maximum to shorter wavelengths. The details and signifi-cance of this phenomenon are discussed in greater detail in the following chapters.

The chemical reactivity of the bases depends primarily upon the substituents. Both parent compounds, purine and pyrimidine (II and III, R = H), are very stable to oxidizing agents and concentrated acids, but are easily reduced. This behavior resembles that of benzene or pyridine. Because the conjugated ring has a deficiency of electrons, these compounds are electrophilic and lose some of their stability when positions 2, 4 and/or 6 are occupied by substituents which can serve as electron donors.

The chemical reactions of the bases which have been useful in the study of nucleo-tides include deamination of 8-azaguanine, adenine, guanine, cytosine, hydroxy-methylcytosine, or methylcytosine with nitrous acid[19, 21, 30, 31], and replacement of the amino group by a hydroxyl group. If the pyrimidine contains amino or hydroxyl groups in positions C_4 and C_6, nitrous acid can be used to substitute a nitroso group at C_5[32]. Formaldehyde reacts with the amino groups to form the methene group, $CH_2 = N$[33]. This latter reaction has been particularly useful in studies of the role of the amino group in determining the properties of synthetic polynucleotides[34].

The nomenclature conventionally used in naming the purine and pyrimidine

TABLE 3

VALUES OF THE pK'S OF NUCLEOTIDES AND THEIR COMPONENTS

molecule	base pK	sugar pK	secondary phosphate pK	primary phosphate pK
adenine	4.2[3],9.8[3]			
adenosine	3.5[4]	12.5[4]		
adenosine-5'-phosphate	3.8[1]		6.1[1]	0.9[4]
adenosine-5'-diphosphate	3.9[1]		6.3[1]	
adenosine-5'-triphosphate	4.1[1]		6.5[1]	
adenosine-2'- and 3'-phosphate (mixture)	3.7[4]		6.0[4]	0.9[4]
uracil	9.5[2]			
uridine	9.2[4]	12.5[4]		
uridine-5'-phosphate	9.5[1]		6.4[1]	1.0[4]
uridine-5'-diphosphate	9.4[1]		6.5[1]	
uridine-5'-triphosphate	9.5[1]		6.6[1]	
uridine-2'-and 3'-phosphate (mixture)	9.4[4]		5.9[4]	1.0[4]
cytosine	4.6[2],12.2[2]			
cytidine	4.2[4]	12.3[4]		
cytidine-5'-phosphate	4.5[1]		6.3[1]	0.8[4]
cytidine-5'-diphosphate	4.6[1]		6.4[1]	
cytidine-5'-triphosphate	4.8[1]		6.6[1]	
cytidine-2'-phosphate	4.36[6]		6.17[6]	
cytidine-3'-phosphate	4.28[6]		6.0[6]	
guanine	3.3[3],9.2[3],12.3[3]			
guanosine	1.6[4],9.2[4]	12.3[4]		
guanosine-5'-phosphate	2.4[1],9.4[1]		6.1[1]	0.7[1]
guanosine-5'-diphosphate	2.9[1],9.6[1]		6.3[1]	
guanosine-5'-triphosphate	3.3[1],9.3[1]		6.5[1]	
guanosine-2'-and 3'-phosphate (mixture)	9.3[4],2.4[4]		6.0[4]	0.7[4]
hypoxanthine	8.8[2],12.0[2]			
inosine	8.8[4]	12.3[4]		
thymine	9.8[5]			

[1] Pabst Laboratories circular OR-10, 1956.
[2] H. TAYLOR, Doctoral Thesis, London, 1946.
[3] H. TAYLOR, J. Chem. Soc., (1948) 765.
[4] P. LEVENE AND H. SIMMS, J. Biol. Chem., 65 (1925) 519.
[5] P. LEVENE, L. BASS AND H. SIMMS, J. Biol. Chem., 70 (1926) 229.
[6] L. CAVALIERI, J. Am. Chem. Soc., 74 (1952) 5804.

bases has been adopted without regard to the actual tautomeric form of the bases existing, for example, in water. As will be shown below, the most prevalent form of the bases is the keto, amino form. Consequently, the correct nomenclature for the bases should be keto, aminopurines and pyrimidines. This terminology will be used throughout the remainder of this text.

Tautomeric structures of the bases

The question of the prevailing tautomeric forms of the purine or pyrimidine bases, alone or as nucleosides and nucleotides, remained an issue long after their basic primary structures had been clarified. It has only been by means of infra-red spectroscopy that, within the past few years, the actual tautomeric forms of the bases have been determined with certainty.

One of the problems presented to the investigator in this field is the fact that the tautomeric structure of interest is generally that existing in aqueous solution. This solvent was long thought to be precluded as a medium for infra-red studies because of the limited transparency of water in the infra-red. However, in recent years it has been found that the transparent regions of H_2O and D_2O are complementary. Almost the entire infra-red spectrum of a given solute may be observed if both of these solvents are used in succession.

The difficulties involved in attempting to make a direct assignment of the observed absorption bands to known groups necessitated an indirect approach, utilizing model compounds of known structure. Miles[35, 36] has successfully used this approach in deciding between possible forms of several purine and pyrimidine bases.

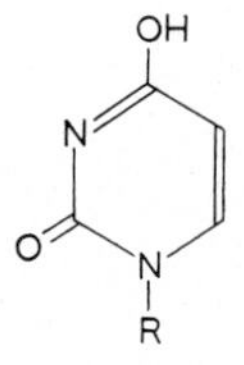

IVa   IVb   IVc 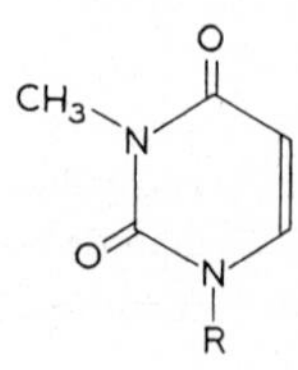   V

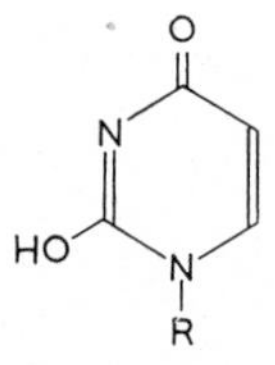

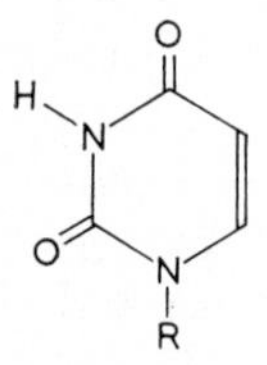

At a pH below its pK of about 9.2, the uracil group of uridine has three possible tautomeric forms, according to whether the C_6 or the C_2 carbonyl group, or neither, is enolized (IVa, IVb, IVc). In D_2O solution uridine has two strong bands at 5.92 μ and 6.05 μ. As this wavelength range is typical of carbonyls, it is highly probable that at least one of these bands arises from a carbonyl group, since with the formation of the glycosidic linkage at N_3, both oxygens cannot be simultaneously enolized. Miles found that the N_1-methyl derivative of uridine (V), which cannot enolize and, hence, must have the diketo form, had a spectrum in the 6 μ region almost identical with that of uridine[35]. This furnished very compelling evidence for the diketo structure (IVc).

VI a	VI b	VI c	VII	VIII

Brown et al.,[37] observed that the ultraviolet absorption spectra of 2-hydroxypyrimidine (VI) and 6-hydroxypyrimidine resembled those of their N-methyl derivatives (VII), which cannot tautomerize, much more closely than those of the corresponding 2-methoxy (VIII) and 6-methoxy derivatives. Additional evidence for the diketo form was obtained by examining the infra-red spectrum of a derivative of the hypothetical 6-enol tautomer of uracil[35]. Thus, the ethyl derivative of 6-enol uridine (IX) was found to have a very different spectrum from that of uridine. The 5.92 μ band had entirely disappeared, but the band at 6.03 μ remained.

The assignment of the two bands in the 6 μ region is still uncertain. Since the C_6 carbonyl should be conjugated and as conjugation usually shifts a band to

IX	X	XI	XII	XIII

longer wavelengths, it is likely that the 6.05 μ band can be assigned to this group and the 5.92 μ band to the unconjugated C_2 carbonyl group. In the case of the ethyl enolate derivative (IX) the 2-carbonyl group becomes conjugated, so that the band shifts to 6.03 μ.

The close structural analogy of thymidine to uridine makes it, a priori, very likely that this nucleoside also has the diketo form. This has been confirmed by examination of the spectrum of the non tautomeric N_1-methyl glucose analog of thymidine which, like its parent compound, was found to have bands at 6.00 and 5.92 μ (X and XI).

Both uracil and thymine have alkaline pK's. According to Sinsheimer et al.[38] the spectra in the 6 μ region of uridine and thymidine are almost identical at pH 7.0, but show a marked divergence at pH 11. This is surprising and it would appear likely that the carbonyl group which enolizes and then ionizes may be different in the two cases. In either case, if the enolate group were at the C_6 position, the chain of conjugation, $C_4=C_5-C_6=N_1-C_2=0$, should be analogous to that in

2-ketopyrimidine. If the enolate were at the C_2 position the conjugated structure should be like that of 6-ketopyrimidine. Comparison of the alkaline infra-red spectra in the 6 μ region of these model compounds with those of uridine and thymidine reveals that thymidine is somewhat like 6-ketopyrimidine and that uridine resembles 2-ketopyrimidine. Although the matching of the bands is by no means decisive, there is a definite inference that uridine enolizes in the C_6 position and thymidine in the C_2 position. The most probable corresponding keto and enol forms of the two bases are, therefore, structures IVc and XII, and XI and XIII, respectively.

The spectrum of uridylic acid in the 6 μ region is very similar to that of uridine, the only difference being a slight shift to longer wavelengths (5.96 vs. 5.92 μ) of the C_2 carbonyl band.

The assignment of many of the infra-red bands of uridine and thymidine is still uncertain. A comparison of these two bases with their dihydro derivatives (XIV

| XIV | XV | XVIa | XVIb | XVII |

and XV) reveals that a band at 6.1–6.2 μ present in the former pair disappears in the dihydro compounds. As this is in the region of the $C=C$ stretching vibration, it appears plausible to assign this band to the $C_4=C_5$ double bond stretching vibration[36].

In the case of the nucleoside, cytidine, two tautomeric forms of the base are possible in neutral and alkaline solution, one of which has an amino group in the C_6 position and the other an imino group in the C_6 position (XVIa and XVIb). The X-ray crystallographic study of Furberg[39] showed that the external nitrogen attached to C_6 bonded 2 hydrogen atoms and that the amino configuration was, therefore, prevalent in the solid state. This, however, would not necessarily be relevant to the state in aqueous solution.

However, Miles[36] observed that cytidine in D_2O had a strong band at 6.08 μ in a position similar to that assigned to the conjugated carbonyl group of uridine ($C_2=O$) and none below 6 μ. As the C_2 carbonyl group of cytidine should be unconjugated for the imino form (XVIb) ($C_6-N_1-C_2=O$) and conjugated for the amino form (XVIa) ($C_6=N_1-C_2=O$), it might be inferred that the amino form predominates in solution.

Somewhat more compelling evidence for the amino tautomer was obtained by comparing the spectrum in the 6 μ region of cytidine with its 6-dimethyl derivative (XVII), which cannot tautomerize. The latter compound has its carbonyl band in almost exactly the same position as does cytidine. The state of conjugation of the C_2 carbonyl group must therefore be the same in both cases. This virtually precludes the existence of an imino form of cytidine in solution. The prevailing structure is XVIa.

In the case of adenosine an amino and imino form are also possible for the adenine base in neutral and alkaline solution (XVIIIa and XVIIIb). Again it has been possible to choose between the two by comparing the spectra of sodium adenylate and the 6-dimethylamino derivative of adenosine (XIX). The close

XVIIIa   XVIIIb   XIX

XX a   XX b   XXI

similarity of the two indicates that the amino form (XVIIIa) is the prevalent form in solution.

The site of proton binding in acid solution for cytidine could conceivably be either the C_6-amino group or the N_1 of the ring. Cytosine possesses a pK at about pH 4.5. It is not possible to decide conclusively between the two possibilities by a comparison of the acid infra-red spectra of cytidine and its dimethyl derivative, because each can exist in either of two tautomeric forms (XXa and XXb).

With respect to adenine, the X-ray studies of Cochran[40] have shown that in the solid state the proton is on the N_1 of the ring. If the acid form of adenine does not change in solution and if that of cytidine is analogous to adenine, one may conclude indirectly that in the acid forms of both bases the proton binding site is the N_1 of the ring.

XXII   XXIII

The hypoxanthine base of inosine might conceivably be either a 6-keto (XXI) or 6-enol form. The evidence for selecting either possibility is not as complete as in the above examples. Brown and Mason[41] observed that solid films of hypoxanthine displayed a prominant band at 5.99 μ and no evidence of a hydroxyl band. Furthermore, 1,7-dimethylhypoxanthine (XXII) had a spectrum in the 6 μ region very similar to the parent compound. The carbonyl band in this instance was displaced to a slightly lower wavelength between 5.85 and 5.96 μ. In addition, 6-hydroxy,7-methylpurine has an NH band at 2.95 μ, which is in the range for cyclic conjugated amides with an orthoquinoid structure. Brown and Mason also

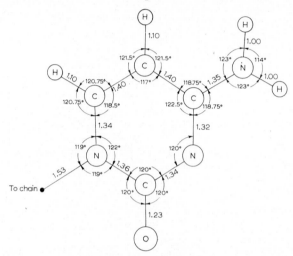

Fig. 2. Structure of cytosine[42].

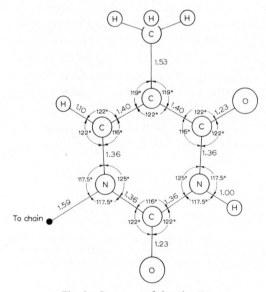

Fig. 3. Structure of thymine[42]

examined the infra-red spectrum of 2-hydroxypurine and found a band in the carbonyl region at 5.97 μ. Thus, the available evidence appears to suggest that all the above hydroxypurines occur in the keto form (XXI and XXII).

It is probably valid to extend the above considerations to the C_6 oxygen of guanine (XXIII). The latter resembles hypoxanthine except for the presence of an external nitrogen at the C_2 position. In view of the results with adenine it is probable that the latter group is also in the amino form. However, the most compelling evidence for the 6-keto, 2-amino form of guanine is the nature of the hydrogen bond it appears to form with cytosine in deoxyribonucleic acid. This would be very difficult to reconcile with any other tautomeric form.

Bond lengths and angles

The bond lengths and angles of the bases have been determined by X-ray crystallographic studies in a number of instances. In all cases the X-ray data indicate that the purine and pyrimidine bases are planar within experimental error. This is of importance with regard to the structures assigned to the ordered polynucleotide systems. In Figs. 2–5 are shown the bond angles and distances for the purine and pyrimidine bases which occur in natural nucleic acid. The data are taken from reference [42].

It is instructive to compare the structure of uracil with that of a pyrimidine derivative which contains no carbonyl groups. If the structure of uracil, as deter-

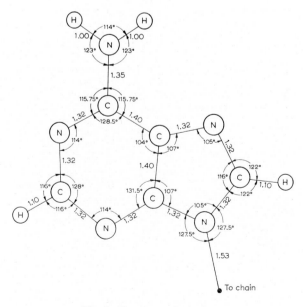

Fig. 4. Structure of adenine [42].

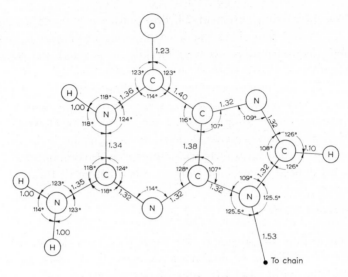

Fig. 5. Structure of guanine[42].

mined by Parry[43], is compared with that of 4-amino-, 2,6-dichloropyrimidine, as reported by Clews and Cochran[44], it is found that the average $C-N$ bond distance in the ring is 1.36 Å in the former and 1.32 Å in the latter (Fig. 6). The significantly larger bond lengths in uracil have been attributed by Pauling and Corey[42] to a lesser degree of double bond character which is predicted if both oxygens are

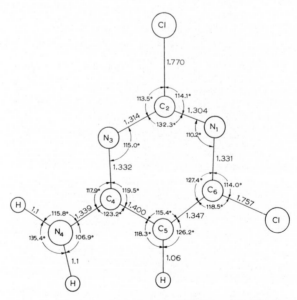

Fig. 6. Structure of 4-amino-, 2, 6 dichloropyrimidine[42].

in the carbonyl state. In the case of 4-amino,2,6-dichloropyrimidine, which has
no keto oxygens, the resonance structure of the ring (XXIV) should be like the
Kekule structure of benzene (XXV). Thus, the C — N bonds should have some

XXIV   XXV

double bond character and should, therefore, be shortened with respect to those
of uracil (IVc), as is indeed the case. In the intermediate case of cytosine (XVIa),
which has one keto oxygen, the mean C — N bond length is 1.34 Å.

The average bond angle for the ring nitrogens of uracil is 124° and that for the
carbon atoms is 118°. In 4-amino,2,6-dichloropyrimidine they are 113° and 124°,
respectively. This is also explicable on the basis of their known structures[42]. The
ring carbons of 4-amino,2,6-dichloropyrimidine form two σ bonds in the ring,
a π bond in the ring and a σ bond outside the ring. The orbitals are sp³ hybrids
and the bond angles would be expected to be the normal tetrahedral angles. The
expected value of the angle between a single and double bond in this instance
is 125° 16′, which is close to the observed value.

The ring nitrogens form two σ bonds and one π bond in the ring, with an
unshared pair in the valence shell. The greater stability of the 2s orbital, as compared with the 2p orbital, will presumably give the orbital occupied by the
unshared pair a large amount of s character. This means that the bond orbitals
must have largely a p character[42].

While a direct estimate of the expected angle between a single and a double
bond cannot be made in this case, a reasonable guess can be made on the basis of
the known difference between the bond angles between two sp³ tetrahedral single
bonds and two pure p single bonds[42]. The values are 109° 28′ and 90°, respectively.
If this same 19° difference occurs between the angle of a single and a double bond
of a ring nitrogen in an aromatic molecule, and the tetrahedral bond angle of a
single and a double bond (125° 16′), then the former angle should be 125° 16′ — 19°
or about 106°. Although the observed nitrogen bond angles are somewhat greater
than this, the agreement is reasonable in view of the roughness of the calculation.

The very different bond angles observed for the ring atoms of uracil arise
logically from its diketo structure. Thus, each of the nitrogen atoms has a hydrogen
atom attached to it and accordingly its bond orbitals are sp³ orbitals, for which
the predicted tetrahedral angle, 125° 16′, is close to the observed value, 124°.
Moreover, the carbon atoms C_2 and C_6 form only single bonds within the ring
and the C — O bond distances of uracil, which are close to 1.24 Å, show the expected
shortening arising from their largely double character.

References p. 61/64

In the case of cytosine the $C-O$ bond distance is 1.23 Å, which is again consistent with its keto structure. While the data are clearly consistent with an amino form for the external nitrogen, the C_6-N bond distance, 1.35 Å, is somewhat short for a single bond. This is attributed by Furberg[39] to the contribution of resonance forms of the type $C=\overset{+}{N}H_2$.

The bond angles and distances cited in Fig. 5 for guanine are obtained from the work of Broomhead[45] upon crystals of guanine HCl monohydrate. By analogy to the other bases, it may probably be assigned a 6-keto,2-aminopurine structure.

THE STRUCTURES OF THE NUCLEOSIDES

The pentose of the purine ribosides has been identified as D-ribose, which on oxidation yields optically active D-ribonic acid, and then optically inactive trihydroxy-glutaric acid[46]. It was first isolated in crystalline form by Levene and Jacobs[47]. Unequivocal identification was obtained by the synthesis of D-ribose[48]. Pyrimidine ribosides also contain D-ribose. One method of identification was based on the hydrolysis and oxidation of cytidine with HBr and Br_2 to yield 5-bromouracil and D-ribonic acid[49].

Ribose forms a variety of glycosides, of which the N-glycosides are present in nucleosides. The nature of the sugar accounts for many of the distinguishing features of RNA as compared with DNA. The position of the glycosidic linkage on the base has been established to be on N_9 of the purines and N_3 of the pyrimidines. The ease of acid hydrolysis of the purine glycosidic linkage appears to preclude a $C-C$ glycoside bond. The evidence for the above conclusions can be briefly summarized as follows.

Because adenosine can be converted to inosine by nitrous acid hydrolysis of the 6-amino group and guanosine to xanthosine by hydrolysis of the 2-amino group, it is apparent that the primary amino groups of these nucleosides are not involved in the glycosidic linkage. This leaves the N-atoms at positions N_1 and N_3 of the pyrimidines and N_1, N_3, N_7 and N_9 of the purines. Positions N_1 and N_3 have been eliminated by methylation of xanthosine (XXVI) to give theophylline riboside (XXVII)[50].

XXVI   XXVII

Ultraviolet absorption studies of adenosine (XVIIIa) and inosine (XXIa) show a close resemblance of the spectra of these compounds to those of 9-methyladenine and 9-methylhypoxanthine, but a marked difference from those of the corresponding 7-methyl derivatives[51]. A corresponding relationship is observed with guanosine[52] and xanthosine[53] and their analogous methyl derivatives. It is concluded, therefore, that the natural purine ribosides are the 9- and not the 7-N-glycosides.

Confirmatory evidence has also been obtained by the action of periodate on adenosine, which yields a dialdehyde identical with the dialdehyde from 9-D-mannopyranosyladenine[54].

The position of the glycosidic linkage of the pyrimidine ribosides has been shown not to involve the substituents of these ribosides in view of the fact that deamination of cytidine to uridine does not result in the loss of the ribose residue. Conversion of uridine to 5-nitrouridine and 5-bromouridine without loss of ribose also indicates that position C_5 is not involved. If substituents are absent on

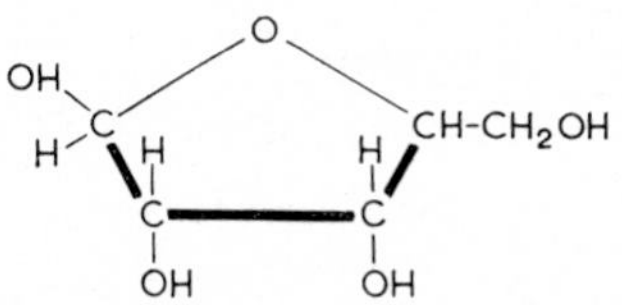

XXVIII

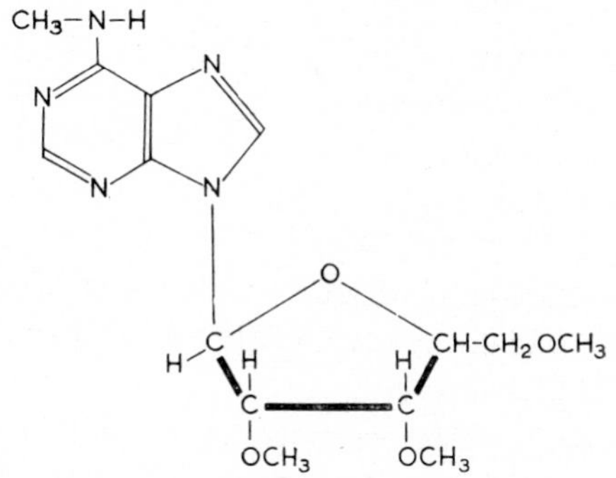

XXIX

positions C_4 and C_5, an N_3-substituted uracil derivative should react with Br_2 and phenylhydrazine to give the corresponding 4,5-diphenylhydrazine derivative[55]. This reaction is thought to be specific for 3'-substituted uracils. This reaction occurs with uridine and is, therefore, evidence for a N_3-glycosidic linkage.

The ring structure of D-ribose in both purine and pyrimidine nucleosides has been shown to be ribofuranose, a five-membered ring (XXVIII). Acetylation and methylation of adenosine, successively followed by deacetylation, yields trimethyl-N_{10}-methyladenosine (XXIX). This can be hydrolyzed by dilute HCl to N_{10}-methyladenine and trimethyl ribose, identified as 2,3,5-trimethyl-D-ribofuranose[56].

Additional evidence for the furanose structure is provided by the behavior of the nucleoside toward tritylchloride, a reagent frequently used for the protection of reactive groups on the sugar (see below). This reagent reacts preferentially with primary hydroxyl groups of sugars, giving trityl ethers. Adenosine gives a mixture of mono- and di-trityladenosine when treated with this reagent (XXX)[57,58]. The former yields a tritosyl derivative which is hydrolyzed by acid to a tritosyladenosine: N_{10}, 2',3'-tritosyladenosine (XXXI). Failure of iodine to replace the tosyl groups indicates that this compound contains an unsubstituted primary hydroxyl group; therefore, the sugar has a furanose structure.

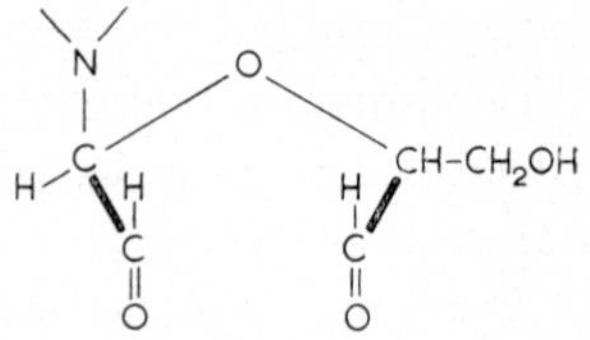

XXXII

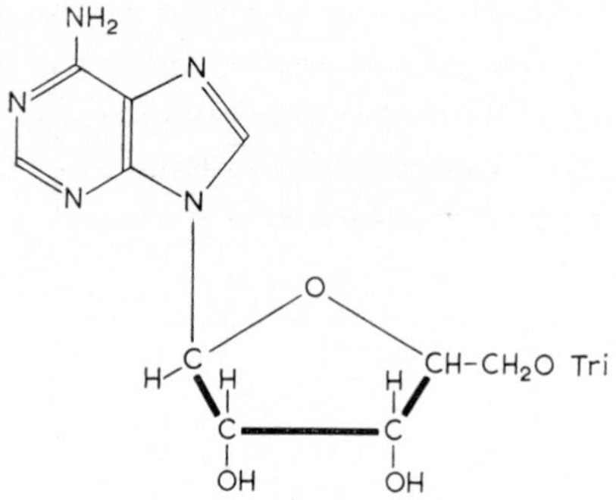

XXX

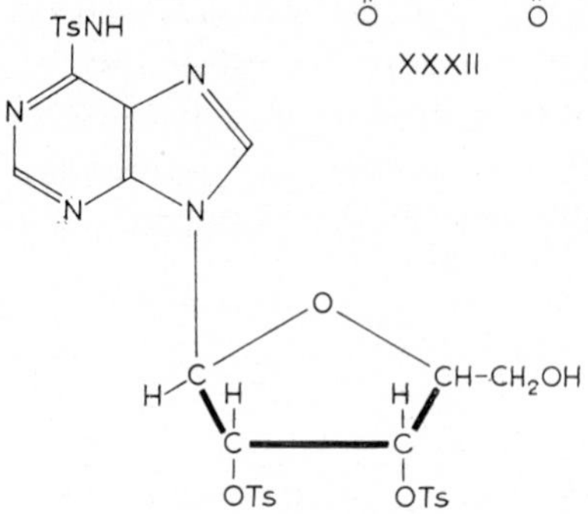

XXXI

The reaction of periodate with ribonucleosides involves one mole of periodate to yield a dialdehyde (XXXII) and no formic acid, a reaction consistent with a furanoside structure[54].

Finally, uridine, inosine, guanosine, and adenosine are converted to the 2′,3′-isopropylidene derivatives (XXXIII)[58–60] by reaction with acetone in the presence of an acidic dehydrating reagent, such as H_2SO_4. These compounds form 5′-tosyl derivatives, which yield the corresponding 5′-iodo-derivatives by a reaction with sodium iodide, reactions which are specific for the furanoside structure.

The configuration of the glycosidic linkage of the ribonucleotides has also been determined by the action of periodate on the nucleoside. The dialdehyde (XXXII) which is obtained is the same compound as is obtained by periodate oxidation of glucosyladenine synthesized from α-acetobromoglucose. Assuming, as is very likely, that optical inversion occurs during the formation of glucosides from the latter compound, it would appear, therefore, that the configuration of the natural glycosides must be the β-configuration.

Other evidence for the β-configuration of the natural nucleosides has been obtained from X-ray studies[39] and by the behavior of the isopropylidene derivatives of the nucleosides. For example, 2′,3′-isopropylidene-5′-p-toluene-sulfonyladenosine isomerizes to a cyclo-nucleoside (XXXIV)[62]. Such isomerization cannot take place with the α-glycosides.

The synthesis of nucleosides with the correct ring structure and glycosidic configuration added final proof of the structure and configuration of the natural nucleosides. Wright et al.[63] report the synthesis of a mixture of adenosines with both the α- and β-configuration. The C_2, and C_3, hydroxyl groups of a ribofuranosyl halide, 5-O-benzoyl-D-ribofuranosyl bromide, were protected by a cyclic carbonate. This compound was heated in boiling xylene with chloromercuri-6-benzamidopurine and the protecting groups removed by hydrolysis with sodium methylate in methanol. The adenosine isomers were separated on cellulose powder with butanol : water (86 : 14) eluent. The anomeric relationship was established by oxidizing the two compounds with periodate and reducing with sodium borohydride. The products had equal and opposite specific optical rotations.

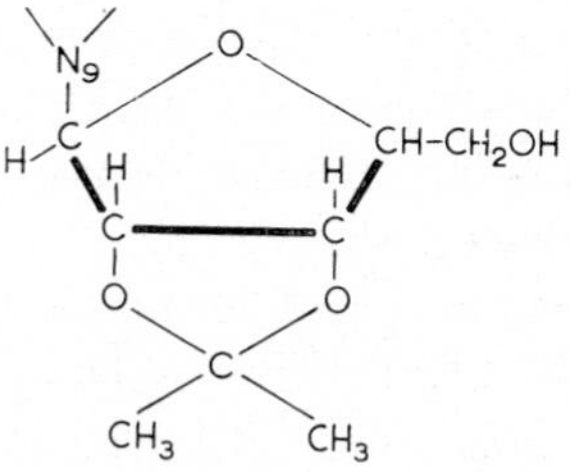

XXXIII

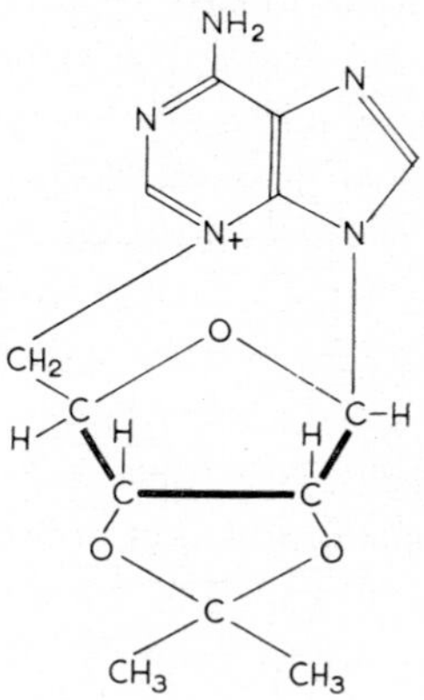

XXXIV

The deoxyribose of deoxyribonucleotides has been identified as 2-deoxy-D-ribose[64]. It is obtained with difficulty by hydrolysis of DNA because of its ease of conversion to levulinic acid during acid hydrolysis. More successful methods include mild acidic hydrolysis of deoxyguanosine and deoxyinosine[65,66]. The benzylphenylhydrazone of the sugar is readily formed[64]. Except for the sign of rotation it is indistinguishable from 2-deoxy-L-ribose. Synthesis of the sugar for unequivocal identification was accomplished by a conversion of D-arabinal into 2-deoxy-D-ribose through the action of dilute H_2SO_4[67].

Methods already described for the ribonucleosides have also been used with the deoxyribonucleosides to establish the position of the glycosidic linkage at the N_3 and N_9 positions of the pyrimidines and purines, respectively[52,68,69]. Similarly, the ring structure of 2-deoxy-D-ribose in nucleosides has been established as a furanose[61].

Anderson et al.[70], confirmed the β-configuration of deoxyribonucleosides by the synthesis of cyclodeoxynucleosides from 5'-O-tosylnucleosides in a reaction analogous to that for the synthesis of the cyclic ribonucleosides[62]. Presumably, the other deoxynucleosides have the same configuration.

Preparation and properties

Nucleosides can be prepared from RNA by the action of alkali, which produces as intermediates the nucleotides:

$$RNA \rightarrow nucleotides \rightarrow nucleosides + orthophosphate$$

This complete hydrolysis can be accomplished by heating with concentrated ammonium hydroxide under pressure at 176–180° for 3–5 hours[71]. In addition, direct hydrolysis of the nucleotides by alkali or enzymatic means[72] can be used. Similar procedures cannot be applied to DNA because of the resistance of the phosphodiester linkage between two deoxyribose residues to alkaline hydrolysis. However, enzymatic degradation of the polymer followed by hydrolysis of the nucleotide by nucleotide phosphatases can provide a satisfactory method for the production of deoxynucleosides[73].

The nucleosides are readily separated by paper and ion exchange resin chromatography. As in the case of the free bases, non-polar solvents are satisfactory in paper chromatography. Similar systems are also used in ion exchange separations.

The presence of the glycosidic linkage alters somewhat the pK's of the bases of nucleosides (see Table 3, p. 25). For example, the pK of adenine at 4.15 shifts to 3.5 in adenosine; that of cytosine shifts from 4.60 to 4.2 in cytidine, and that of guanine from 3.3 to 1.6 in guanosine. In other words, the acid dissociation constant is strengthened by the presence of the sugar. This effect probably stems from the influence of the substituent upon the tautomeric forms of the base.

A second group of pK values attributable to the hydroxyl groups of the sugar is present in the nucleosides. These are in the vicinity of pH 12, which compares with the first acid dissociation constant of a sugar. Associated with this pK is a change in the absorption curve of the nucleoside in the ultraviolet region.

The spatial structures of the nucleosides have not been examined in as great detail as those of the corresponding bases. The first detailed X-ray study was made of cytidine by Furberg[74, 75]. He confirmed the furanose structure of D-ribose and the β-configuration of the glycosidic linkage. The position of the glycosidic bond is at N_3. In addition, the six atoms of the pyrimidine ring were found to lie in the same plane, as shown earlier by Clews and Cochran[44] and by Pitt[76] with substituted pyrimidines. The glycosidic bond $N_3 - C_1$ has a distance of 1.47 Å, corresponding to a single bond. This lies in the plane of the pyrimidine ring and forms angles of 109° and 115° with the adjacent bonds in D-ribose. The pyrimidine and D-ribose rings are mutually perpendicular.

Other X-ray studies have been performed on uridine, adenosine and guanosine by Furberg[39] and on heavy atom derivatives of nucleosides by Zussmann[77] and Huber[78].

NUCLEOTIDES

Phosphate esters of nucleosides are known as nucleotides. The isomers, nucleoside-2'-phosphate and nucleoside-3'-phosphate, as well as the cyclic phosphate compound, nucleoside-2′ : 3′-phosphate, can be obtained by mild alkaline hydrolysis of RNA [79, 80]. A fairly complete hydrolysis of RNA can be accomplished by a 24 hour digestion in 1.0 N NaOH at room temperature. Recently, however, it has been shown that not all the internucleotide bonds are hydrolyzed under these conditions. The adenylic-adenylic bond appears to be particularly resistant to alkaline hydrolysis.

Enzymatic hydrolysis of ribonucleic acid by pancreatic ribonuclease yields the pyrimidine nucleoside-3′-phosphates [81, 82]. However, the yield is not quantitative and this method is not ordinarily used for the production of nucleotides. The 5′-isomer can also be obtained from ribonucleic acid by the action of nucleases which split the $C_{3'} - O$ bond of the phosphodiester linkage [83, 84].

The pyrimidine nucleotides of deoxyribonucleic acid can be obtained by acid hydrolysis of DNA [85, 86]. The products are 3′-phosphates and small amounts of 3′,5′-diphosphates. Enzymatic digestion of DNA with deoxyribonuclease yields in addition the purine nucleotides [87]. Either the 3′- or 5′-isomers can be prepared, according to the enzyme chosen. Pancreatic deoxyribonuclease I, which requires Mg^{++} or other divalent cation, yields the 5′-isomer [88]; deoxyribonuclease II from spleen or thymus, which does not require Mg^{++}, yields the 3′-isomers [89, 90]. However, a high proportion of oligonucleotides is also present in the deoxyribonuclease digests.

Nucleotides are easily separated into purified fractions by paper or ion exchange chromatography. Because of the presence of the phosphate group, this is usually accomplished with polar solvents and anionic resins, respectively. In general, for the separation of the isomeric forms of the nucleotides, two or more solvent systems must be used. One system may be used to separate the different groups of isomers; a second system can then be used to separate the isomers. Dowex-1-Cl⁻ or Dowex-2-Cl⁻ or formate are the most frequently used ion exchange resins [18, 91–93].

Structure and synthesis of the 2′- and 3′-nucleotides

Levene and Harris [94] assumed that only one isomer of the nucleotides was produced by the alkaline hydrolysis of RNA, namely, the 3′-isomer. Their techniques could clearly distinguish between the 5′-isomer and the 2′- or 3′-isomer, but they could not distinguish between the 2′- and 3′-isomers. Since the rate of hydrolysis of the presumed 3′-phosphate ester had been shown to be considerably faster than that of the 5′-phosphate ester, the phosphodiester linkage [95] was believed to be 2′, 3′.

The original assumptions of Levene and Harris were subsequently proven false by Carter and Cohn [91, 96, 97] when in 1949 they isolated two isomeric nucleotides a and b from the so-called nucleoside-3′-phosphates by ion exchange chromatography with Dowex-1-formate and an ammonium formate elution system. Brown and Todd synthesized adenylic acids a and b through the action of dibenzylphosphorochloridate on 5′-O-trityladenosine [98], although it could not be established at that time whether adenylic acid a corresponded to the 2′- or 3′-isomer.

Cavalieri[99] determined the pK's and densities of solutions of the a and b isomers of adenylic acid. He found that solutions of the b isomer had greater densities and that the pK of the adenine group was lower for the b than for the a isomer. If the difference can be explained by the greater charge separation of the b isomer, then the b isomer should be adenosine-3'-phosphate (XXXV) and the a isomer adenosine-2'-phosphate (XXXVI).

XXXV   XXXVI

Khym and Cohn reached the same conclusion from studies of the hydrolysis products of the adenylic acids on the acid form of sulfonic acid resin[100]. This resin catalyzes the cleavage of the glycosidic linkage at N_9. The rate of glycosidic cleavage was sufficiently fast, despite the presence of some phosphate cyclization (see below), to permit the identification of the ribose-2'-phosphate and ribose-3'-phosphate. Ribose-2'-phosphate can be distinguished from the 3'-isomer by the fact that it is reduced to the optically active ribitol phosphate. Ribose-3'-phosphate, when reduced, shows no optical activity.

Unequivocal proof of the structure of the a isomer of adenylic acid was finally obtained by Brown et al.[101, 102]. 5'-O-acetyladenosine was acetylated with acetic anhydride in pyridine to yield, among other products, a derivative subsequently identified as 3',5'-O-diacetyladenosine (XXXVII). This compound was phosphoryl-

XXXVII   XXXVIII

ated with O-benzylphosphorous O,O-diphenylphosphoric anhydride to yield 3',5'-O-diacetyladenosine-2'-benzylphosphite. Treatment with N-chlorosuccinimide and hydrolysis with pyridine gave the corresponding diacetyladenosine benzyl phosphate derivative (XXXVIII). This was hydrogenated with PtO_2 and Pd-carbon catalysts to yield 3',5'-diacetyladenosine-2'-phosphate, which was then hydrolyzed at the $C_{3'}$ and $C_{5'}$ positions with methanolic ammonia to yield adenosine-2'-phosphate, chromatographically identical with adenylic acid a. Therefore, adenylic acid b must be adenosine-3′-phosphate, a conclusion also reached by X-ray diffraction studies[101] of crystals of adenylic acid b.

The proof of the structure of the initial diacetyladenosine (3′,5′-O-diacetyladenosine) (XXXVII) was obtained by treatment with p-MeC$_6$H$_4$SO$_2$Cl to give the diacetyl-tosyl derivative. This compound is cleaved by methanol-HCl to adenine and methyl-tosyl-D-ribofuranoside. Methylation of this compound showed the presence of the tosyl group on C$_2$.

The isomeric structures of the pyrimidine nucleotides, cytidylic acids a and b, were also demonstrated by Cavalieri from density and pK measurements to correspond to the 2′- and 3′-isomers, respectively[99]. Baron and Brown[103] found that cytidylic acids can be degraded with hydrazine to ribose phosphate without phosphoryl migration. The position of the phosphate on the ribose was then determined to be 2′- for the a and 3′- for the b isomer. Comparison of the infra-red spectra of the cytidylic acids and deoxycytidylic acid (3′-isomer only) by Michelson and Todd[104] indicated that the b isomer was cytidine-3′-phosphate. Recently, Alver and Furberg[105] reached the same conclusion from X-ray crystallographic studies of the b isomer.

The synthesis of uridylic acid a was accomplished by Brown et $al.$ using a method similar to those developed for the synthesis[106] of adenylic acid a. 5′-O-acetyluridine was acetylated to give 3′,5′-O-diacetyluridine. This was phosphorylated with dibenzylphosphorochloridate, followed by removal of the acetyl groups to yield uridylic acid a. The identity of 3′,5′-di-O-acetyluridine was established by the following conversions: 3′,5′-di-O-acetyluridine → 3′, 5′-di-O-acetyl-2′-toluene-p-sulfonyl uridine → O^2, 2′-cyclo-uridine → 3-β-D-arabofuranosyluracil.

Nucleotides containing a cyclic phosphate ester

The sugar phosphate bond of the nucleotide is an ester linkage. The lability of the inter-nucleotide linkage to acid or alkaline hydrolysis depends to a large degree upon the presence of a neighboring hydroxyl group. RNA, which has a free C$_{2′}$ hydroxyl group, is readily hydrolyzed by alkali, whereas DNA is not. The reasons for the lability of the ribose-phosphate linkages were clarified by the discovery of an intermediate, the cyclic nucleoside-2′ : 3′-phosphate, which has an internal phosphodiester linkage between the C$_{2′}$ and C$_{3′}$ positions of the ribose.

XXXIX   XI

(XXXIX). The formation of a cyclic phosphate compound is a general property of phosphate esters to which there is a neighboring *cis* hydroxyl group. The concept that a cyclic intermediate is necessary for the easy hydrolysis of a phosphate ester was first proposed by Fono[107] and confirmed by the studies of Brown and Todd[98, 108]. Involved is a transesterification. The reaction is catalyzed by hydrogen or hydroxyl ions.

The mechanism originally proposed by Brown and Todd[109] postulated the formation of a neutral triester of orthophosphoric acid (XL), in which R can be a benzyl group, hydrogen, C_5' of a nucleotide, etc. This hypothetical unstable intermediate was thought to be then attacked by water to remove the R group and form the cyclic phosphate nucleotide (XXXIX) and ROH. The simplified view was subsequently modified[109] with the suggestion that the process depends upon an acid- or base-catalyzed attack by the vicinal hydroxyl group of the $P-O-C$ bond. The R group is simultaneously removed as an alkoxy anion. This view is supported by the findings of Lipkin, Talbert and Cohn[110] who found that the alkaline hydrolysis of RNA in $H_2^{18}O$ yields nucleotides containing only one atom of ^{18}O per atom of phosphorus instead of the two predicted by the original version of the mechanism.

The isolation of cyclic intermediates in the digests of ribonuclease-treated RNA suggests that the mechanism of action of ribonuclease is similar to that of alkaline hydrolysis[108, 111]. The synthesis of cyclic phosphate nucleosides by the action of hydrogen or hydroxyl ions, or of ribonuclease, on RNA gives very low yields, primarily because of the tendency of the compound to undergo further hydrolysis to the 2'- or 3'-isomer[112] by the action of alkali and to the 3'-isomer by that of ribonuclease[113, 114]. This occurs with either RNA or the mononucleotide as the source material.

Brown *et al.*, developed the first procedure for the direct synthesis of the cyclic compounds with reasonably large yields[112], although the product contained a large number of by-products which were difficult to separate. Trifluoroacetic anhydride is mixed with a dried mixture of the 2'- and 3'-isomers and stored for 18 hours at 20°. Presumably a mixed anhydride forms between the nucleotide and the trifluoroacetyl group. The remaining acetic anhydride is removed by evaporation and the residue hydrolyzed in a methanol–ammonia solution to yield the cyclic compound.

A second procedure has been developed by Khorana *et al.*[115, 116], based on the reaction of dicyclohexylcarbodiimide with the 2'- or 3'-isomer. The reaction is carried out in aqueous pyridine which is subsequently removed by extraction with ether. The yields are low because of the property of the 5-membered ring of the cyclic phosphate nucleosides to form N-phosphorylureas with dicyclohexylcarbodiimide (XLI).

Recently, Khorana *et al.*[117], were able to increase their yields of the cyclic compounds to 90% of the theoretical yield by using the tri-n-alkylammonium salts of the nucleotides, which are more soluble in anhydrous media. In the absence of water the subsequent reaction of the cyclic phosphate group with the carbodiimide reagent is blocked.

The preparation of 6-membered phosphate derivatives of ribonucleotides, *i.e.*, cyclic 3' : 5'-phosphate nucleosides (XLII), proved to be indispensible for the synthesis of the specific 3',5'-phosphodiester linkage of a dinucleotide[118]. The ease

XLI   XLII

with which the 5-membered ring is formed between $C_{2'}$ and $C_{3'}$ of the ribose precludes the use of the a and b isomers. However, if a nucleoside-5'-phosphate is used with the carbodiimide reagent, a 3' : 5'-cyclic nucleotide is formed. Smith and Khorana[118] report a yield of 60% with uridine-5'-phosphate, provided that the concentration of UMP is very low. At higher concentrations the nucleotide polymerizes (see below).

The 6-membered and 7-membered cyclic phosphate derivatives do not undergo a subsequent reaction with the carbodiimide reagent, in contrast to the case of the 5-membered cyclic structure. This has been used as a means of distinguishing the 5-membered structures from the 6- and 7-membered structures. Both the 6- and 7-membered rings may be synthesized by the action of dicyclohexylcarbodiimide on 3-hydroxypropyl monophosphate and butane-1,4-diol monophosphate. These derivatives differ from the 5-membered structure in having 1 and 2 methene groups, respectively, between the two ester linkages[117].

Five-membered cyclic phosphate derivatives of the deoxyribonucleotides cannot be formed because of the absence of adjacent *cis* hydroxyl groups on the sugar. However, it is possible to form 6-membered cyclic phosphate compounds[119]. Treatment of the pyridinium salt of thymidine-5'-phosphate with dicyclohexyl-carbodiimide in tri-*n*-butylamine and pyridine yields P^1, P^2-dithymidine-5'-pyro-phosphate (XLIII). Heating a pyridine solution of this compound for four hours

XLIII

at 100° yields a small quantity of cyclic thymidine-3' : 5'-phosphate. This derivative
is sensitive to both alkaline and acid hydrolysis, the former yielding about 80%
thymidine-3'-phosphate and 20% thymidine-5'-phosphate, the latter yielding only
the base, thymine. A more direct synthesis without the pyrophosphate intermediate
occurs if the thymidine-5'-phosphate is highly diluted. The intermediate (XLIV)
is the same as that for the synthesis of the dinucleotide, thymidylyl-3',5'-thymidine
diphosphate.

XLIV

Identification of the cyclic 3' : 5'-phosphate derivative of thymidine, and of the
other cyclic compounds, can be based in part on the failure of efforts to demonstrate a secondary phosphoryl dissociation. In the case of adenosine-2' : 3'-phos-
phate, the pK of 6.0, characteristic of the non-cyclic nucleotide, disappears. The
hydrolytic reactions catalyzed by hydroxyl ions always give the isomeric mixtures
of the 2'- and 3'- or of the 3'- and 5'-compounds. The presence of the cyclic
phosphate ring renders the glycosyl bond sensitive to acid cleavage[119]. In addition
to the information these cyclic compounds have provided regarding the structure
of the nucleic acids, they are also valuable as intermediates in the chemical and,
as briefly described in Chapter 1, the enzymatic synthesis of the phosphodiester
linkage. This subject will be considered in the latter part of this chapter.

Synthesis of 5'-nucleotides

Of equal interest, however, is the biologically active group of nucleotides containing the phosphate on $C_{5'}$. It is beyond the scope of this text to consider in any
detail the enzymatic methods used for the synthesis of these compounds. Our
attention will be directed primarily to the chemical methods, as these procedures
have shed considerable light on the possible pathways involved in enzymatic
synthesis and degradation of the nucleotides. The subject can be divided into
two areas, that devoted to the synthesis of nucleoside-5'-phosphate compounds
and that devoted to the synthesis of nucleoside-5'-pyrophosphate compounds.
The former are of interest with regard to the chemical synthesis of the phosphodiester linkage, the latter in the enzymatic synthesis of the phosphodiester
linkage.

A basic requirement for the phosphorylation of a particular hydroxyl group of the
sugar moiety of the nucleoside is the protection of the remaining reactive hydroxyl

groups from the action of the phosphorylating agent. Some outlines of the principles employed to accomplish this goal have been indicated in the discussions above on the synthesis of the a and b isomers. For the synthesis of the 5'-isomers some modifications are necessary.

The original procedure introduced by Levene and Tipson[58, 60] for the synthesis of ribonucleotides involved the dehydration of the sugar by the formation of a cyclic isopropylidene derivative of the C_2', and C_3' hydroxyl groups (XXXIII), p. 37. This derivative is formed by the action of a dehydrating agent, such as zinc chloride, H_2SO_4, or copper sulfate in acetone. Todd recommends zinc chloride for the synthesis of 2',3'-O-isopropylidene derivatives of adenosine[120], guanosine[121], cytidine[122]; and copper sulfate and H_2SO_4 for 2',3'-O-isopropylidene uridine[123]. The mixture is refluxed for several hours, cooled, and the acetone removed by evaporation. For the synthesis of the adenosine derivative[58], the residue is rendered alkaline by the addition of barium hydroxide, neutralized by the addition of solid CO_2, heated to 80°, and filtered hot. The filtrate is cooled to crystallize out the adenosine derivative. For the synthesis of the guanosine derivative[124], the syrup remaining after removal of the acetone is dissolved in 2-ethoxyethanol, to which dry ether is added to crystallize the isopropylidene derivative. The latter is recrystallized from hot water. The uridine derivative is prepared in a manner similar to that for the adenosine derivative, except that calcium hydroxide is used instead of barium hydroxide[60]. The cytidine derivative is also prepared in the same manner with barium hydroxide[124].

In contrast to the general method for the protection of the 2'- and 3'-hydroxyl groups of the ribonucleosides, the method used for the deoxyribonucleosides involves a protection first of the C_5'-hydroxyl group, then of the C_3'-hydroxyl group. A method has been described for the synthesis of thymidine-5'-phosphate[125] and deoxycytidine-5'-phosphate[126] by Michelson and Todd. The nucleoside is mixed with triphenylmethyl chloride in anhydrous pyridine and left standing at room temperature for one week. The product, 5'-O-trityl thymidine or 5'-O-trityl deoxycytidine, is crystallized from pyridine by dilution with ice water.

XLV

XLVI

The C_3'-OH group is then acetylated with acetic anhydride in pyridine[127]. The product is crystallized by dilution with water. From thymidine there is obtained

3'-O-acetyl-, 5'-O-trityl-thymidine, and from deoxycytidine there is obtained N,O³'-diacetyl,O⁵'-tritylcytidine. The triphenylmethyl group is removed from both compounds by hydrolysis in acetic acid to yield 3'-O-acetyl thymidine and N,O³'-diacetyldeoxycytidine (XLV, XLVI).

Phosphorylation of the nucleoside derivatives can be brought about by a variety of agents. One of the early reagents used was dibenzyl phosphorochloridate, $(C_6H_5CH_2)_2POCl$. This compound is prepared from dibenzyl phosphite immediately before use. Dibenzyl phosphite is a product of the reaction of phosphorus trichloride with benzyl alcohol and diethylaniline in benzene[128]. Dibenzyl phosphite is allowed to react with chlorine in carbon tetrachloride at $-10°$ to give the unstable phosphorylation reagent[128,129].

For the synthesis of adenosine-5'-phosphate; 2',3'-O-isopropylidene-adenosine is phosphorylated with dibenzyl phosphorochloridate to yield 2',3'-O-isopropylidene-adenosine-5'-dibenzyl phosphate[130]. The benzyl groups are removed by hydrogenation with Pd carbon and PdO, and the isopropylidene ring hydrolyzed with sulfuric acid to yield adenosine-5'-phosphate.

Guanosine-5'-phosphate has been prepared by phosphorylation of the isopropylidene derivative with phosphoryl chloride[124], which is added to a solution of the nucleoside derivative in a mixture of anhydrous dimethylformamide and pyridine. The isopropylidene ring is then hydrolyzed with H_2SO_4.

Uridine-5'-phosphate requires a more tedious procedure than the above. The isopropylidene derivative is converted to 5'-O-toluene-p-sulfonyl-2',3'-O-isopropylidene-uridine by reacting with toluene-p-sulfonyl chloride in anhydrous pyridine. This product is then iodinated with sodium iodide in acetone at 100° for two hours to yield 5'-iodo-5'-deoxy-2',3'-O-isopropylidene-uridine. Phosphorylation of the iodo derivative by refluxing with silver dibenzyl phosphate in benzene yields dibenzyl 2',3'-O-isopropylidene-uridine-5'-phosphate[131], which is then converted to uridine-5'-phosphate by methods similar to those used for the preparation of adenosine-5'-phosphate.

Cytidine-5'-phosphate is prepared by methods analogous to those used for the synthesis of adenosine-5'-phosphate[124].

Thymidine-5'-phosphate[125] and deoxycytidine-5'-phosphate[126] are also prepared by the use of dibenzylphosphorochloridate[132].

Chambers et al.[133], have prepared guanosine-5'-phosphate from the isopropylidene derivative by phosphorylation with tetra p-nitrophenyl pyrophosphate. The intermediate, 2',3'-isopropylideneguanosine-5'-di-p-nitrophenyl phosphate, was hydrolyzed in alkaline methyl cyanide to yield 2',3'-isopropylideneguanosine-5'-p-nitrophenyl hydrogen phosphate. The p-nitrophenyl group was removed by the action of crude snake venom, and the isopropylidene group hydrolyzed by acid. This procedure gives yields as high as 70%.

Hall and Khorana[134] used phosphorus pentoxide and 85% phosphoric acid as the phosphorylating system for the synthesis of uridine-5'-phosphate, starting with the isopropylidene derivative of uridine. The reaction is carried out at 60° for two hours; the mixture neutralized with lithium hydroxide to pH 9, to remove the phosphate as the insoluble tri-lithium salt; and the solution chromatographed on a Dowex 2 ion-exchange column for the separation of UMP from uridine. The final yield of a barium salt was 65%. For maximum yields of the nucleotide, the phosphorylation should not be allowed to continue longer than two hours. At longer time intervals increasing amounts of uridine-2',3'- and 3',5'-diphosphate are synthesized (23.1% after 3.5 hours).

The synthesis of uridine-5'-phosphate is also described by Levene and Tipson[60], Gulland and Hobday[135], and Hall and Khorana[136].

Properties of the nucleotides

The addition of the phosphate group to the pentose portion of the nucleosides has the expected effect upon the electrophoretic and proton-binding properties of these molecules. Thus adenylic, guanylic, and cytidylic acids exist largely as zwitterions at pH's acid to the pK's of their respective bases.

In addition to the pK arising from the base itself, all of the nucleotides possess a pK close to 1.0, which arises from the primary phosphate ionization, and a second pK near 6.0, which represents the secondary phosphate ionization. The sugar dissociation at about 12.5, which is observed for nucleosides, is not found for nucleotides.

Table 3 (p. 24) includes values for the base pK's of the nucleotides. There is generally a slight alkaline displacement from the corresponding value for the nucleoside. This is explicable in terms of the electrostatic effect of the negatively charged phosphate[137-140]. Jordan[137] has made use of the theory of Kirkwood and Westheimer to compute the separation of charged groups. The magnitude of the shift in the base pK will, of course, depend upon the position of the phospho-monoester group and is different for 2'-, 3'-, and 5'-nucleotides.

Jordan has computed the fractions of nucleotide in the zwitterionic form, using the known constants for the binding of a proton by the bases and the phosphate groups[137]. In the cases of adenylic and cytidylic acids the nucleotide is almost 100 per cent. zwitterionic in the iso-electric region. In the case of guanylic acid there is an appreciable concentration of other ionic forms, because of the relatively low guanine pK.

Cavalieri[141] and Loring et al.[142], have made careful hydrogen ion titrations of cytidylic acids a and b in an effort to correlate the magnitude of the observed pK with the position of the phosphate group on the sugar. A higher pK, according to the concepts of Kirkwood and Westheimer[139,140], corresponds to a closer proximity of two oppositely charged groups. Cavalieri obtained pK values of 4.36 and 6.17 for cytidylic acid a and 4.28 and 6.0 for cytidylic acid b. Therefore, the a isomer is cytidine-2'-phosphate and the b isomer cytidine-3'-phosphate, in agreement with conclusions reached by other techniques.

In general, the state of ionization of the phosphate group has little influence upon the ultaviolet absorption curve of the base, which is only slightly different for the nucleoside and nucleotide[142]. Minor differences have been reported between the 2'-, 3'-. and 5'-isomers of cytidylic acid[142].

The structure of nucleotides has not been studied extensively by X-ray crystallographic methods, despite the importance of such information in interpreting X-ray diffraction data upon polynucleotides. The Watson-Crick model of DNA[144] has been based primarily on the information available regarding the structure of the nucleosides. Recently Alver and Furberg[105] have completed a study of

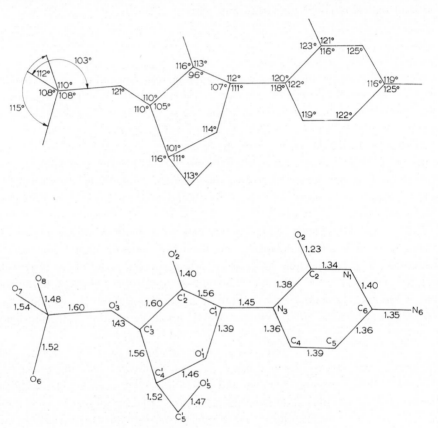

Fig. 7. Bond lengths and angles for cytidylic acid b[105].

cytidylic acid b, the results of which are summarized in Fig. 7, taken from their paper. Confirming previous studies with cytidine[74], the N-glycosidic linkage was found to be of the β-type. Also the ribose and pyrimidine rings were found to be mutually perpendicular. However, two new findings were made which conceivably might require some minor modification of previous ideas regarding the configuration of nucleotides in DNA and other helical polynucleotides.

The first of these is the configuration of the phosphate group located at $C_{3'}$. Instead of having the tetrahedral angle assumed in most current models of polynucleotides the $C_{3'} - O_{3'} - P$ angle is 121°, a value also found in dibenzylphosphate[145]. The $O_{3'} - P$ bond is in transposition with respect to the ribose ring and parallel to the $N_3 - C_{1'}$ bond, with a separation of about 1.6 Å. In current polynucleotide models[144, 146] these bonds are placed nearly perpendicular to one another.

The second new finding deals with the shape of the ribose moiety. Atoms $C_{1'}$, $O_{1'}$, $C_{3'}$ and $C_{4'}$ lie in nearly the same plane, but $C_{2'}$ is out of this plane by approximately 0.5 Å with its oxygen atom, $O_{2'}$, almost in the plane. Cytidine, in contrast, has the $C_{3'}$ atom out of the plane by about 0.5 Å[74]. The combination of the ring puckering and the wide angle formed by the $C_{3'} - O_{3'} - P$ bonds makes the molecule a rather extended one.

The other features of the nucleotide structure are similar to those previously found for cytidine[74]. The $N_3 - C_{1'}$, whose bond-length is 1.45 Å, corresponding to a single bond, lies in the plane of the pyrimidine ring and forms angles of 111° and 112° with the ribose $C_{1'} - O_{1'}$ and $C_{1'} - C_{2'}$ bonds respectively. The $C_6 - N_6$ bond to the amino group is only 1.35 Å in length, indicating considerable double bond character. The angles of the amino group form a flattened pyramid.

Alver and Furberg conclude that, with respect to current models of helical polynucleotides, this structure of cytidylic acid b requires no major modifications except possibly those suggested by the wide $C_{3'} - O_{3'} - P$ angle and the unexpected kind of ring puckering. The latter, however, may be unique for D-ribose and not a feature of D-deoxyribose.

THE NUCLEOSIDE-5′-PYROPHOSPHATES

We now direct our attention to the synthesis of the nucleoside pyrophosphates, which, as mentioned earlier, are of interest because of the role of these derivatives in the synthesis of polynucleotides by enzymatic means, In most instances the starting materials for the preparation of the nucleoside di- or triphosphates are the nucleoside-5′-phosphates.

The early methods developed by Todd's group involved the phosphorylation of adenosine-5′-benzyl phosphate[130], a derivative obtained by the acid hydrolysis of the 2′,3′-isopropylidene adenosine-5′-dibenzyl phosphate, the synthesis of which has been described above. The silver salt of the monobenzyl ester is phosphorylated with dibenzyl chlorophosphonate to give adenosine-5′-tribenzyl pyrophosphate (XLVII). Catalytic hydrogenation removes the benzyl groups to yield ADP. If the tribenzyl derivative is heated with a tertiary base, one benzyl group is lost from the

XLVII

terminal phosphate[147, 148]. The resulting dibenzyl derivative can be phosphorylated again with dibenzyl chlorophosphonate to give a tetrabenzyl ester of ATP. Catalytic hydrogenation removes the benzyl groups to yield ATP.

Similar methods have been used for the synthesis of UDP. One of these[149] involves the phosphorylation with silver tribenzyl pyrophosphate of the derivative 2',3'-isopropylidene, 5'-iodo,5'-deoxyuridine (XLVIII), to yield the intermediate

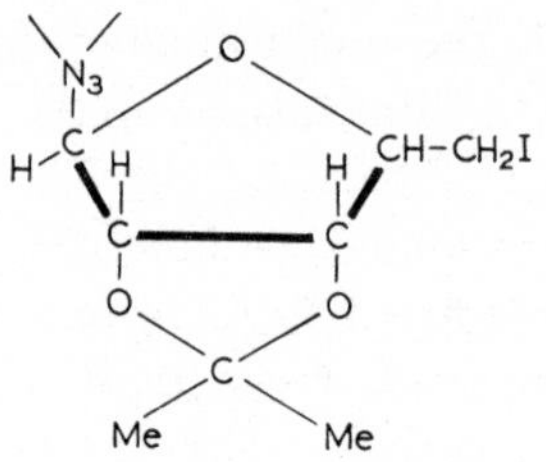

XLVIII 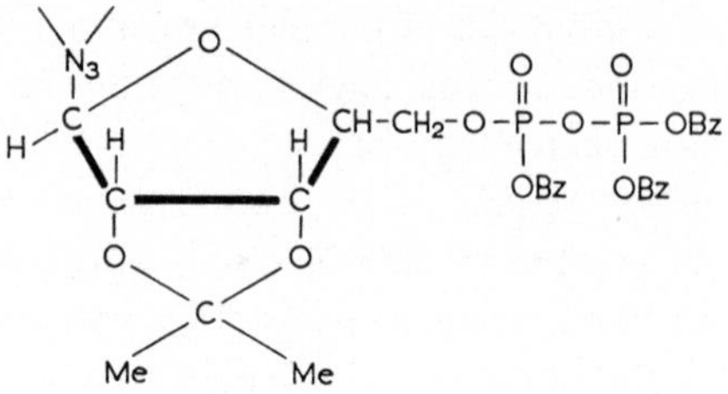   XLIX

2',3'-isopropylidene-5'-tribenzyl pyrophosphate (XLIX). Acid hydrolysis and hydrogenation remove the protective groups to yield UDP.

The other procedure involves phosphorylation of 2',3'-isopropylidene-uridine-5'-benzyl chlorophosphonate (L) with triethylammonium dibenzyl phosphate[150]. The protecting groups are removed by the usual methods.

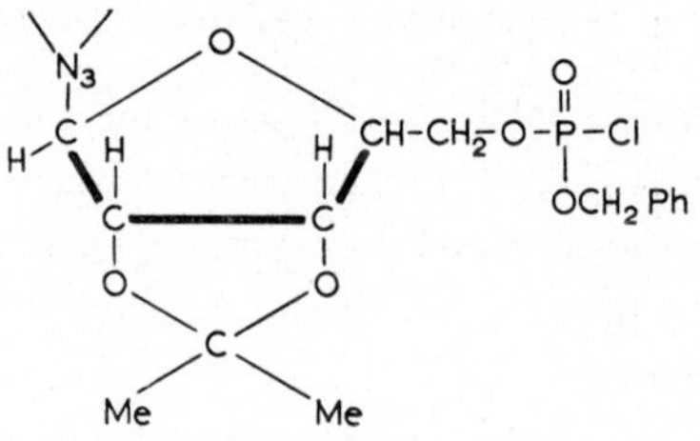

L

Khorana[151] has introduced another general method which does not require the protection of the $C_{2'}$ and $C_{3'}$ hydroxyl groups. The starting material is the nucleoside-5'-phosphate. The reagent, dicyclohexyl carbodiimide LI, is used for the synthesis of an intermediate which is then attacked by the phosphorylating group. The principle of the reaction is similar to that involved in the synthesis of cyclic phosphate nucleosides[115, 116].

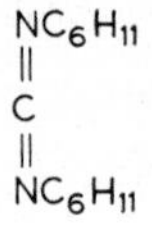

LI 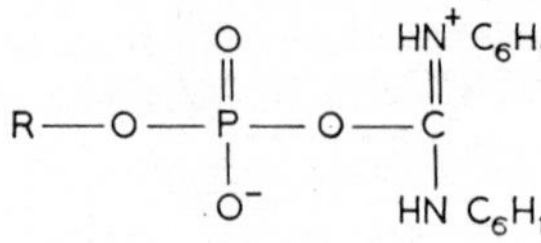   LII

In the presence of a monoester of phosphoric acid, the carbodiimide reagent probably forms the transient derivative, LII. This adduct can then be attacked by a second phosphate ester to form a symmetrical pyrophosphate or, in the presence of excess concentrations, by phosphoric acid to yield the unsymmetrical pyrophosphate compound, LIII, and the carbodiimide derivative, LIV. The unsymmetrical pyrophosphate derivative can undergo a second reaction with the carbodiimide reagent to yield, in the presence of excess phosphoric acid, the triphosphate compound.

LIII   LIV

For the synthesis of ADP and ATP the reaction is carried out in aqueous pyridine[151]; the per cent. yields of the two nucleotides are governed in part by the ratio of AMP to phosphoric acid and by the quantity of pyridine, water and the carbodiimide reagent. Maximum yields of ADP were 44% of the initial AMP; of ATP 56% of the initial AMP, each being dependent upon the experimental conditions.

This method has also been used for the synthesis of UDP and UTP from UMP[152] and of GDP and GTP from GMP[153]. The yields of the guanosine derivatives have proved to be low, primarily because of the low solubility of the carbodiimide derivatives in aqueous pyridine.

The solubility difficulty may be overcome by the use of the tri-n-butylammonium salts of the nucleoside-5'-phosphates[154]. A characteristic result of the use of this salt is the proportionately higher yield of the triphosphate derivatives. A possible explanation offered by Smith and Khorana is the formation of a cyclic metaphosphate of the triphosphate nucleoside, which accumulates in the reaction mixture. The authors also describe an interesting "dismutation" reaction, which takes place on incubating ADP with the carbodiimide reagent, yielding mixtures of AMP and ATP.

The common competing reaction in the synthesis of the pyrophosphate esters is the formation of symmetrical compounds represented by P^1P^2 dithymidine-5'-diphosphate (XLIII) and P^1P^2 diadenosine-5'-diphosphate, both prepared from the coupling of two nucleoside-5'-phosphate molecules. In addition, the compound, P^1P^4 diadenosine-5'-tetraphosphate can be prepared from ADP. It is believed that the hydrolysis of this compound can occur between P^1 and P^2 (or P^3 and P^4) to yield a mixture of AMP and ATP; or between P^2 and P^3 to yield ADP, thus accounting for the "dismutation" observed by Smith and Khorana[154].

Smith and Khorana[154] have defined the conditions necessary for optimum yields of polyphosphate derivatives of adenosine, cytidine, guanosine, uridine, deoxycytidine and deoxyguanosine, starting with the tri-n-butylammonium salts of the nucleoside-5'-phosphate compounds.

A third method for the synthesis of nucleoside polyphosphates has been described recently by Chambers and Khorana[155]. The objectives of this procedure included the prevention of the excessive side reactions encountered in the carbodiimide method. In principle, the nucleoside-5'-phosphate compound is converted to a derivative which contains a highly reactive $P-X$ linkage, in which the phosphorus is electrophilic. The derivative is subsequently attacked at the $P-X$ linkage by an anion, such as phosphoric acid or another phosphomonoester. Phosphoramidic acid and its esters were found to meet the requirements for X.

Unlike the carbodiimide method, the phosphoramidic method requires the protection of the reactive hydroxyl groups. 2',3'-di-O-Acetyladenosine (LV) is

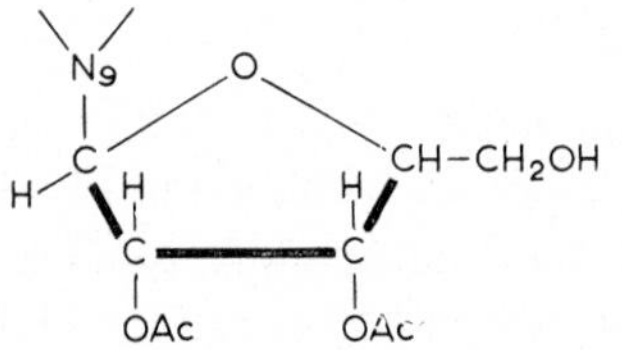

LV 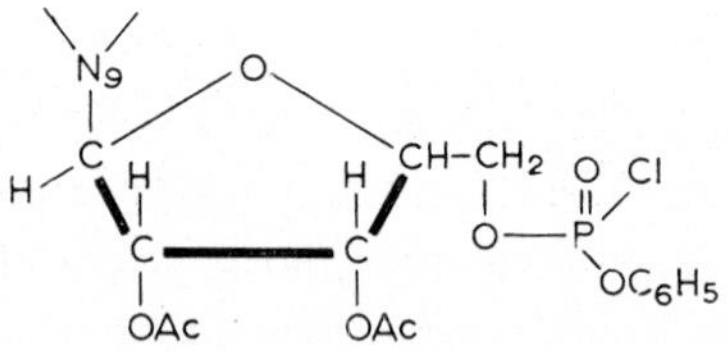   LVI

phosphorylated with phenylphosphorodichloridate[156] in the presence of quinoline to yield the intermediate, 2',3'-di-O-acetyladenosine-5'-phenylphosphorochloridate (LVI) which, when treated with ammonia, becomes LVII. The acetyl and phenyl groups are removed by hydrolysis with lithium hydroxide to yield adenosine-5'-phosphoramidate (LVIII).

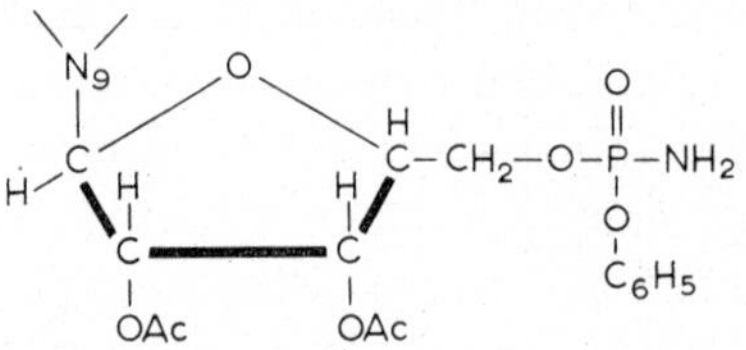

LVII 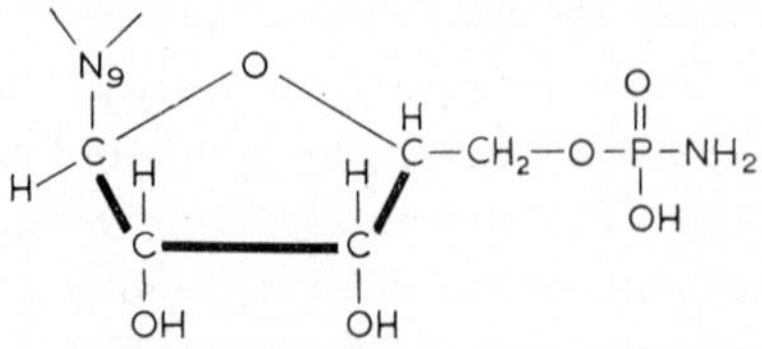   LVIII

The 1,3-dicyclohexylguanidinium salt of the phosphoroamidate derivative is then reacted with an 85% solution of phosphoric acid in o-chlorophenol solvent, a 2-phase system which must be agitated continuously for successful synthesis of the pyrophosphate compound. The yield of ADP as prepared by Chambers and Khorana was 49% of the initial AMP.

Clark et al.[157] have synthesized ADP and ATP with monobenzylphosphoraamidate.

The phosphoramidate reaction can also be used for the synthesis of a variety of coenzymes containing a pyrophosphate group. Uridine di-phosphate glucose and flavin adenine dinucleotide[158], as well as coenzyme A[159], have been synthesized by means of phosphoramidate derivatives of the nucleotides.

The properties of the polyphosphate nucleotides have not been studied as extensively as the monophosphate derivatives, possibly because their discovery, with the exception of ADP and ATP, has been relatively recent.

The pK values of the homologous series of nucleotides show an increase as the number of phosphate groups increase, reflecting the effect of the electrostatic field discussed above. In Table 3 are given the pK values for the proton binding sites of the adenine, guanine, and cytidine series; the secondary phosphate dissociation of these and the uracil series; and the enol groups of the uracil and guanine series[160].

THE CHEMICAL SYNTHESIS OF THE PHOSPHODIESTER LINKAGE

The development of methods for the synthesis by purely chemical methods of the phosphodiester linkage has been a natural consequence of the earlier synthetic studies devoted to the phosphorylation of specific sugar hydroxyl groups of the nucleosides. Michelson and Todd[161] were able to synthesize dithymidine monophosphate and dithymidine diphosphate which possessed the 3',5'-phosphodiester linkage. This was rendered possible by the difference in reactivity of the two hydroxyl groups. The procedure of Michelson and Todd involved the synthesis of a nucleoside phosphate with the $C_{3'}$ hydroxyl protected, its conversion to a phosphorochloridate derivative, and the phosphorylation by the latter of the $C_{3'}$ hydroxyl of a second nucleoside.

The derivative 3',5'-di-O-acetylthymidine (cf. LV) was converted by the action of ammonia in ethanol to a mixture of 5'-O-acetylthymidine and 3'-O-acetylthymidine, which were separated by countercurrent distribution. The 5'-O-isomer was then treated with O-benzylphosphorous O,O-diphenylphosphoric anhydride in the presence of 2,6-lutidine, to yield 5'-O-acetylthymidine-3'-benzyl phosphite. The reaction of N-chlorosuccinimide with the latter produced 5'-O-acetylthymidine-3'-benzyl phosphorochloridate (cf. LVI).

In the next step, the phosphorochloridate was allowed to react with 3'-O-acetylthymidine in the presence of excess 2,6-lutidine. A complex mixture of products was obtained. After removal of the acetyl and benzyl groups by hydrolysis, the final mixture was fractionated by ion exchange chromatography to yield thymidine-3'-phosphate, the dinucleoside monophosphate thymidylyl-5',3'-thymidine, and di-(thymidine-3')-P^1P^2 pyrophosphate (cf. XLIII, p. 43).

By a variant of the above procedure it was also possible to synthesize the true dinucleotide thymidylyl-5',3'-thymidine-5'-phosphate (LIX).

The method of Michelson and Todd has not been used extensively and is not satisfactory for the synthesis of polynucleotides beyond the dinucleotide stage. A major drawback of the method is the simultaneous production of a number of difficultly separable by-products.

Khorana *et al.*[162] introduced a different approach to the problem. Instead of relying on the phosphorylating properties of the benzylphosphorochloridate derivative to attack selectively the $C_{5'}$ hydroxyl group of a nucleotide, the phosphorolysis reaction was brought about by the action of *p*-toluenesulfonyl chloride.

The mechanism was believed to involve the activation of the phosphomonoester group of the nucleoside-5'-phosphate, which then was attacked by the hydroxyl group of a nucleoside or nucleotide, *i.e.*, phosphorolysis took place. From a mixture of thymidine-5'-phosphate and 5'-tritylthymidine, a yield of 45% of thymidylyl-5',3'-thymidine was obtained.

Subsequent studies showed that dicyclohexylcarbodiimide was superior to the *p*-toluene derivative[163]. A detailed study of the properties and mechanism of phosphodiester synthesis was carried out by Gilham and Khorana[164]. The $C_{5'}$ hydroxyl group of the nucleoside or nucleotide attacking the carbodiimide derivative must be protected to prevent the synthesis of $C_{5'} - C_{5'}$ phosphodiester linkages. This can be accomplished by acetylation or by the addition of the triphenylmethyl (trityl) group. For better stoichiometry it is also desirable to protect the $C_{3'}$ hydroxyl group of the activated nucleotide to minimize self-condensation.

Thymidylyl-5',3'-thymidine was synthesized in 66% yield from 5'-O-tritylthymidine and 3'-O-acetylthymidine-5'-phosphate in anhydrous pyridine[163], to which was added the carbodiimide reagent. After 48 hours at room temperature, the dinucleoside phosphate product, 3'-O-acetylthymidylyl (5',3'),(5'-O-trityl)-thymidine, was isolated and the protecting groups removed by acid and alkaline hydrolysis. A 50% yield could be obtained without protecting the $C_{3'}$ hydroxyl group, provided that there was present an excess of 5'-O-tritylthymidine, which prevented the self-condensation of thymidine-5'-phosphate. *p*-Toluenesulfonyl chloride was the activating agent.

The true dinucleotide, thymidylyl-5',3'-thymidine-5'-phosphate, was prepared from the reaction of 5'-O-dibenzylphosphorylthymidine and 3'-O-acetylthymidine-5'-phosphate using the carbodiimide reagent. The yield was 35–40%. Similarly, deoxyadenylyl-5',3'-thymidine-5'-phosphate has been prepared in 40% yield.

The dinucleotides can also be prepared from the dinucleoside monophosphate compounds by phosphorylation of the free $C_{5'}$ or $C_{3'}$ hydroxyl group. The trityl intermediate formed in the synthesis of the dinucleoside phosphate compound is used. For the synthesis of thymidylyl-5',3'-thymidine-5'-phosphate the intermediate is treated with acid to remove the trityl group at $C_{5'}$ and then phosphorylated at the $C_{5'}$ position with dibenzylphosphorochloridate. Similarly, thymidylyl-3',5'-thymidine-3'-phosphate is prepared after removal of the 3'-O-acetyl group by alkaline hydrolysis.

It is probable that the mechanism of phosphodiester synthesis is not a simple phosphorolytic attack by the $C_{3'}$ hydroxyl group on the activated $C_{5'}$ phosphate group of the nucleotide, a mechanism which presumably occurs in the synthesis of phosphodiesters with alkyl phosphates and alcohol[165]. Gilham and Khorana believe rather that an intermediate condensation product of the activated nucleotide is first synthesized: P^1, P^2-dithymidine-5'-diphosphate (cf. XLIII, p. 43), which is subsequently activated by the carbodiimide reagent to permit phosphorolysis of the adduct by the $C_{3'}$ hydroxyl group of the nucleoside or nucleotide. Evidence for this sequence of events is furnished by the accumulation of the acetylated derivative of P^1, P^2-dithymidine-5'-diphosphate in the reaction mixture *before* the occurrence of any phosphorylation of the nucleotide takes place. Subsequently, it was shown[166] that these pyrophosphate derivatives can serve as starting material for the synthesis of the phosphodiester linkage. As these derivatives are not suitable phosphorylating agents without the presence of the carbodiimide reagent, it must be assumed that an active intermediate must be formed. However, it has not yet been isolated.

Tener *et al.*[119], extended the study of the synthesis of phosphodiester bonds beyond the dinucleotide state[162, 163, 167]. Two classes of polymer are formed from thymidine-5'-phosphate: linear and cyclic. Both *p*-toluene-sulfonyl chloride and dicyclohexylcarbodiimide reagents are effective in polymerizing this nucleotide. The reaction is carried out in anhydrous pyridine with the pyridinium salt of thymidine-5'-phosphate. With low concentrations of *p*-toluenesulfonyl chloride, the only product isolated is P^1,P^2-dithymidine-5'-diphosphate. At higher concentrations the oligonucleotides are formed.

The products of the reaction are separated by aminoalkyl-substituted cellulose columns: diethylamino-ethyl (DEAE) cellulose and (ECTEOLA) cellulose. The elution system is a gradient of lithium chloride or stepwise elution with 0.05, 0.01, 0.15 and 0.25 M lithium chloride. This method of fractionating oligonucleotides has proven to be extremely useful and has almost become the standard procedure for this purpose. The separation of the linear and cyclic oligonucleotides by cellulose columns is not complete and must be supplemented by paper chromatography with the solvent system isopropyl alcohol–ammonia–water (7 : 1 : 2, by volume).

In a large scale preparation the yields of the various oligonucleotides varied from a maximum of 15–20% for the cyclic dinucleotide to a minimum of 0.5% for the cyclic pentanucleotide. The percent yields of the linear oligonucleotides were 3, 5, 7, 6, and 3% for the mono-, di-, tri-, tetra- and penta-nucleotides. The yields for the cyclic nucleotides were 15–20, 5–6, 3 and 0.5% for the di-, tri-, tetra-, and pentanucleotides, respectively.

Identification of the linear oligonucleotides, which contain a phosphomonoester terminal group at $C_{5'}$, is based on the increased mobility of the polymer, as determined by paper electrophoresis, at pH 7.5 as compared with that at pH 3.5; on electrometric titrations, which showed that the ratio of the number of primary phosphoryl dissociations to secondary phosphoryl dissociations was 3 and 4 for tri- and tetranucleotides, respectively; and on the removal of the $C_{5'}$ phosphate group with snake venom phosphomonoesterase. The identification of the cyclic oligonucleotides, which do not contain a phosphomonoester terminal group, was based on the absence of a secondary phosphoryl dissociation and on their stability toward 0.1 N HCl at 100°, which readily hydrolyzes the pyrophosphate linkage of P^1, P^2-dithymidine-5'-diphosphate. Unequivocal proof of the cyclic structure of the dinucleotide was obtained by the synthesis of the cyclic derivative from the linear dinucleotide in an 80% yield with the carbodiimide reagent in pyridine. Each cyclic oligonucleotide has the same electrophoretic mobility as its homologous linear oligonucleotide at pH 3.5.

Both the linear and cyclic oligonucleotides are readily hydrolyzed by snake venom phosphodiesterase, the former more rapidly than the latter. The product is thymidine-5'-phosphate. Acid hydrolysis at 100° in 1 N HCl for 3 hours yields thymidine-3',5'-diphosphate and thymidine-3'-phosphate. Treatment with spleen diesterase yields thymidine-3'-phosphate. Thus, the phosphodiester linkage is clearly the 5',3' form.

If the position of one of the oligonucleotides can be established in the elution sequence from the cellulose column, the others can be identified by their relative sequence which is in the order mono-, di-, tri-, tetra-, penta-, etc. Tener, *et al.*[119] believe that polymers with up to eleven units are synthesized by this method, although the chromatographic separation of the higher homologs is not feasible with the systems presently available. Presumably, the higher homologs are linear, judging from the rapid decrease in yield of cyclic oligonucleotides as the degree of polymerization increases.

The synthesis of an homologous series of oligonucleotides does not require the protection of reactive hydroxyl groups in the deoxyribonucleotide series, although, of course, as shown by the results of Tener et al.[119], failure to protect these groups results in some self-condensation or cyclization of the polymer. In order to block the self-condensation reaction, Tener et al.[168] used a mixture of 3'-O-acetylthymidylic acid and thymidine-5'-phosphate in a molar ratio of 1:2 and obtained 4 times more linear dinucleotide than cyclic dinucleotide, compared with a ratio of 1:4 in the absence of the acetylated derivative.

The stepwise synthesis of mixed oligonucleotides has also been extended beyond the dinucleotide stage[169] to tri-nucleoside-diphosphate polymers. Two modifications were introduced. The dinucleotide is reacted with the carbodiimide reagent first to form the fully substituted pyrophosphate derivative (LX), a condensation product of two molecules of the dinucleotide, where R and R' (LX) are the nucleoside components. Then the mononucleotide is added. The ratio of the mononucleotide to dinucleotide is increased from 1 : 1[164] to 2 : 1 to increase the yield with respect to the diester product.

The requirement that the dinucleotide be converted to the fully substituted pyrophosphate derivative stems from the necessity of preventing the synthesis of intermediates of the type LXI, which might be formed between the dinucleotide and mononucleotide and would probably be inefficient as phosphorylating agents.

The stepwise synthesis of thymidylyl-5',3'-thymidylyl-5',3'-thymidine was accomplished by reacting thymidylyl-(5',3')-(5'-O-trityl)-thymidine with dicyclohexylcarbodiimide for one hour and then with two equivalents of 3'-O-acetylthymidine-5'-phosphate for two days at room temperature. The trityl derivative of the trinucleoside diphosphate was isolated in 68% yield and catalytically hydrogenolysed to give the desired product.

A mixed trinucleoside diphosphate was prepared from deoxyadenylyl-(5',3')-5'-O-tritylthymidine and N,O$_{3'}$-diacetyldeoxycytidine-5'-phosphate. The intermediate derivative was treated with alkali to remove the acetyl groups and yield deoxycytidylyl-5',3'-deoxyadenylyl-(5',3')-5'-O-trityl-thymidine in 37% yield. The yield is believed to be low in part because of the reactivity of the unprotected C$_6$ amino group of the adenine base. Removal of the trityl group is complicated by the acid lability of the adenosine glycoside bond. Catalytic hydrogenolysis is also unsatisfactory, because of the susceptibility of the cytosine ring to hydrogenation. A reasonably good yield (83%) was obtained by mild acid hydrolysis in 80% aqueous acetic acid at room temperature for 26 hours.

It is pointed out by Gilham and Khorana[169] that a major problem in the synthesis of higher mixed oligonucleotides is the decreasing solubility of the intermediates in the organic solvents, a problem also present in the synthesis of oligonucleotides of the ribonucleotide series[170].

The structure of these mixed oligonucleotides was confirmed by the identification of the enzymatic digestion products with spleen phosphodiesterase as the 3'-isomers of the corresponding deoxynucleotides.

The emphasis in organic synthesis of the phosphodiester bond has been directed toward activating the C$_{5'}$ phosphomonoester group for subsequent phosphorolysis. An alternative procedure would be to activate the C$_{3'}$ phosphoryl group in an analagous manner. Turner and Khorana[166] have accomplished the synthesis of oligonucleotides from thymidine-3'-phosphate. These differ from the previous series of oligonucleotides by having a terminal C$_{3'}$-phosphomonoester rather than a C$_{5'}$-phosphomonoester. Incidental to this study was the development of a synthetic method for the production of thymidine-3'-phosphate from 5'-O-tritylthymidine and p-nitrophenyl phosphorodichloridate in pyridine. After removal of the trityl group of the intermediate by mild acid hydrolysis, the product thymidine-3'-p-nitrophenyl phosphate was obtained in 94–97% yields. Alkaline hydrolysis of this product to remove the p-nitrophenyl group was unsuccessful because of the formation of the cyclic intermediate, thymidine-3' : 5'-phosphate, which then was hydrolyzed into a mixture of the 3'- and 5'-isomers. The p-nitrophenyl group was successfully removed by mild alkaline hydrolysis of the trityl derivative; the trityl group was then removed by acid hydrolysis. No migration of the phosphoryl group could occur under these conditions. The final yield of thymidine-3'-phosphate was 75%.

The nucleotide was condensed by the method described earlier to form the pyrophosphate derivative, P^1, P^2-dithymidine-3'-diphosphate. This substance was then treated with an excess of the carbodiimide reagent for four days at room temperature to bring about the polymerization. Both linear and cyclic oligonucleotides were synthesized. The linear polymers were identified by methods similar to those used in the identification of the $C_{5'}$ phosphomonoester terminal polymers. The terminal phosphate group was removed by prostate phosphomonoesterase to yield a series of homologous compounds identical with those obtained in the previous case by the removal of the $C_{5'}$ phosphomonoester group by the same enzyme. Hydrolysis of the polymer by spleen phosphodiesterase yielded only the thymidine-3'-phosphate nucleotide, indicating that the $C_{5'}$ hydroxyl group was free and that the $C_{3'}$ position was occupied by a phosphate group.

The cyclic oligonucleotides were, of course, identical with those obtained from cytidine-5'-phosphate polymerization.

The ribonucleotide series

The synthesis of the diester linkages in the ribonucleotide series has presented a difficult problem because of the presence of the *cis* $C_{2'}$ hydroxyl group. Michelson *et al.*,[171] was able to synthesize the dinucleoside, adenylyl-2',5'-uridine by condensing 3',5'-di-O-acetyladenosine-2'-benzylphosphorochloridate with 2',3'-di-O-acetyluridine and then removing the protective groups in the usual way.

Later Hall, Todd and Webb[172] synthesized the dinucleotide adenylyl-5',3'-uridine-5'-phosphate. The reaction occurred through the formation of a mixed anhydride with a nucleoside phosphorochloridate derivative (1) and either 2,6-lutidine diphenylphosphate or trifluoroacetate (*cf.* XL, p. 41).

Recently, Michelson[170] demonstrated the synthesis of a mixture of ribonucleotide polymers from nucleoside-2' : 3'-phosphate substrates. The polynucleotides contain 2',5'- and 3',5'-phosphodiester linkage which are apparently distributed randomly throughout the polymer chain. The mechanism of polymerization is, therefore, reminiscent of that catalyzed by ribonuclease[173] in which the substrate were also the 2' : 3'-cyclic phosphate nucleosides.

The polymerization is brought about by the action of tetraphenylpyrophosphate.

Presumably, an unstable pyrophosphate intermediate (LXII) of the kind postulated by Khorana (LX) is formed. The second step is the phosphorolysis of this derivative by the $C_{5'}$ hydroxyl group at a second nucleotide to form the dinucleotide. In view of the experience of Khorana and his associates with the mechanism of polymerization of the deoxyribonucleotides via the formation of a fully saturated pyrophos-

LXII   LXIII

phate intermediate, *i.e.*, LX, this concept of Michelson's appears reasonable. A fundamental weakness of this method of phosphodiester synthesis is inherent in the structure of the intermediate LXII which provides for no specificity toward $C_{3'}$ or $C_{2'}$ ester formation.

The synthetic polymers are readily hydrolyzed by alkali to the 2'- and 3'-isomers. If nucleoside-2' : 3'-cyclic phosphate,5'-phosphate is included in the reaction mixture, this nucleotide appears at the front end of the polymer and can be isolated from the alkaline digests of the polymer as uridine-2',5'-diphosphate and uridine-3',5'-diphosphate. The average length of the polymers obtained ranged from 4 to 8 nucleotide units, the upper lengths being limited by the insolubility of the higher homologs in organic solvents.

Positive identification of the 2',5'-phosphodiester linkage is based on the failure of up to 50% of the polyuridylic acid ester linkages to be hydrolyzed by either ribonuclease or spleen phosphodiesterase, both of which are specific for the 3',5'-phosphodiester linkage.

In addition to tetraphenylpyrophosphate (formed from diphenylphosphorochloridate), other acid anhydrides have been found capable of initiating the polymerization of the cyclic phosphate nucleosides. These include diphenyl phosphoric-benzyl phosphorus anhydride. The products obtained by the action of this compound on adenosine-2' : 3'-phosphate included polyadenylic acid with a 5'-benzyl phosphite group at the head and a cyclic 2' : 3'-phosphate at the tail.

It will be recalled that the polymerization of cyclic phosphate nucleosides by ribonuclease resulted in the synthesis only of the 3',5'-phosphodiester linkage[173]. Furthermore, the intermediate in the hydrolysis of polyribonucleotides by ribonuclease is the cyclic phosphate nucleoside. It would appear, therefore, that the mechanism of action of the enzyme may be somewhat similar to that occurring with the acid anhydrides.

The need for a specific synthesis of the 5',3'-phosphodiester linkage of the ribonucleotide series obviously requires a different approach than that developed by Michelson with mixed anhydrides. Investigators in Khorana's laboratory also approached the problem via the cyclic phosphate nucleosides. Tener and Khorana[116] were able to synthesize alkyl ribonucleoside phosphates by acid catalysis of mixtures of the 2' : 3' cyclic phosphate with an alcohol. The reaction occurs as a result of the reactivity of the cyclic nucleoside-2' : 3'-phosphate intermediate which is phosphorylyzed by an alcohol to yield the alkyl derivative (LXIII). This is similar to a reaction catalyzed by ribonuclease and by spleen phosphodiesterase[174]. Unfortunately, the former reaction will not take place with any degree of success if the alcohol is replaced by a nucleoside.

Quite recently, Smith and Khorana[118] announced the successful chemical synthesis of uridylyl-5',3'-uridine. Uridine-5'-phosphate, under conditions of high dilution, is converted to its cyclic 3' : 5'-phosphate derivative by the action of dicyclohexylcarbodiimide. The cyclic phosphate, in the free acid form, was treated with dihydropyran in anhydrous dioxane to yield its 2'-O-tetrahydropyranyl derivative.

Alkaline hydrolysis of the latter compound produced a mixture of the 2'-tetrahydropyranyluridine-3'- and 5'-phosphates, whose triphenylmethyl derivatives were prepared and then separated chromatographically. The derivative 5'-triphenylmethyl-, 2'-tetrahydropyranyluridine-3'-phosphate was reacted with 2',3'-di-O-acetyluridine in the presence of dicyclohexylcarbodiimide to yield, after removal of protective groups, uridylyl-5',3'-uridine and uridine.

Thus, it appears that the specific chemical synthesis of the 3',5'-phosphodiester linkage has been accomplished for the case of polyribonucleotides as well as polydeoxyribonucleotides.

REFERENCES

1 W. COHN, *Biochim. et Biophys. Acta*, 32 (1959) 569.

2 D. DUNN AND J. SMITH, *Biochem. J.*, 68 (1958) 627.

3 M. ADLER, B. WEISSMANN AND A. GUTMAN, *J. Biol. Chem.*, 230 (1958) 717.

4 J. LITTLEFIELD AND D. DUNN, *Biochem. J.*, 68 (1958) 8P.

5 L. BOSCH, E. HARBERS AND C. HEIDELBERGER, *Cancer Res.*, 18 (1958) 335.

6 E. HARBERS AND C. HEIDELBERGER, *Fed. Proc.*, 17 (1958) 237.

7 S. ZAMENHOF, K. RICH AND R. DEGIOVANNI, *J. Biol. Chem.*, 232 (1958) 651.

8 D. DUNN AND J. SMITH, *Biochem. J.*, 67 (1957) 494.

9 H. AMOS, *Abstr. Intern. Congr. Biochem. 4th Meeting, (Vienna)*, (1958) 127.

10 H. MANDEL AND R. MARKHAM, *Biochem. J.*, 69 (1958) 297.

11 P. LEVENE, *J. Biol. Chem.*, 53 (1922) 441.

12 E. VISCHER AND E. CHARGAFF, *J. Biol. Chem.*, 176 (1948) 715.

13 H. LORING, J. FAIRLEY AND H. SEAGRAN, *J. Biol. Chem.*, 197 (1952) 823.

14 S. KERR, K. SERAIDARIAN AND M. WARGON, *J. Biol. Chem.*, 181 (1949) 761, 773.

15 J. SMITH AND R. MARKHAM, *Biochem. J.*, 46 (1950) 509.

16 R. HOTCHKISS, *J. Biol. Chem.*, 175 (1948) 315.

17 A. MARSHAK AND H. VOGEL, *J. Biol. Chem.*, 189 (1951) 597.

18 W. COHN, *Science*, 109 (1949) 377.

19 G. WYATT, *Biochem. J.*, 48 (1951) 584.

20 K. DIMROTH, L. JAENICKE AND I. VOLLBRECHTSHAUSEN, *Z. physiol. Chem.*, 289 (1952) 71.

21 E. FISCHER, *Ber.*, 30 (1897) 2226.

22 W. TRAUBE, *Ann.*, 331 (1904) 64.

23 W. TRAUBE, *Ber.*, 33 (1900) 1371, 3035.

24 E. FISCHER AND G. ROEDER, *Ber.*, 34 (1901) 3751.

25 H. STEUDEL, *Z. physiol. Chem.*, 30 (1900) 539.

26 H. WHEELER AND H. MERRIAM, *Am. Chem. J.*, 29 (1903) 478.

27 H. WHEELER AND T. JOHNSON, *Am. Chem. J.*, 29 (1903) 492.

28 T. JOHNSON AND R. COGHILL, *J. Am. Chem. Soc.*, 47 (1925) 2838.

29 G. WYATT AND S. COHEN, *Nature*, 170 (1952) 1072.

30 J. DAVOLL, *J. Am. Chem. Soc.*, 73 (1951) 3174.

31 L. CAVALIERI, A. BENDICH, J. TINKER AND G. BROWN, *J. Am. Chem. Soc.*, 70 (1948) 3875.

32 B. LYTHGOE, A. TODD AND A. TOPHAM, *J. Chem. Soc.*, (1944) 315.

33 H. FRAENKEL-CONRAT, *Biochim. et Biophys. Acta*, 15 (1954) 307.

34 R. BEERS AND R. STEINER, *Nature*, 181 (1958) 30.

35 H. MILES, *Biochim. et Biophys. Acta*, 22 (1956) 247.

36 H. MILES, *Biochim. et Biophys. Acta*, 27 (1958) 46.

37 D. BROWN, E. HOERGER AND S. MASON, *J. Chem. Soc.*, (1955) 211.

38 R. SINSHEIMER, R. NUTTER AND G. HOPKINS, *Biochim. et Biophys. Acta*, 18 (1955) 13.

39 S. FURBERG, *Acta Chem. Scand.*, 4 (1950) 751.

40 W. COCHRAN, *Acta Cryst.*, 4 (1951) 81.

41 D. BROWN AND S. MASON, *J. Chem. Soc.*, (1957) 682.

42 L. PAULING AND R. COREY, *Arch. Biochem. Biophys.*, 65 (1956) 164.

43 G. PARRY, *Acta Cryst.*, 7 (1954) 313.

44 C. CLEWS AND W. COCHRAN, *Acta Cryst.*, 1 (1948) 4.

45 J. BROOMHEAD, *Acta Cryst.*, 4 (1951) 92.

46 P. LEVENE AND W. JACOBS, *Ber.*, 42 (1909) 1198; 44 (1911) 746.

47 P. LEVENE AND W. JACOBS, *Ber.*, 41 (1908) 2703.

48 W. VAN EKENSTEIN AND J. BLANKSMA, *Chem. Weekblad*, 10 (1913) 664.

49 P. LEVENE AND F. LAFORGE, *Ber.*, 45 (1912) 608.

50 P. LEVENE, *J. Biol. Chem.*, 55 (1923) 437.

51 J. GULLAND AND E. HOLIDAY, *J. Chem. Soc.*, (1936) 765.

52 J. GULLAND AND L. STORY, *J. Chem. Soc.*, (1938) 692.

53 J. GULLAND, E. HOLIDAY AND T. MACRAE, *J. Chem. Soc.*, (1934) 1639.

54 B. LYTHGOE, H. SMITH AND A. TODD, *J. Chem. Soc.*, (1947) 355.

55 P. LEVENE, *J. Biol. Chem.*, 63 (1925) 653.

[56] P. LEVENE AND R. TIPSON, *J. Biol. Chem.*, 94 (1932) 809.

[57] H. BREDERECK, *Z. physiol. Chem.*, 223 (1934) 61.

[58] P. LEVENE AND R. TIPSON, *J. Biol. Chem.*, 121 (1937) 131.

[59] P. LEVENE AND R. TIPSON, *J. Biol. Chem.*, 111 (1935) 313.

[60] P. LEVENE AND R. TIPSON, *J. Biol. Chem.*, 106 (1934) 113.

[61] P. LEVENE AND R. TIPSON, *J. Biol. Chem.*, 109 (1935) 623.

[62] V. CLARK, A. TODD AND J. ZUSSMAN, *J. Chem. Soc.*, (1951) 2952.

[63] R. WRIGHT, G. TENER AND H. KHORANA, *Chem. and Ind.*, (1957) 954.

[64] P. LEVENE, L. MIKESKA AND T. MORI, *J. Biol. Chem.*, 85 (1930) 785.

[65] P. LEVENE AND T. MORI, *J. Biol. Chem.*, 83 (1929) 803.

[66] P. LEVENE AND E. LONDON, *J. Biol. Chem.*, 83 (1929) 793.

[67] G. FELTON AND W. FREUDENBERG, *J. Am. Chem. Soc.*, 57 (1935) 1637.

[68] J. GULLAND AND L. STORY, *J. Chem. Soc.*, (1938) 259.

[69] H. BREDERECK, G. MULLER AND E. BERGER, *Ber.*, 73 (1940) 1058.

[70] W. ANDERSEN, D. HAYES, A. MICHELSON AND A. TODD, *J. Chem. Soc.*, (1954) 1882

[71] P. LEVENE AND W. JACOBS, *Ber.*, 43 (1910) 3150.

[72] H. LORING, M. HAMMELL, L. LEVY AND H. BORTNER, *J. Biol. Chem.*, 196 (1952) 821.

[73] L. HEPPEL AND R. HILMOE, *J. Biol. Chem.*, 188 (1951) 665.

[74] S. FURBERG, *Nature*, 164 (1949) 22.

[75] S. FURBERG, *Acta Cryst.*, 3 (1950) 325.

[76] G. PITT, *Acta Cryst.*, 1 (1948) 168.

[77] J. ZUSSMANN, *Acta Cryst.*, 6 (1953) 504.

[78] M. HUBER, *Acta Cryst.*, 10 (1957) 129.

[79] P. LEVENE, *J. Biol. Chem.*, 33 (1918) 425.

[80] E. CHARGAFF, B. MAGASANIK, E. VISCHER, C. GREEN, R. DONIGER AND D. ELSON, *J. Biol. Chem.*, 186 (1950) 51.

[81] R. MARKHAM AND J. SMITH, *Biochem. J.*, 52 (1952) 552.

[82] R. MERRIFIELD AND D. WOOLLEY, *J. Biol. Chem.*, 197 (1952) 521.

[83] W. COHN AND E. VOLKIN, *J. Biol. Chem.*, 203 (1953) 319.

[84] L. SHUSTER, *J. Biol. Chem.*, 229 (1957) 289.

[85] P. LEVENE, *J. Biol. Chem.*, 126 (1938) 63.

[86] C. DEKKER, A. MICHELSON AND A. TODD, *J. Chem. Soc.*, (1953) 947.

[87] W. KLEIN AND S. THANNHAUSER, *Z. physiol. chem.*, 231 (1935) 96.

[88] J. SMITH AND R. MARKHAM, *Biochim. et Biophys. Acta*, 8 (1952) 350.

[89] J. KOERNER AND R. SINSHEIMER, *J. Biol. Chem.*, 228 (1957) 1039.

[90] U. LAURILA AND M. LASKOWSKI, *J. Biol. Chem.*, 228 (1957) 49.

[91] W. COHN, *J. Am. Chem. Soc.*, 72 (1950) 1471.

[92] E. VOLKIN, J. KHYM AND W. COHN, *J. Am. Chem. Soc.*, 73 (1951) 1533.

[93] R. BERGKVIST AND A. DEUTSCH, *Acta Chem. Scand.*, 8 (1954) 1877.

[94] P. LEVENE AND S. HARRIS, *J. Biol. Chem.*, 101 (1933) 419.

[95] P. LEVENE AND R. TIPSON, *J. Biol. Chem.*, 109 (1935) 623.

[96] C. CARTER AND W. COHN, *Fed. Proc.*, 8 (1949) 190.

[97] C. CARTER, *J. Am. Chem. Soc.*, 72 (1950) 1466.

[98] D. BROWN AND A. TODD, *J. Chem. Soc.*, (1952). 44

[99] L. CAVALIERI, *J. Am. Chem. Soc.*, 75 (1953) 5268.

[100] J. KHYM AND W. COHN, *J. Am. Chem. Soc.*, 76 (1954) 1818,

[101] D. BROWN, G. FASMAN, D. MAGRATH, A. TODD, W. COCHRAN AND M. WOOLFSON, *Nature*, 172 (1953) 1184.

[102] D. BROWN, G. FASMAN, D. MAGRATH AND A. TODD, *J. Chem. Soc.*, (1954) 1448.

[103] F. BARON AND D. BROWN, *J. Chem. Soc.*, (1955) 2855.

[104] A. MICHELSON AND A. TODD, *J. Chem. Soc.*, (1954) 34.

[105] E. ALVER AND S. FURBERG, *Acta Chem. Scand.*, 13 (1959) 910.

[106] D. BROWN, A. TODD AND S. VARADARAJAN, *J. Chem. Soc.*, (1956) 2388.

[107] A. FONÓ, *Arkiv. Kemi Minerol. Geol.*, 24A, No. 33 (1947) 14, 15.

[108] D. BROWN AND A. TODD, *J. Chem. Soc.*, (1952) 52.

[109] D. BROWN AND A. TODD, *J. Chem. Soc.*, (1953) 2040.

[110] D. LIPKIN, R. TALBERT AND M. COHN, *J. Am. Chem. Soc.*, 76 (1954) 2871.

111 R. MARKHAM AND J. SMITH, *Nature*, 168 (1951) 406.
112 D. BROWN, D. MAGRATH AND A. TODD, *J. Chem. Soc.*, (1952) 2708.
113 R. MARKHAM AND J. SMITH, *Biochem. J.*, 52 (1952) 558.
114 D. BROWN, C. DEKKER AND A. TODD, *J. Chem. Soc.*, (1952) 2715.
115 C. DEKKER AND H. KHORANA, *J. Am. Chem. Soc.*, 76 (1954) 3522.
116 G. TENER AND H. KHORANA, *J. Am. Chem. Soc.*, 77 (1955) 5349.
117 H. KHORANA, G. TENER, R. WRIGHT AND J. MOFFATT, *J. Am. Chem. Soc.*, 79 (1957) 430.
118 M. SMITH AND H. KHORANA, *J. Am. Chem. Soc.*, 81 (1959) 2911.
119 G. TENER, H. KHORANA, R. MARKHAM AND E. POL, *J. Am. Chem. Soc.*, 80 (1958) 6223.
120 A. TODD, in S. COLOWICK AND N. KAPLAN, Eds. *Methods in Enzymology*, Vol. III, Academic Press, New York, 1957, p. 812.
121 *Ibid.*, p. 817.
122 *Ibid.*, p. 823.
123 *Ibid.*, p. 819.
124 A. MICHELSON AND A. TODD, *J. Chem. Soc.*, (1949) 2476.
125 A. MICHELSON AND A. TODD, *J. Chem. Soc.*, (1953) 951.
126 A. MICHELSON AND A. TODD, *J. Chem. Soc.*, (1954) 34.
127 J. DAVOLL AND B. LOWY, *J. Am. Chem. Soc.*, 73 (1951) 1650.
128 F. ATHERTON, H. OPENSHAW AND A. TODD, *J. Chem. Soc.*, (1945) 382.
129 A. TODD, *Methods in Enzymology*, Vol. III, 1957, p. 811.
130 J. BADDILEY AND A. TODD, *J. Chem. Soc.*, (1947) 648.
131 S. CHRISTIE, D. ELMORE, G. KENNER, A. TODD AND F. WEYMOUTH, *J. Chem. Soc.*, (1953) 2947
132 J. BADDILEY, IN E. CHARGAFF AND J. DAVIDSON, *The Nucleic Acids*, Vol. I, 1955, p. 175.
133 R. CHAMBERS, J. MOFFATT AND H. KHORANA, *J. Am. Chem. Soc.*, 77 (1955) 3416.
134 R. HALL AND H. KHORANA, *J. Am. Chem. Soc.*, 77 (1955) 1871.
135 J. GULLAND AND H. HOBDAY, *J. Chem. Soc.*, (1940) 746.
136 R. HALL AND H. KHORANA, *J. Am. Chem. Soc.*, 76 (1954) 5056.
137 D. JORDAN, *Progr. Biophys. and Biophys. Chem.*, 2 (1951) 51.
138 N. BJERRUM, *Z. physik. Chem.*, 106 (1923) 219.
139 J. KIRKWOOD AND F. WESTHEIMER, *J. Chem. Phys.*, 6 (1938) 506.
140 F. WESTHEIMER AND J. KIRKWOOD, *J. Chem. Phys.*, 6 (1938) 513.
141 L. CAVALIERI, *J. Am. Chem. Soc.*, 74 (1952) 5804.
142 H. LORING, H. BORTNER, L. LEVY AND M. HAMMELL, *J. Biol. Chem.*, 196 (1952) 807.
143 G. BEAVEN, E. HOLIDAY AND E. JOHNSON, *The Nucleic Acids*, Vol. I, 1955, p. 493.
144 F. CRICK AND J. WATSON, *Proc. Roy. Soc., London*, A223 (1954) 80.
145 J. DUNITZ AND J. ROLLET, *Acta Cryst.*, 9 (1956) 327.
146 S. FURBERG, *Acta Chem. Scand.*, 6 (1952) 634.
147 A. MICHELSON AND A. TODD, *J. Chem. Soc.*, (1949) 2487.
148 J. BADDILEY, A. MICHELSON AND A. TODD, *J. Chem. Soc.*, (1949) 582.
149 N. ANAND, V. CLARK, R. HALL AND A. TODD, *J. Chem. Soc.*, (1952) 3665.
150 G. KENNER, A. TODD AND F. WEYMOUTH, *J. Chem. Soc.*, (1952) 3675.
151 H. KHORANA, *J. Am. Chem. Soc.*, 76 (1954) 3517.
152 R. HALL AND H. KHORANA, *J. Am. Chem. Soc.*, 76 (1954) 5056.
153 R. CHAMBERS AND H. KHORANA, *J. Am. Chem. Soc.*, 79 (1957) 3752.
154 M. SMITH AND H. KHORANA, *J. Am. Chem. Soc.*, 80 (1958) 1141.
155 R. CHAMBERS AND H. KHORANA, *J. Am. Chem. Soc.*, 80 (1958) 3749.
156 E. BAER AND H. STANCER, *J. Am. Chem. Soc.*, 75 (1953) 4510.
157 V. CLARK, G. KIRBY AND A. TODD, *J. Chem. Soc.*, (1957) 1497.
158 J. MOFFATT AND H. KHORANA, *J. Am. Chem. Soc.*, 80 (1958) 3756.
159 J. MOFFATT AND H. KHORANA, *J. Am. Chem. Soc.*, 81 (1959) 1265.
160 Pabst Laboratories, *Circular OR-10*, 1956.
161 A. MICHELSON AND A. TODD, *J. Chem. Soc.*, (1955) 2632.
162 H. KHORANA, G. TENER, J. MOFFATT AND E. POL, *Chem. and Ind. (London)*, (1956) 1523.
163 H. KHORANA, W. RAZZELL, P. GILHAM, G. TENER AND E. POL, *J. Am. Chem. Soc.*, 79 (1957) 1002.
164 P. GILHAM AND H. KHORANA, *J. Am. Chem. Soc.*, 80 (1958) 6212.
165 M. SMITH, J. MOFFATT AND H. KHORANA, *J. Am. Chem. Soc.*, 80 (1958) 6204.

[166] A. TURNER AND H. KHORANA, *J. Am. Chem. Soc.*, 81 (1959) 4651.

[167] H. KHORANA, G. TENER, W. RAZZELL AND R. MARKHAM, *Fed. Proc.*, 17 (1958) 253.

[168] G. TENER, P. GILHAM, W. RAZZELL, A. TURNER AND H. KHORANA, *Ann. N. Y. Acad. Sci.*, 81 (1959) 757.

[169] P. GILHAM AND H. KHORANA, *J. Am. Chem. Soc.*, 81 (1959) 4647.

[170] A. MICHELSON, *Nature*, 181 (1958) 303.

[171] A. MICHELSON, L. SZABO AND A. TODD, *J. Chem. Soc.*, (1956) 1546.

[172] R. HALL, A. TODD AND R. WEBB, *J. Chem. Soc.* (1957) 3291.

[173] L. HEPPEL, P. WHITFIELD AND R. MARKHAM, *Biochem. J.*, 60 (1955) 8.

[174] L. HEPPEL AND P. WHITFIELD, *Biochem. J.*, 60 (1955) 1.

Chapter 3

The Primary Structure of Polynucleotides

In analogy to the protein case, the term *primary structure* will be used to refer to the nucleotide composition, the mode of internucleotide linkage, and the sequential arrangement of nucleotides in a macromolecular polynucleotide. The discussion must inevitably be centered upon the first and second of these, as next to nothing is known about the third.

As soon as it had become evident that, when carefully prepared by mild procedures, both ribonucleic acid (RNA) and deoxyribonucleic acid (DNA) could be obtained as polymers of high molecular weight, the question of the manner of linkage of the individual nucleotide units acquired major interest. Once the basic chemistry of the nucleotides themselves was well understood the number of possibilities became severely restricted.

Hydrogen ion titration data upon DNA and RNA early indicated that secondary and tertiary phosphate ionizations were present only to a minor extent[1,2]. It was thereby apparent that the vast majority of internucleotide linkages in either case must be of the phosphodiester type and that ether or pyrophosphate linkages could be eliminated from consideration. The basic primary structure of the natural nucleic acids thus emerged as of the following type:

$$
\begin{array}{c}
\text{base}-\text{sugar}-\text{PO(OH)} \\
| \\
\text{base}-\text{sugar}-\text{PO(OH)} \\
| \\
\text{base}-\text{sugar}-\text{PO(OH)}
\end{array}
$$

Despite the wide range of base compositions occurring for RNA or DNA from various sources, it is possible to generalize as to the primary structure of both types. No exceptions to the general mode of linkage to be discussed subsequently have been observed and the evidence for it will be considered without regard to the particular source of the DNA or RNA. There can, of course, be no guarantee that exceptions to the general scheme cannot occur.

If it is granted that all, or almost all, of the linkages are of the phosphodiester type, we can restrict the possibilities in the case of RNA to phosphodiester linkages of the types 2′–3′, 2′–5′, and 3′–5′; as well as alternating 2′–2′, 3′–3′, or 5′–5′

(Fig. 8). In the case of DNA the absence of a 2′-ribose hydroxyl restricts the possibilities further to the 3′–5′ or alternating 3′–3′ and 5′–5′ linkages.

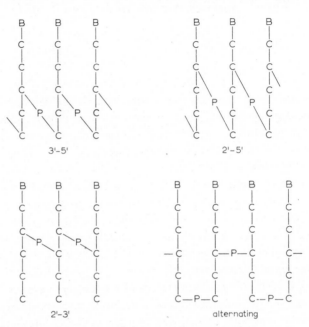

Fig. 8.   Possible modes of linkage for RNA.

The preceding refers, of course, to the mode of linkage for the primary chains. The possibility of branching also exists and will be discussed for the individual systems for which evidence is available.

In all cases the basic method of attack has been to hydrolyze selectively the phosphodiester bonds by chemical or enzymatic means and to isolate and characterize the products. In the more recent stages of the work the use of phosphodiesterases of known specificity has proved invaluable.

Much of the work to be discussed subsequently would have been almost impossible prior to the introduction of chromatographic means of analyzing nucleotide and oligonucleotide mixtures. The use of partition paper chromatography in particular has become a standard procedure in investigations of this type.

ENZYMATIC PROBES OF POLYNUCLEOTIDE STRUCTURE

Before continuing with a detailed consideration of the structures of the individual polynucleotides it is desirable to summarize what is known of the chemical and enzymatic probes of structure which were used in the investigations which clarified this problem.

   a.   Hydrolysis by purified snake venom phosphodiesterase. This enzyme, which falls in the category of relatively non-specific phosphodiesterases, has been separated and purified by a number of fractionation procedures, most of which involve the use of chromatographic columns[3-7]. It is possible to obtain preparations which are free from 5'-nucleotidase activity. The enzyme occurs in the venom of a variety of poisonous snakes, including *Crotalus* and *Bothrops*.

It was early shown by Cohn and Volkin[8] that such preparations catalyze the hydrolysis of RNA to a mixture of nucleoside-5'-phosphates, pyrimidine-3', 5'-diphosphates, and purine nucleosides. As the products were mononucleotides or nucleosides exclusively it was evident that no specificity requirements with regard to the purine or pyrimidine base were present. The nature of the products indicated that the activity of the enzyme was confined to esters of nucleoside-5'-phosphates, which were cleaved so as to leave the phosphate in the 5'-position. This conclusion was strengthened by the finding that the hydrolysis of adenosine-5'-benzyl phosphate is catalyzed by the enzyme[9] but not that of adenosine-3'-benzyl phosphate.

The origin of the pyrimidine nucleoside-3', 5'-diphosphates in RNA digests presented some difficulty. The explanation appears to lie in a specificity requirement of the enzyme with regard to the nature of the end group. Polynucleotides and oligonucleotides terminating in a nucleoside-5'-phosphate are hydrolyzed rapidly; oligonucleotides with a nucleoside-3'-phosphate terminal group are resistant[10,11]. In all probability the action of the enzyme is stepwise and proceeds preferentially from the chain terminus. The presence of a secondary phosphate in the 3'-position inhibits its action.

Oligonucleotides terminating in a non-esterified nucleoside are attacked by this enzyme, although at a slower rate than the analogous 5'-terminal polymers[12]. The products of hydrolysis are 5'-mononucleotides plus a nucleoside residue corresponding to the end group.

The inhibitory effect of a 3'-terminal phosphate is not absolute as a slow hydrolysis occurs at enzyme concentrations roughly 1,000 times greater than required to produce a comparable rate for 5'-oligonucleotides[11]. The rate of hydrolysis in the case of 3'-terminal polynucleotides is dependent upon the chain length and increases for longer chains[12].

Thus a plausible explanation for the occurrence of nucleoside-3',5'-diphosphates in RNA digests would appear to be that sufficiently long 3'-terminal polynucleotides can be split in the interior of the chain, possibly by a second enzyme contaminant, yielding a polynucleotide without a phosphomonoester end group and one with both a 5'- and a 3'-terminal group. The former could be readily hydrolyzed, the latter might be attacked from the 5' end[12]. The splitting off of the final 3'-terminal nucleotide group would proceed via hydrolysis of its 3'-5' linkage, thereby producing a nucleoside diesterified in both the 3' and 5' positions.

As the prior action of ribonuclease upon RNA would result in the production of oligonucleotides and polynucleotides terminating in a pyrimidine nucleoside-3'-phosphate, it is likely that the extensive occurrence of the corresponding 3', 5'-diphosphates in the digests of Cohn and Volkin is thereby explicable[8]. Crestfield and Allen have found that, if RNA is subjected to digestion by pancreatic ribonuclease, subsequent treatment with a large excess of venom phosphodiesterase results in the production of pyrimidine nucleoside-3', 5'-diphosphates amounting to 60 per cent of the pyrimidine content of the original RNA [13].

Oddly enough, nucleoside-2': 3'-cyclic phosphates are hydrolyzed by this enzyme to yield nucleoside-3'-phosphates [14]. It is possible that this activity may arise from a second enzyme contaminant.

Oligonucleotides formed from DNA and containing a deoxyribose group are attacked in a manner similar to the oligoribonucleotide case in both the specificity requirements and the nature of the products [15, 16]. If the DNA is subjected to prior treatment with deoxyribonuclease I, which produces 5'-terminal oligonucleotides solely, the action of venom phosphodiesterase results in nucleoside-5'-monophosphates exclusively.

Boman has obtained evidence that the action of venom phosphodiesterase upon DNA is markedly accelerated by calcium [16].

The mode of action of venom phosphodiesterases is illustrated by Fig. 9.

b. Hydrolysis by whole snake venom. Unfractionated snake venoms generally contain phosphomonoesterases in addition to phosphodiesterases. In addition to

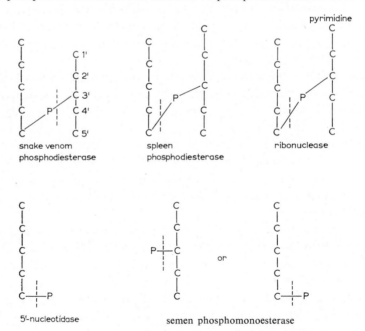

Fig. 9. Specificity of the various phosphoesterases. The dotted lines indicate the points of attack. The symbol —P— represents the phosphodiester linkage:

$$\underset{\text{OH}}{\overset{\displaystyle\overset{\textstyle O}{\overset{\|}{}}}{—O—P—O—}}$$

the diesterase described above, unfractionated preparations of the venom of *Crotalus adamanteus* contain a 5'-nucleotidase, so that the mixture converts 3'–'5 polynucleotides to the constituent nucleosides[17]. These preparations are free from 3'-nucleotidase activity.

c. Hydrolysis by spleen phosphodiesterase. This enzyme fraction, whose purification is described by Heppel and Hilmoe[18] has a mode of action almost exactly converse to the venom phosphodiesterase discussed earlier. Thus RNA is hydrolyzed to 3'-mononucleotides. This suggests that the action of this enzyme is confined to esters of nucleoside-3'-phosphates, which are split so as to leave the phosphate attached to the 3'-position (Fig. 9). In conformity with this view it has been found that alkyl esters of nucleoside-3'-phosphates are hydrolyzed by this enzyme[12], but not the esters of nucleoside-5'-phosphates.

The finding that RNA is hydrolyzed to mononucleotides indicates that there are no obvious specificity requirements with respect to the bases. The spleen phosphodiesterase fraction described by Heppel and Hilmoe likewise resembles venom phosphodiesterase in that it catalyzes the hydrolysis of polydeoxyribonucleotides as well as polyribonucleotides. The products of hydrolysis are 3'-mononucleotides in both cases.

Again in analogy to the phosphodiesterase of snake venom, the activity of this enzyme is definitely influenced by the nature of the monoesterified terminal group of the polynucleotide. Oligoribonucleotides and oligodeoxyribonucleotides with a terminal 5'-phosphate are resistant to hydrolysis, while those ending in a nucleoside-3'-phosphate are attacked readily. However, there is some evidence that the inhibition is not absolute and that at sufficiently high enzyme levels a slow hydrolysis of the 5'-terminal polymers occurs.

This diesterase apparently will not attack 2'–5' linkages. Thus an adenosine-uridine dinucleoside monophosphate with a 2'–5' phosphodiester linkage has been synthesized and shown to be inert[19].

Maver and Greco have reported the isolation of a second spleen fraction which did not hydrolyze polydeoxyribonucleotides, but which had otherwise similar properties[20].

d. Hydrolysis by bull semen 5'-nucleotidase. Soluble enzymes capable of catalyzing the hydrolysis of nucleoside-5'-phosphomonoester groups are fairly widely distributed in nature. They are found in mammalian tissues, snake venoms, and potatoes, among other sources[21, 22].

The properties of the 5'-nucleotidase of bull semen have been investigated by Heppel and Hilmoe[23]. Purified preparations could be obtained which were free from 3'-nucleotidase activity and apparently quite specific for the nucleoside-5'-phosphomonoester linkage (Fig. 9). No evidence for any base specificity was obtained. Nucleotides terminating in a nucleoside-5'-phosphate are converted to the corresponding nucleoside. Phosphodiester linkages are not attacked.

Apparently the presence of a purine or pyrimidine base is not necessary for its action as ribose-5-phosphate was hydrolized at a rate comparable to that of the nucleotides. Glucose-6-phosphate was inert however. It appears therefore that the specificity of this enzyme is confined to the nature of the sugar-phosphate ester[23].

e. Hydrolysis by human seminal plasma phosphomonoesterase. This enzyme (or enzymes) has a broader specificity than the 5'-nucleotidase discussed above and catalyzes the hydrolysis of both the 3'- and 5'-phosphomonoester derivatives of the common nucleosides (Fig. 9). Oligonucleotides terminating in a nucleoside-3'-phosphate or nucleoside-5'-phosphate are converted to the corresponding polymer terminating in a nucleoside[17]. Unfortunately, most preparations of this enzyme appear to contain a phosphodiesterase contaminant.

f. Hydrolysis by pancreatic ribonuclease. This enzyme may be regarded as a highly specific phosphodiesterase, whose action upon mixed polynucleotides is confined to esters of pyrimidine nucleoside-3'-phosphates. These are cleaved so as to leave the phosphate in the 3'-position of the pyrimidine nucleoside[10, 24, 25, 26].

Because of its rigid specificity requirements, pancreatic ribonuclease converts RNA to a complex mixture of uridine-3'-phosphate, cytidine-3'-phosphate, and a series of oligonucleotides each of which terminates in a pyrimidine nucleoside-3'-phosphate[10, 24]. The clarification of the specificity of pancreatic ribonuclease occurred largely as a consequence of the work of Markham and Smith[24] and of Volkin and Cohn[10].

This picture of the specificity of this enzyme is reinforced by the observations of Brown and Todd, who found that ribonuclease catalyzed the hydrolysis of benzyl esters of pyrimidine nucleoside-3'-phosphates but not the corresponding esters of 2'-phosphates[27].

This enzyme is quite sensitive to any modification of the pyrimidine base. Thus N-methyl uridine-3'-methyl phosphate is inert[12]. On the other hand there is evidence that 2-thiouracil may be substituted for uracil[28].

The base specificity of pancreatic ribonuclease was shown by Markham and Smith to be responsible for the presence of a resistant "core" in ribonuclease digests of natural RNA[24]. This "core" was demonstrated to originate from sequences of purine nucleotides in the original RNA molecule.

Markham and Smith were able to demonstrate that pancreatic ribonuclease hydrolysis proceeds via the formation of a 2' : 3' cyclic phosphate terminal intermediate. The readiness with which this transient intermediate accumulated in ribonuclease digests of RNA suggested that its subsequent ribonuclease-catalyzed hydrolysis is slow relative to the initial step.

The specificity of pancreatic ribonuclease is illustrated by Fig. 9.

g. Hydrolysis by pancreatic deoxyribonuclease. This enzyme, which is also commonly referred to as deoxyribonuclease I, is distinguished from the other deoxyribonucleases of Class II by its activity in neutral solution and the requirement for magnesium or certain other divalent cations.

The specificity of this enzyme cannot be said to have been clarified to an extent comparable to the case of pancreatic ribonuclease. Its action is confined to polydeoxyribonucleotides and no activity with regard to polyribonucleotides has been found[12].

The products of its exhaustive hydrolytic action upon DNA are primarily oligonucleotides terminating in a nucleoside-5'-phosphate, although some mononucleotides are present in the digest[29-33]. Most of our knowledge of the base specificity of pancreatic deoxyribonuclease has been obtained from studies of the relative frequency of occurrence of the various oligonucleotides[30].

Thus it has been found that dinucleotides with sequences of the following type were abundant: pPypPy, pPupPu and pPypPu*. Sequences of the type pPupPy were very rare. This has been regarded as evidence that the pPupPy bond was preferentially hydrolyzed[30].

This conclusion was strengthened by the observation that the trinucleotide ApApTp was split into ApA and pTp by this enzyme. However, it was also observed that oligonucleotides smaller than trinucleotides were not attacked, irrespective of whether they contained a pPupPy sequence.

The origin of the mononucleotides present in DNA digests is still obscure. Obviously they cannot arise solely from the hydrolysis of the pPupPy linkage.

h. Hydrolysis by deoxyribonuclease II. This term is reserved for the deoxyribonuclease with an acid pH optimum and no Mg^{++} requirement. It has been found in spleen[20], in *M. pyrogenes*[34], and in thymus[35].

The products of its action upon DNA are mononucleotides and oligonucleotides, apparently with 3'-phosphomonoester terminal groups[35].

i. Alkaline hydrolysis under mild conditions. This method of degrading ribonucleic acid, whose use dates from the very beginnings of such investigations, remained incompletely understood until recent times. Exhaustive degradation by 1 *M* NaOH at room temperature converts polyribonucleotides to a mixture of nucleoside monophosphates, each of which occurs in two isomeric forms corresponding to the nucleoside 2'- and 3'-monophosphates.

This finding, which somewhat confused the earlier investigations of the structure of RNA, was finally shown by Brown and Todd to be an artifact of the hydrolysis[27], which proceeds via the formation of a transient intermediate which has been identified as a cyclic 2' : 3' terminal phosphate. Subsequent hydrolysis of this group occurs with roughly equal readiness at either position and thus gives rise to both isomers. Markham and Smith[24] have succeeded in isolating such cyclic intermediates by careful alkaline hydrolysis of RNA.

---

* Here and in the sections to follow the convention will be followed of representing a 5'-ester of a nucleoside by placing a "p" to the *left* of the symbol for the nucleoside and a 3'-ester by placing the "p" to the *right*. Thus:

pA   represents adenosine-5'-phosphate
Ap   represents adenosine-3'-phosphate
ApA   represents adenosine dinucleoside-3',5'-monophosphate
ApAp represents adenosine 3',5' dinucleoside-diphosphate (with a terminal 3',phosphate)
pApA represents adenosine 3',5' dinucleoside-diphosphate (with a terminal 5',phosphate)
Pu   represents purine; Py represents pyrimidine.

The phosphodiester linkage between two deoxyribonucleosides is relatively stable to alkali, as the absence of 2'-hydroxyls in this case prevents the formation of the 2' : 3' cyclic phosphate intermediate.

At elevated temperatures (100°) prolonged exposure to alkali results in the splitting of the nucleoside phosphate bonds with the liberation of inorganic phosphate.

j. Acid hydrolysis under mild conditions. Treatment with 0.1*M* HCl for four hours at room temperature serves to hydrolyze the cyclic 2' : 3' nucleoside phosphates[36] to phosphomonoesters. More drastic conditions, such as higher concentrations of acid or elevated temperatures, result in extensive hydrolysis of phosphodiester linkages as well as a preferential splitting of purine riboside linkages.

THE MODE OF LINKAGE OF NATURAL RIBONUCLEIC ACID

It was early found that the mild alkaline degradation of ribonucleic acids resulted in their conversion to a mixture of their constituent mononucleotides. From such a hydrolysate of yeast RNA, Carter and Cohn were able to isolate two isomeric adenylic acids, called *a* and *b*[37]. It was subsequently shown that all of the constituent mononucleotides were obtained as analogous pairs[38-40].

The *a* and *b* nucleotides were identified by Brown and Todd, with the corresponding nucleoside 2'- and 3'-monophosphates. More recent studies have indicated that the *a* nucleotides are probably the 2'-phosphates and that the *b* nucleotides are the 3'-phosphates.

The problem of the origin of the isomeric nucleotides in RNA hydrolysates was clarified largely through the work of Brown and Todd. Early studies of Bailly and Gaume had showed that while glycerol-α-phosphate is stable to alkali, its methyl ester is readily hydrolyzed under alkaline conditions to methanol and a mixture of glycerol-α- and -β-phosphates[41]. This and other investigations showed that an exception to the general stability of alkyl and dialkyl phosphates to alkali occurs when a hydroxyl group is adjacent to the phosphoryl group.

Brown and Todd discovered that adenosine-2'-benzyl phosphate and adenosine-3'-benzyl phosphate were both converted by alkali treatment to benzyl alcohol and a mixture of adenosine-2'- and -3'-phosphates[42]. In contrast, adenosine-5'-benzyl phosphate, which has no vicinal hydroxyl, was found to be stable to alkali[9].

On the basis of these and other results, Brown and Todd proposed the following mechanism for the hydrolysis of dialkyl phosphates with a vicinal hydroxyl. On their model the reaction proceeds via the formation of a labile cyclic intermediate, as is illustrated in Fig. 10 for the case of esters of ribonucleoside phosphates.

The plausbility of this model for the alkaline hydrolysis of esters of ribonucleoside-3'-phosphates is enhanced by the fact that the 2'- and 3'-phosphates are in the cis configuration. Conclusive proof of the correctness of this model was furnished by the finding of Markham and Smith that cyclic 2' : 3' phosphates

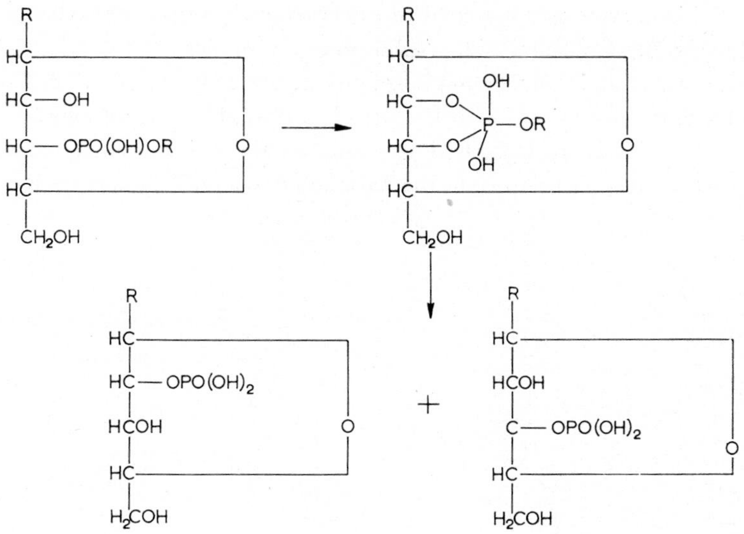

Fig. 10.

could be isolated and identified as intermediates in the alkaline hydrolysis of RNA[24].

The mechanism of Brown and Todd provided the essential key to an understanding of the alkaline breakdown of RNA. In view of the demonstrated stability of esters of nucleoside-5'-phosphates, it was evident that each phosphodiester linkage must include either a 2'- or a 3'-hydroxyl, since the hydrolysis proceeds all the way to mononucleotides. If phosphodiester linkages between two 5'-positions were present, it would be expected that alkali-stable dinucleotides would be present in the digest. The mechanism of Brown and Todd indicated that the linkages could proceed exclusively from the 2'- or from the 3'-position.

This model also served to eliminate the possibility of 2'-3' or alternating 2'-2' and 3'-3' phosphodiester linkages. In both cases, the only available free hydroxyl adjacent to the phosphodiester linkages would occur at the terminal nucleotide residue. Thus alkaline hydrolysis in either case would have to proceed stepwise by removal of mononucleotide units from the end of the polyribonucleotide chain. The relevant chemical evidence, however, favors simultaneous rather than stepwise attack and under the proper conditions a variety of oligonucleotide intermediates can be isolated[43].

The sole remaining possibilities were 2'-5' or 3'-5' linkages. It remained for enzymatic studies to decide conclusively between these possibilities. Thus it was found that spleen phosphodiesterase catalyzed the hydrolysis of RNA to the constituent nucleoside-3'-phosphates exclusively[44,45]. As no evidence for the occurrence of any cyclic intermediate was obtained in the case of this enzyme, it followed that the original phosphodiester linkages must be of the 3'-5' type exclusively. Further corroborative information came from the finding that the activity of this enzyme was confined to esters of nucleoside-3′-phosphates, while the analogous esters of nucleoside-2′-phosphates were inert.

Finally, it was found that venom phosphodiesterase converted RNA to 5′-mononucleotides[46]. In conclusion, it may be stated that it would be exceedingly difficult to reconcile all the above evidence with any other mode of linkage than the 3′–5′.

The question as to the nature of the basic internucleotide linkage of RNA can

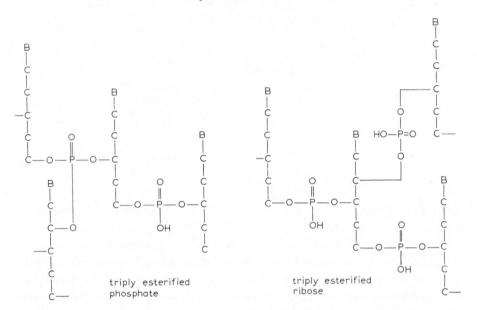

Fig. 11. Schemes of branching for RNA.

be regarded as having been settled fairly decisively. There remains the problem of branching. In this connection it is probably unjustified to retain the unitarian approach followed in the discussion of the mode of linkage of the linear sequence. Until we have much more compelling evidence to the contrary than is available now, it is probably safer to examine this question for each RNA separately.

There are two alternative ways in which branching could occur. The first of these is from the main chain, via the formation of phosphotriester linkages. The alternative model invokes the presence of a normal phosphodiester linkage between a 2′-position in the main chain and a 3′ (or 2′) position in the first nucleoside residue of the branch (Fig. 11).

In either case the presence of branches should be reflected by the occurrence of secondary phosphate ionizations arising from the phosphomonoester groups at the chain termini. In fact, it was evidence of this type which led originally to the suggestion that branching might occur. Also the extent of liberation of inorganic phosphate by phosphomonoesterases would be an index of the degree of branching.

Cox and co-workers have obtained hydrogen ion titration curves for a carefully prepared high molecular weight sample of RNA from *Aerobacter aerogenes*[47].

Within experimental error, there was no evidence for any secondary phosphate ionization in the pH range 5.75–8.0. This would place an upper limit to the number of branches in this RNA molecule at about one per 300 nucleotides, or less. These results are in contrast to earlier work upon RNA from other sources which appeared to indicate the occurrence of secondary phosphates to an appreciable extent[48].

Markham and Smith found that, if the RNA from turnip yellow mosaic virus were subjected to complete alkaline hydrolysis after prior treatment with phosphomonoesterase, about one residue in 65 was isolated as a nucleoside[49]. Without a prior knowledge of the molecular weight, it is impossible to decide conclusively between rather short chain lengths and an important degree of branching as the origin of the high proportion of end groups thereby indicated. However, if complete alkaline hydrolysis was carried out without prior treatment with phosphomonoesterase, the material was converted quantitatively to nucleotides. This equivalent of ribose and phosphate precludes the existence of branches originating from a ribose 2'-position. Branching from a triply esterified phosphate in the main chain cannot be excluded on this basis, but was believed to be unlikely by the authors[49].

The RNA from presumably degraded tobacco mosaic virus has likewise been subjected to complete alkaline hydrolysis[50]. Along with mononucleotides, small amounts of nucleoside and nucleoside diphosphate (3',5') were present[50]. This would be consistent with a linear polynucleotide containing a single nucleoside-5'-phosphate terminal group. Since the nucleoside and nucleoside diphosphate contents of the digest were equivalent, the only kind of branching which could be consistent with these results would involve two kinds of branches present to about the same extent. One of these would originate from a triple phosphate ester on the main chain and would involve the 5'-position of the first residue in the branch; the other would arise via a 2'–3' phosphodiester linkage from the main chain to the branch. That such an arrangement could occur fortuitously is, of course, very unlikely and the alternative explanation, that these preparations are essentially unbranched, is probably preferable.

Both the two preceding investigations suffer from the severe drawback of being based upon extensively degraded preparations. To what extent this might tend to mask the occurrence of branching in the original intact molecule is difficult to say.

More recent work upon less degraded preparations has resulted in a considerable downward revision of the estimated number of 5'-terminal phosphate groups in intact RNA from tobacco mosaic virus[51]. At present, there is in fact little positive evidence for the occurrence, in measurable amounts, of *any* end groups in native, as opposed to degraded, samples of RNA from this source[52]. Thus a rough upper limit can be set to the number of possible branches at about one per several hundred nucleotide units.

Cohn and Volkin made enzymatic degradation studies upon RNA from mammalian liver and thymus and from yeast[8]. It was found that nucleosides and nucleoside diphosphates were produced in relatively large and equivalent quantities by the action of venom phosphodiesterase. This result was originally interpreted in terms of branching from triply esterified ribose. However, subsequent observations found a very wide variability in the amounts of diphosphates formed[53]. An alternative explanation later advanced by Cohn was that the original preparations had been extensively degraded by contaminating nuclease and that an interpretation in terms of branching was unnecessary[53].

The over-all situation with regard to branching is that in no case is there very compelling evidence for it; in several instances there is incompletely conclusive evidence against it, and in at least one case there is decisive evidence against it. Again, it must be stressed that any generalization about this point is probably premature.

The base compositions of ribonucleic acids from a wide variety of sources have been determined. In general, it can be stated that the results not only show a very wide range of compositions but have also failed to bring out any particular regularity of base ratios.

For example, the mole ratio of purines to pyrimidines varies from 2.6 for pig pancreas RNA[54] to 0.66 for a fraction of the RNA from rat liver nuclei[55]. The ratio of adenine plus uracil to guanine plus cytosine varies from 0.63 for ox liver RNA[56] to 1.12 for yeast RNA[56].

The sole evidence for any definite pattern of composition lies in the relative constancy of the adenine plus cytosine to guanine plus uracil ratio, which is close to unity for many RNA's[57]. However, even in this case, large deviations occur in some instances.

On the whole, studies of the base composition of RNA are not encouraging with regard to any generalized picture of its secondary structure.

MODE OF LINKAGE OF DEOXYRIBONUCLEIC ACIDS

In the case of DNA the 2'-hydroxyl of ribose is missing so that the possible positions of the phosphodiester linkages are limited. The only two possibilities are linkages which are exclusively 3'–5' or which alternate between 3'–3' and 5'–5'.

It proved possible to eliminate conclusively the second of these possibilities by enzymatic studies. By consecutive treatment of DNA with deoxyribonuclease and venom phosphodiesterase an almost quantitative recovery of the constituent mononucleotides in the form of deoxyribonucleoside-5'-phosphates could be made[58]. This indicates that almost all the phosphodiester linkages must be of the 3'–5' type.

Further direct evidence in support of this model came from the identification of dinucleotides containing the 3'–5' linkage in deoxyribonuclease digests of DNA[59].

Finally it may be mentioned that the relative stability of DNA to alkali is fully consistent with the 3'–5' linkage in view of the absence of a vicinal 2'-hydroxyl and serves to reinforce the mechanism of Brown and Todd for the hydrolysis of the analogous linkage in RNA.

It thus appears that the basic primary linkages of the linear RNA and DNA chains are similar. There remain the questions of branching and of chain interruptions.

The doubly stranded character of DNA, which will be discussed in more detail in a later chapter, raises the possibility that interruptions might occur in each strand. As the two strands are held together by interbase hydrogen bonding a considerable number of such interruptions could still be consistent with a very high molecular weight.

Each interruption of this type should be similar to a chain terminus and should result in the presence of a phosphomonoester group. This should be recognizable from hydrogen ion titration data, as the pK of the secondary phosphate dissociation is at about pH 6.

As more accurate titration data have become available and as values for the base compositions have become more precisely known, estimates of the number of secondary phosphates have been revised sharply downward. According to Cox and Peacocke, the hydrogen ion titration curve of herring sperm DNA can be accounted for entirely without the necessity of invoking *any* secondary phosphate ionization[60]. Or, in other words, the amount of the latter does not exceed the limits of experimental uncertainty. Thus the number of monoesterified phosphates must be less than about one per three hundred nucleotide units. This rules out chain interruption as a major factor in the structure.

Branching to any important extent is likewise improbable in view of the low phosphomonoester content. Furthermore electron microscopic observations of thymus DNA have failed to show any evidence for branching[61].

In summary, the evidence to date as to the structure of the native DNA's which have been examined is most consistent with long linear chains of nucleotides joined by 3′–5′ phosphodiester linkages. Branching probably does not occur to any important degree, if at all.

In contrast to the case of RNA, the base composition of DNA exhibits, as is well-known, a well-defined pattern. Thus, despite a wide variation with source of over-all composition, the DNA's so far examined show the following regularities[62]:

adenine = thymine
guanine = cytosine
adenine + guanine = cytosine + thymine
adenine + cytosine = guanine + thymine

These regularities provided an essential basis for the Watson–Crick model of DNA. They have been found to hold, within experimental uncertainty, for DNA's from many sources, including mammalian tissues, fish sperm, wheat germ, yeast, bacteria, and bacteriophage. To date only one exception has been convincingly shown to exist[63].

The preceding relationships refer, of course, to the base composition of DNA preparations averaged over the entire system. In actuality a considerable hetero-geneity of composition is generally present for DNA from a particular source.

Bendich and co-workers have fractionated calf thymus DNA chromatographi-cally and determined the base composition of the various fractions[64]. Discon-certingly enough, they have found that while the unfractionated material obeyed the above relationships, quite appreciable deviations occurred for the fractions. The discrepancies were particularly large in the case of the guanine–cytosine ratios, values as low as 0.75 having been found. These results clearly require confirmation. If correct, they may necessitate a major revision of our current ideas as to DNA secondary structure, as will be discussed in a later chapter.

The bases occurring in natural DNA are not always limited to the familiar four of adenine, guanine, thymine, and cytosine. In some instances 5-methyl cytosine replaces part of the cytosine, particularly in the case of plant DNA's[62]. In the DNA from wheat germ, as much as six per cent of this base has been identified. This base has also been found in DNA from calf thymus, bovine spleen and sperm, and herring sperm.

In the DNA from several species of bacteriophage, including T2, T4, and T6, cytosine is replaced by 5-hydroxymethyl cytosine[62]. Under exceptional circum-stances 6-N-methyl adenine partially replaces adenine[65].

THE PRIMARY STRUCTURE OF THE BIOSYNTHETIC POLYRIBONUCLEOTIDES

After it became clearly established that biosynthetic polyribonucleotides of high degree of polymerization could be produced *in vitro*, the pressing question at once arose as to their mode of linkage. In view of the known structure of the nucleotide monomers and the empirical formulae of the polymers any mode of linkage other than the phosphodiester was most unlikely. However, a direct confirmation of this was desirable. In addition, the problem existed whether the phosphodiester linkages were exclusively between the 3′ and 5′ positions of the ribose ring, as is the case with natural RNA and DNA. In the case of the polymers of two or more nucleotides there was also the question of the sequential arrangement of the nucleotides, in particular whether the linear distribution was random or not.

In the case of the biosynthetic polynucleotides produced by the enzyme from *Azotobacter vinelandii*, the above uncertainties can be said to have been fairly completely resolved, largely through the work of Heppel, Ochoa, and co-work-ers[66-72]. The method of approach was the biochemically familiar one of con-trolled chemical and enzymatic degradation to identifiable products. The speed and thoroughness with which the problem yielded to this kind of attack may, in large measure, be attributed to the volume of information on the specificity of the various esterases which was built up by the efforts of many workers in the field of natural nucleic acids.

The chemical structure of biosynthetic polymers of a single nucleotide

The techniques discussed in the preceding section provided a potentially very powerful means of attack upon the problem of the chemical structure of the biosynthetic polynucleotides. In the hands of Heppel, Oritz, and Ochoa this approach has successfully established the mode of linkage of the polynucleotides produced by the action of the *Azotobacter* enzyme[17, 66].

The above workers examined the products of enzymatic degradation of polymers of adenylic acid, uridylic acid, cytidylic acid and inosinic acid.

In the case of poly A, alkaline hydrolysis under mild conditions gave rise to a mixture of 2'- and 3'-adenosine monophosphate. This type of behavior is expected for a phosphodiester linkage and is encountered in the case of natural RNA. The presence of a phosphate group in the 2'-position in the product has been shown to be a consequence of the hydrolysis mechanism, which proceeds via the formation of a 2' : 3' cyclic phosphate intermediate.

Incubation of poly A with spleen phosphodiesterase yielded adenosine-3'-monophosphate. Also exhaustive degradation with purified snake venom phosphodiesterase produced adenosine-5'-monophosphate. In view of the known specificity of these enzymes this evidence is almost conclusive in establishing the 3'–5' phosphodiester linkage for poly A. If the incubation with spleen phosphodiesterase was carried out in the presence of ethanol the methyl ester of 3'-AMP was obtained as well as 3'-AMP itself. The various schemes of hydrolysis of poly A are shown in Fig. 12.

Corroborative evidence for the 3'–5' linkage was sought by isolating and identifying oligonucleotides as transient intermediates in the enzymatic hydrolysis of poly A. Failure to isolate such intermediates in the case of hydrolysis by the spleen and snake venom phosphodiesterases led to the use of a phosphodiesterase-containing ammonium sulfate fraction isolated from guinea pig liver nuclei. Treatment of poly A with this material resulted in a complex mixture of 5'-AMP and a series of di-, tri-, and tetranucleotides, which were isolated chromatographically.

After isolation the oligonucleotides were identified by quantitative conversion to adenosine-5'-monophosphate in all cases. This indicated that the terminal phosphate was in the 5'-position in each case.

The dinucleotide pApA was converted by treatment with phosphomonoesterase to the dinucleoside monophosphate ApA. Alkaline hydrolysis of the latter yielded adenosine and AMP in 1 : 1 mole ratio.

The trinucleotide pApApA was transformed into the trinucleotide diphosphate ApApA by the action of phosphomonoesterase. Alkaline hydrolysis of this material resulted in adenosine and AMP in a 1 : 2 mole ratio.

Thus all of the available evidence obtained for poly A is consistent with its existence in the form of linear chains united by the 3'–5' phosphodiester linkage. No evidence was obtained for the presence of any other type of linkage or for the occurrence of any appreciable degree of branching.

References p. 92/93

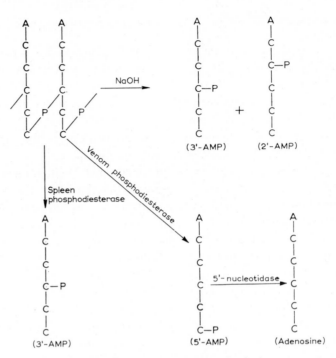

Fig. 12. Enzymatic hydrolysis of poly A.

The results obtained by the above methods in the case of poly U were entirely analogous. Thus incubation with purified snake venom phosphodiesterase converted poly U to uridine-5′-monophosphate. Hydrolysis by spleen phosphodiesterase yielded uridine-3′-monophosphate. Alkaline hydrolysis gave the expected mixture of uridine 2′- and 3′-monophosphates which were identified chromatographically, by their conversion to uridine by human seminal plasma phosphomonoesterase, and by their resistance to hydrolysis by bull semen 5′-nucleotidase.

The results with poly C were altogether similar to those with poly U. Thus poly C was converted to 2′-CMP and 3′-CMP by alkaline hydrolysis, to 3′-CMP by digestion with spleen phosphodiesterase, and to 5′-CMP by snake venom phosphodiesterase. Similar statements can be made in the case of poly I. The lack of success in preparing poly G in reasonable yield and degree of polymerization has precluded any analogous structural determination in this case.

There exists as yet no structural determination comparable in thoroughness to the above in the case of the polymers produced by the other available enzyme systems. This is unfortunate, as much of the physical data to be discussed in later chapters was obtained with polynucleotides prepared with the enzyme from *M. lysodeikticus*. However, in view of the essentially identical physical properties of the *Azotobacter* and *M. lysodeikticus* polynucleotides it would appear *a priori* to be entirely reasonable to assume the 3′–5′ phosphodiester linkage in the latter case as well, in the absence of any conflicting evidence.

The action of ribonuclease upon polynucleotides

Before proceeding to a consideration of structural determinations upon polymers containing more than one nucleotide it is desirable to discuss the mechanism of the action of ribonuclease upon synthetic polynucleotides in view of its pertinence to this problem.

From investigations of the mode of action of pancreatic ribonuclease upon natural RNA it is known that this enzyme will not hydrolyze 3′–5′ phosphodiester linkages joining two purine nucleosides [24] in a mixed polynucleotide. Its action is limited to 3′-5′ (or cyclic 3′ : 2′) phosphodiester linkages in which the 3′ esterification is on a pyrimidine nucleoside. In all cases the ultimate product of hydrolysis has a phosphomonoester group in the 3′ position.

Heppel, Ortiz, and Ochoa examined the hydrolysis of poly U by pancreatic ribonuclease [17]. In this case it was possible to isolate intermediate products of

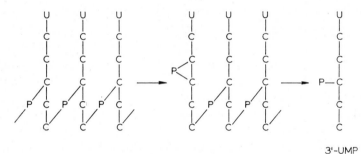

3′-UMP

Fig. 13. Hydrolysis of poly U by ribonuclease.

hydrolysis. Exhaustive hydrolysis gave of course 3′-UMP exclusively. However, at low levels of ribonuclease activity it was possible to isolate and identify a homologous series of oligonucleotide intermediates (Fig. 13). In accordance with the mechanism of ribonuclease hydrolysis proposed by Markham and Smith these proved to have cyclic-terminal 2′ : 3′ phosphate groups [24].

For a given time of hydrolysis the concentration of each cyclic-terminal oligonucleotide passed through a maximum with increasing ribonuclease concentration. This maximum was progressively displaced to higher ribonuclease concentrations with decreasing size of the oligonucleotide.

The above is consistent with a rate of hydrolysis of the cyclic bond which is slow in comparison with that of the 3′–5′ phosphodiester linkage, in agreement with the earlier work of Markham and Smith [24].

The identification of the cyclic terminal mono- and oligonucleotides was carried out as folows: Uridine 2′ : 3′ cyclic-terminal phosphate was identified chromatographically, by its resistance to human seminal plasma phosphomonoesterase, and by its acquired susceptibility to the latter after treatment with HCl, which is known to split cyclic-terminal phosphates.

Analogously the dinucleotide UpU $(2' : 3')$ p was inert to semen phosphomonoesterase prior to HCl treatment. Consecutive treatment with HCl and semen phosphomonoesterase yielded the dinucleoside monophosphate UpU, which was hydrolyzed by alkali to uridine and UMP in a 1 : 1 mole ratio.

Similar studies were made of the hydrolysis of poly C by ribonuclease with entirely analogous results.

Chemical structure of copolymers containing two or more different nucleotides

Heppel, Oritz and Ochoa[66] have also made structural studies of copolymers of adenylic and uridylic acids (poly AU) as well as of a copolymer containing all four ribonucleotides (poly AGUC). In these cases, in addition to the problem of establishing the mode of linkage, there also existed the question of whether the sequential distribution of nucleotides was random. The method of attack was the now familiar one of degradation of the copolymers by enzymatic and alkaline hydrolysis and subsequent characterization of the products.

Most of the work upon poly AU was carried out with a copolymer containing adenylic and uridylic acids in an approximately 1 : 1 mole ratio. Exhaustive alkaline hydrolysis gave rise to a mixture of the 2'- and 3'-adenosine and uridine monophosphates. Treatment with spleen phosphodiesterase yielded 3'-AMP and 3'-UMP. Incubation with purified snake venom phosphodiesterase converted the copolymer to 5'-AMP and 5'-UMP. Thus, as in the case of polymers containing a single nucleotide, the evidence from enzymatic degradation is conclusively in favor of the 3'–5' phosphodiester linkage.

The absence of any specificity with regard to the purine or pyrimidine base precluded the use of the above diesterases in settling the question of sequence. However, the known specificity of ribonuclease rendered this enzyme appropriate for this purpose.

Extensive digestion of poly AU with ribonuclease yielded a mixture of 3'-UMP and what proved to be a homologous series of oligonucleotides with a 3'-terminal phosphate: ApUp, ApApUp, ApApApApUp. In no case was more than about 10 per cent of the products in the form of oligonucleotides higher than the pentanucleotide and usually the fraction of larger polynucleotides was much less than this.

The products of ribonuclease hydrolysis were separated by means of paper chromatography and paper electrophoresis. Their identification was carried out as follows:

The dinucleotide ApUp was converted by the action of human seminal plasma phosphomonoesterase to the 3'–5' dinucleotide monophosphate ApU. The latter was identified by alkaline hydrolysis to uridine and AMP (2' and 3').

The trinucleotide ApApUp was identified by treatment with phosphomonoesterase followed by alkaline hydrolysis. The final products were uridine and AMP (2' and 3') in mole ratio 1 : 2.

The homologous tetra- and pentanucleotides were identified in an analogous manner.

Since ribonuclease does not attack 3'–5' phosphodiester linkages which bridge two adenosine residues, the fact that virtually all the adenosine could be recovered in the form of oligonucleotides of very short chain length indicates that the distribution of adenosine units must be relatively random and that very extended sequences of the latter do not occur.

More quantitative evidence of the sequential distribution was obtained by the use of a 1 : 1 AU copolymer prepared from 5'-ADP labeled with ^{32}P in both phosphate groups and non-radioactive UDP. Complete alkaline hydrolysis converted the copolymer to a mixture of the 2' and 3' isomers of AMP and UMP. Thus wherever a labeled phosphate was esterified at the 3' position of a uridine residue a labeled UMP was obtained in the products of hydrolysis. Wherever the esterification was to the 3' position of an adenosine residue the latter acquired the ^{32}P label. Hence the ratio of the specific radioactivity of the AMP in the alkaline hydrolysate to that per mole of phosphate in the original ADP was equal to the fraction of adenosine groups linked to other adenosine groups in the copolymer.

In an experiment where the specific radioactivity per mole phosphate of the original ADP was 980 c.p.m. the AMP in the hydrolysate was found to have a specific radioactivity of 425 and the UMP a specific radioactivity of 518. This corresponded to a fractional cross-linking of 518/980 or 0.53. Thus 53% of the adenosine units were preceded by uridine units in the polynucleotide chain. This figure is very close to the 50% expected if the arrangement was completely random.

Still further information was obtained by examination of the products of ribonuclease digestion of the above ^{32}P labeled copolymer (Fig. 8). After exhaustive degradation by this enzyme the resultant mono- and oligonucleotides were isolated by paper electrophoresis at pH 3.5, eluted, and determined spectrophotometrically. Each oligonucleotide was subsequently subjected to complete alkaline hydrolysis and the specific radioactivity of its terminal UMP unit was determined. If the terminal UMP had, in the original sequence occurring in the copolymer, been followed by a labeled AMP unit the radioactivity of the latter would be acquired by the terminal UMP in its 3'-phosphomonoester group, as Fig. 14 shows. It if had been followed by another UMP unit the 3'-phosphomonoester group would invariably be non-radioactive.

Thus the sequence . . . Up*ApApUp**A . . . gives rise to the trinucleotide ApApUp*, with radioactive 3'-UMP. The sequence . . . Up*ApApUp*U yields the same trinucleotide ApApUp, but with invariably non-radioactive UMP. Similarly the sequences . . . Up*ApUp**A . . . and Up*ApUp*Up . . . yield ApUp containing radioactive and non-radioactive 3'-UMP, respectively. Similar statements may be made about the sequences . . . UpApApApUp*Ap . . . and UpApApApUpUp, etc.

In this manner measurements of the specific radioactivity of the UMP moiety of each of the oligonucleotide products of ribonuclease digestion yield the relative frequency with which such a sequence is followed by an AMP unit or a UMP unit

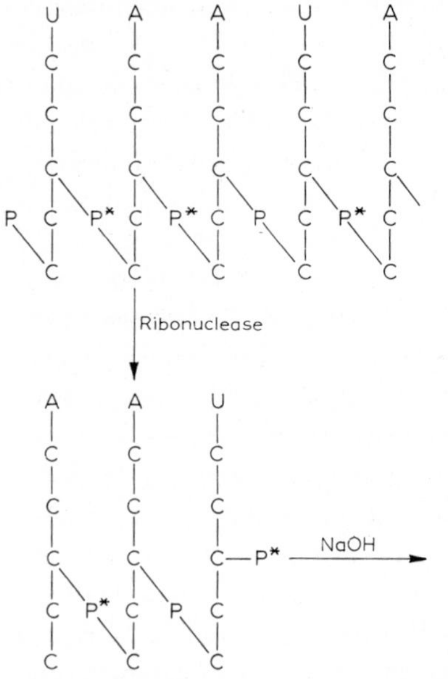

Fig. 14. Scheme of degradation of ^{32}P-labeled poly AU by pancreatic ribonuclease.

in the original copolymer. If the nucleotide sequence in the latter were completely random the two probabilities would be equal in all cases and the specific radioactivity of the terminal 3'-UMP unit of each oligonucleotide would be equal to one-half the specific radioactivity per mole phosphate in the original labeled ADP. Thus, for the 1 : 1 copolymer with 980 c.p.m. per μmole AMP, the specific radioactivity of the terminal 3'-UMP unit of each oligonucleotide should be one-half this figure or 490 c.p.m., if the distribution were completely random. Table 4 shows the results.

TABLE 4

SPECIFIC RADIOACTIVITY OF OLIGONUCLEOTIDE PRODUCTS OF RIBONUCLEASE DIGESTION OF POLY AU

Sequence	Specific radioactivity of terminal U (c.p.m. per μmole)	Fraction of sequences occurring as:
pUp*Up*	427	pUp*UpA, 0.44; pUp*UpU, 0.56
pUp*ApUp*	523	pUp*ApUpA, 0.53; pUp*ApUpU, 0.47
pUp*ApApUp*	515	pUp*ApApUpA, 0.53; pUp*ApApUpU, 0.47
pUp*ApApApUp*	500	pUp*ApApApUpA, 0.52; pUp*ApApApUpU, 0.48

The letters in italics represent the fragment isolated in the RNA-ase digest. In each case the fragment was preceded by a uridylic residue.

Hence it may be said that the measured specific radioactivities are, within experimental uncertainty, equal to those predicted on the basis of a completely random distribution. Thus the distribution of nucleotides in the AU copolymer produced by the *Azotobacter* enzyme may be regarded as essentially random.

Studies were also made upon an AGUC copolymer of all four ribonucleotides in mole ratio $1:0.5:1:1$. Complete alkaline hydrolysis gave rise to a mixture of the 3′ and 2′ isomers of the corresponding mononucleotides. Incubation with snake venom phosphodiesterase yielded the 5′ isomers of AMP, GMP, UMP, and CMP. Treatment with spleen phosphodiesterase produced the corresponding 3′-nucleotide monophosphates. Thus AGUC copolymer, like the AU copolymer, appears to possess the 3′–5′ phosphodiester linkage.

Detailed studies of the nucleotide sequence have not yet been made in this case. However, the products of ribonuclease digestion have been shown to include the dinucleotides ApUp, ApCp, GpUp and GpCp. Hence all possible cross-linkings of the AMP units appear to occur. This fact, together with the more detailed information available for the AU copolymer, makes it rather likely that the nucleotide distribution is essentially random in this case also.

In the case of AU copolymers produced by the action of the *Azotobacter* enzyme it has been shown by Grunberg-Manago that the ratio of AMP to UMP in the product roughly parallels the ADP to UDP ratio in the reaction mixture, although some divergence occurs at low values of the latter[73, 74].

POLYNUCLEOTIDES SYNTHESIZED BY THE POLYASE OF YEAST

Grunberg-Manago has recently succeeded in identifying and concentrating from yeast extract an enzyme (or mixture of enzymes) capable of catalyzing rapid exchange between inorganic ^{32}P and the terminal phosphate of ADP[73, 74]. The uptake of phosphate apparently does not require any co-factor and, unlike the analogous processes which are catalyzed by the *Azotobacter* or *M. lysodeikticus* enzymes, it is inhibited by Mg^{++}. In the presence of Mg^{++} ($2 \cdot 10^{-2}M$) this enzyme system serves to catalyze the formation of phosphate from ADP.

Incubation of the enzyme with ADP and phosphate in the presence of Mg^{++} is accompanied by the formation of a polymeric material, identified as such by its immobility on a paper chromatogram and by its non-dialyzability. When incubation is carried out in the presence of ^{32}P labeled phosphate the latter is incorporated directly into the polymer.

The polynucleotide, which is produced in low yield, precipitates from the reaction mixture as a complex with protein. It is as yet uncertain whether the latter is the enzyme itself or some other component of the probably complex mixture.

The information available about the properties of the deproteinated polymer is as yet scanty. However, what is known is sufficient to indicate that it must have a very different structure from the corresponding polymers produced by the *Azotobacter* enzyme.

Thus the polymer produced from ADP by the yeast enzyme differs in mobility and ultraviolet spectrum from the poly A produced by the *Azotobacter* polyase.

Unlike the latter its spectrum is virtually identical in acid and in alkaline solution. Furthermore, it gives no evidence of interaction with poly U. Again, in contrast with the usual poly A, the yeast polymer reacts with formaldehyde only slowly and to a limited extent.

This polymer retains a negative mobility at pH 3.75. As this pH is sufficiently acid to the adenine pK for virtually all of the latter to be positively charged it appears likely that the yeast polymer contains extra phosphate groups, in addition to those involved in nucleotide diesters, which are sufficient to endow it with a net negative charge under these conditions.

The evidence cited above indicates that this polynucleotide cannot correspond completely to the linear 3′–5′ phosphodiester linked type discussed earlier. In confirmation of this view exhaustive alkaline or enzymatic hydrolysis gives rise o products which cannot be identified with 3′-AMP, 5′-AMP, or adenosine.

STRUCTURE OF POLYRIBONUCLEOTIDES SYNTHESIZED BY CHEMICAL METHODS

Michelson has recently succeeded in synthesizing several polynucleotides of low degree of polymerization by purely chemical means[75,76]. His procedure begins with the nucleoside-2′ : 3′-cyclic phosphate, which is polymerized by the action of tetraphenylpyrophosphate at room temperature. In this manner polymers and copolymers of all four ribonucleotides have been prepared. The terminal nucleotide is a 2′ : 3′ cyclic phosphate in all cases.

The probable nature of the reaction mechanism makes it unlikely that a unique type of phosphodiester linkage can be present in the oligonucleotide products. This is borne out by the properties of the latter, which are consistent with those expected for linear polymers containing the 3′–5′ and 2′–5′ diester linkages to about the same extent.

Thus mild acid treatment splits the terminal 2′ : 3′ cyclic phosphate groups to produce oligonucleotides terminating in a nucleoside 2′ or 3′ phosphate. Complete alkaline hydrolysis gives rise to a mixture of 2′ and 3′ nucleoside monophosphates. No alkaline stable nucleoside-5′-phosphates were observed. Treatment with whole rattlesnake venom yields the expected mixture of nucleosides.

The purine polynucleotides were resistant to the action of ribonuclease. However the poly U produced in this manner was hydrolyzed to a mixture of uridine-3′-monophosphate and a series of very short oligonucleotides including dimers, trimers, and possibly tetramers. The latter components, representing about half the original sample, were resistant to ribonuclease and presumably contained 2′–5′ phosphodiester linkages exclusively. These oligonucleotides were separated by paper chromatography and the terminal phosphate of each was removed by treatment with semen monoesterase to yield a homologous series each of whose members terminated in a nucleoside: UpU, UpUpU, UpUpUpU. The composition of these was confirmed by complete alkaline hydrolysis to nucleotides and terminal nucleoside. The chain lengths were determined by the mole ratio of terminal nucleoside to total nucleotide phosphate in each case.

From end group analyses it appeared that the degree of polymerization of these polynucleotide preparations was not higher than about 15 at the upper limit.

CHEMICAL STRUCTURE OF BIOSYNTHETIC DNA

Questions very similar to those which have been discussed for the case of the biosynthetic polyribonucleotides naturally arose in the case of the high molecular weight polydeoxyribonucleotides produced *in vitro* by the enzyme from *E. coli*[77-82]. In addition, since a definite primer requirement existed in this case, it was of great interest to determine whether the natural DNA employed exerted any directive influence in the composition of the biosynthetic product, or whether the incorporation of nucleotides was essentially random.

To recapitulate, the *E. coli* enzyme is specific for *deoxy*ribonucleoside triphosphates. For extensive synthesis of new DNA to occur, all four nucleoside triphosphates must be present, as well as Mg^{++} and primer DNA.

Kornberg and co-workers have examined the influence of the base composition of the primer DNA upon that of the products[79]. Primer DNA's of varying base composition were isolated from a number of sources, including calf thymus, *Mycobacterium phlei*, *A. aerogenes*, *E. coli*, and T_2 coliphage. The net amount of new DNA synthesized ranged from 4 times the primer content in the case of *M. phlei* primer to over ten times for the other primers. Thus, with the exception of the *M. phlei* case, over 90 per cent of the base composition of the product was derived from the nucleoside triphosphate substrate pool.

TABLE 5

BASE COMPOSITION OF BIOSYNTHETIC DNA

Primer DNA source	Primer Composition (relative)				Product Composition (relative)			
	A	T	G	C	A	T	G	C
M. phlei	0.65	0.66	1.35	1.34	0.66	0.80	1.17	1.34
A. aerogenes	0.90	0.90	1.10	1.10	1.02	1.00	0.97	1.01
E. coli	1.00	0.97	0.98	1.05	1.04	1.00	0.97	0.98
Calf Thymus	1.14	1.05	0.90	0.85	1.19	1.19	0.81	0.83
T_2 bacteriophage	1.31	1.32	0.67	0.70	1.33	1.29	0.69	0.70

Nevertheless, as Table 5 shows, it was found that the base composition of the biosynthetic product showed a definite parallel to that of the primer. This held true for primers of widely varying composition. The nucleotide composition of the synthetic material was found to be independent, within wide limits, of the relative concentrations of the four nucleoside triphosphates in the substrate pool.

In all cases the composition of the products was consistent with the Watson-

Crick pairing, the adenine content being equivalent to the thymine and the guanine to the cytosine. In addition, the $(A+T)/(G+C)$ ratio of the product was established early in the reaction at a value close to that of the primer and showed only minor variation thereafter, irrespective of the extent of synthesis of excess DNA in most cases.

However, the equivalence in composition of primer and product was generally imperfect, especially in the *M. phlei* case. A possible origin of this divergence, particularly after long incubation times, is the simultaneous production of the adenylic–thymidylic (AT) copolymer, which can be produced by the *E. coli* enzyme in the absence of any primer, but only after a lag period of several hours. Alternatively, it might reflect the heterogeneity of composition of the primer DNA. If some components served as more efficient primers than others, the composition of the product would be distorted to some extent.

From the preceding it is evident that the primer DNA exerts a definite directive influence upon the over-all composition of the products. Whether this directive influence extends to sequence as well is still uncertain although quite probable. An obvious test for this would be, of course, to utilize a biologically active DNA as the primer and to observe whether the synthesis of additional DNA was paralled by an increase in activity.

This has in fact been attempted, using the transforming principle from *Diplococcus pneumonias*. The results were negative but their conclusiveness was uncertain, in view of the presence of some deoxyribonuclease impurity in the enzyme preparations.

It has further been found by Kornberg and co-workers that the naturally occurring purine and pyrimidine bases may, to some extent, be replaced by structural analogues[78]. All of such analogues which were acceptable to the enzyme shared an unimpaired capacity to form the hydrogen bonded base pairs of the Watson–Crick type. Thus, thymine could be replaced by uracil or 5-bromouracil (presented as deoxynucleoside triphosphates). Cytosine could be replaced by 5-bromocytosine or 5-methyl cytosine. Similarly, guanine was replaceable by hypoxanthine, but not by xanthine. However, the synthesis occurred at a reduced rate in most cases.

Direct analysis of the uracil-containing polymer showed that the uracil nucleotides were chemically incorporated into the biosynthetic DNA via phosphodiester linkages.

Kornberg and co-workers have also investigated the nature of the phosphodiester linkage of biosynthetic DNA. When ^{14}C-TTP was present in the reaction mixture, labeled thymine occurred in the products. Upon exhaustive digestion of the DNA with pancreatic deoxyribonuclease and subsequent separation of the products upon a Dowex-1 acetate column, the digest was found to contain about 6 per cent mononucleotides and about 15 percent dinucleotides, the balance consisting of higher oligonucleotides. From the dinucleotide fraction it was possible to isolate radioactive dinucleotides containing TMP and each of the four nucleotides. Of these, the CT and TT dinucleotides were selected for further examination.

All of the phosphate was esterified and essentially none of it was liberated by bull semen 5'-nucleotidase. Approximately half the phosphate was liberated by human semen phosphomonoesterase. When either 5'-nucleotidase or human semen phosphomonoesterase was added in combination with snake venom phosphodiesterase, complete conversion to the nucleosides occurred. This indicated that the internucleotide phosphodiester linkage was of the 3'–5' type, just as in the case of natural DNA and RNA.

While the presence of all four deoxynucleoside triphosphates is essential for any extensive synthesis of new DNA, it has nevertheless been found that a single deoxynucleoside triphosphate can be incorporated into DNA to an extent about one-thousandth of that for the complete reaction. The number of the single deoxynucleotides incorporated under these circumstances appears to be of the same order of magnitude as the number of DNA chains added to the reaction mixture. The relationship of the incorporation reaction to the complete synthesis of DNA occurring when all four deoxynucleotides are present is still uncertain.

Kornberg and co-workers have studied the products of incubation of radioactive preparations of each of the four nucleoside triphosphates with natural DNA and the *E. coli* enzyme[77]. The labeled preparations used were dA^{32}PPP, dC^{32}PPP, dT^{32}PPP and ^{14}CdCPPP. It was found that in each case the radioactivity sedimented at the same rate as the DNA itself and that the two could not be separated by heat denaturation of the DNA. This result suggested that the incorporation reflected the formation of relatively stable covalent bonds. The extent of incorporation varied from 0.5 to 1 mole of deoxynucleotide per mole of DNA.

In order to determine whether the incorporated ^{32}P was bound by a phosphodiester linkage, it was necessary to hydrolyze the products in such a way as to leave the labeled phosphate attached to the nucleoside which was adjacent to the incorporated nucleotide. If the incorporation occurred via the formation of a 3'–5' phosphodiester linkage, hydrolysis by calf spleen phosphodiesterase should accomplish this, as the labeled phosphate was attached to the original incorporated nucleoside at the 5' position.

Accordingly, enzymatic degradation of the products by the successive action of the DNAase from *M. pyrogenes* and calf spleen phosphodiesterase was carried out. Exhaustive hydrolysis gave rise to the 3'-mononucleotides exclusively. These were identified chromatographically. Further direct evidence for the nature of the nucleotides was furnished by their inertness to 5'-nucleotidase and their hydrolysis to nucleosides by semen phosphomonoesterase. It was found that, whichever nucleoside ^{32}P triphosphate was originally incorporated, the radioactivity was shared by all of the four 3'-deoxyribonucleotides of DNA.

These experiments were consistent with a direct incorporation of radioactive ^{32}P nucleotide at the nucleoside termini of the DNA, with the formation of a 3'–5' phosphodiester linkage. Incorporation at the non-nucleoside end is excluded.

Treatment of the radioactive products with snake venom phosphodiesterase resulted in the release of perchloric acid-soluble ^{32}P phosphate at a much more rapid rate than the over-all splitting. Thus, in one experiment, release of ^{32}P was 90 per cent complete when less than 3 per cent of all the deoxynucleotides had been released. As hydrolysis in this case proceeds in a stepwise manner from the ends of the DNA molecule, this finding confirms the earlier conclusion that the added deoxynucleotide is incorporated directly at the ends of the primer and excludes the possibility of a preliminary pyrophosphorylysis of the original DNA followed by a *de novo* synthesis of fresh DNA.

While the preceding experiments show conclusively that an incorporation of a single nucleotide at the ends of the primer DNA does occur, the pertinence of this finding to the extensive DNA synthesis occurring when all four bases are present remains uncertain.

MODE OF INTERNUCLEOTIDE LINKAGE
OF THE SYNTHETIC POLYNUCLEOTIDES OF KHORANA

As has been discussed in an earlier chapter, Khorana and co-workers have succeeded in synthesizing small oligodeoxyribonucleotides by purely chemical means. The hydrolytic degradation of these polymers by the phosphodiesterases of snake venom and of spleen has been studied with the aim of confirming both the original concept of the structure of the oligonucleotides and the currently accepted picture of the manner of action of the enzymes[83].

Incubation of the pentanucleotide tetraphosphate corresponding to the thymidylic acid monomer with venom phosphodiesterase resulted in the successive appearance of each of the lower homologs, thymidine appearing last. The concentration of each of these, as followed chromatographically, passed through a maximum with time. The ultimate products were thymidine-5'-phosphate and thymidine in a 4:1 mole ratio. This was consistent with a mode of internucleotide linkage which was exclusively 3'–5', as was certainly to be expected from the manner of synthesis. Interestingly enough these results also indicated first, that degradation was stepwise and, second, that it began at the end bearing the 3'-hydroxyl group.

The degradation of the same oligonucleotide with spleen phosphodiesterase likewise followed a stepwise course with thymidine appearing last. The ultimate products were thymidine-3'-phosphate and thymidine in a 4:1 mole ratio. These results were again consistent with an exclusively 3'–5' diester linkage and indicated furthermore that the action of spleen phosphodiesterase was also stepwise, but proceeded from the end bearing the 5'-hydroxyl group.

The work of Khorana and co-workers thus provides a valuable final link in the interdependent chain of evidence which connects our picture of the primary structure of natural polynucleotides with the known specificity of the phosphodiesterases.

POLYNUCLEOTIDES CONTAINING BOTH RIBO- AND DEOXYRIBONUCLEOTIDES

Hurwitz has recently described an interesting enzyme system from *E. coli* which can catalyze the incorporation of ribonucleotide residues into polydeoxyribonucleotides[84]. The requirements for extensive incorporation to occur include, in addition to enzyme, CTP (the *ribo*nucleotide), dATP, dGTP, dTTP, Mg^{++}, Mn^{++}, thymus DNA, and deoxyribonucleotide polymerase (the *E. coli* enzyme of Kornberg and co-workers).

Incubation of this complex mixture resulted in the synthesis of a new polymer, which was rendered largely acid-soluble by the action of either ribonuclease or deoxyribonuclease. If radioactive $C^{32}PPP$ (the 5′-*ribo*nucleotide) was included in the substrate pool, more than 95 per cent of the radioactivity was incorporated into the polymeric material.

Subsequent enzymatic degradation studies indicated that the polymeric material did not consist of a mixture of polydeoxyribonucleotides and polyribonucleotides, but did, in fact, contain a high proportion of copolymer. The combined action of spleen phosphodiesterase and a nuclease obtained from *M. pyrogenes* converted the polymer species to 3′-mononucleotides. All of the 3′-nucleotides so produced were radioactive. In contrast, when the polymer was completely degraded by the action of deoxyribonuclease and snake venom phosphodiesterase to 5′-mononucleotides, the radioactivity was contained in the 5′-CMP fraction exclusively.

The preceding is definitely consistent with the existence of 3′–5′ phosphodiester linkages between CMP and each of the deoxyribonucleotides. Further evidence was obtained from the isolation of radioactive dinucleotides through the action of deoxyribonuclease on the polymer. One of these was identified as cytidylate-adenylate and was found to be degraded to the corresponding 5′-mononucleotides by the action of snake venom phosphodiesterase.

It thus appears that this mixed polynucleotide, like the other natural and biosynthetic polynucleotides, possesses the 3′–5′ phosphodiester linkage.

REFERENCES

[1] P. LEVENE AND H. SIMMS, *J. Biol. Chem.*, 65 (1925) 519.

[2] P. LEVENE AND H. SIMMS, *J. Biol. Chem.*, 70 (1926) 327.

[3] G. BUTLER, in S. COLOWICK AND N. KAPLAN, *Methods in Enzymology*, Vol 2, 1955, p. 565.

[4] H. BOMAN AND U. KALETTA, *Biochim. et Biophys. Acta*, 24 (1957) 619.

[5] R. HURST AND G. BUTLER, *J. Biol. Chem.*, 193 (1951) 91.

[6] R. SINSHEIMER AND J. KOERNER, *J. Biol. Chem.*, 198 (1952) 293.

[7] M. PRIVAT DE GARILHE AND M. LASKOWSKI, *Biochim. et Biophys. Acta*, 18 (1955) 370.

[8] W. COHN AND E. VOLKIN, *J. Biol. Chem.*, 203 (1953) 319.

[9] J. BADDILEY AND A. TODD, *J. Chem. Soc.*, (1947) 648.

[10] E. VOLKIN AND W. COHN, *J. Biol. Chem.*, 205 (1953) 767.

[11] M. PRIVAT DE GARILHE, L. CUNNINGHAM, U. LAURILA AND M. LASKOWSKI, *J. Biol. Chem.*, 224 (1957) 751.

[12] L. HEPPEL AND J. RABINOWITZ, *Ann. Rev. Biochem.*, 27 (1958) 613.

[13] A. CRESTFIELD AND F. ALLEN, *J. Biol. Chem.*, 219 (1956) 103.

[14] C. DEKKER, *Federation Proc.*, 13 (1954) 197.

[15] D. DUNN AND J. SMITH, *Biochem. J.*, 67 (1957) 494.

[16] H. BOMAN, *Ann. N.Y. Acad. Sci.*, 81 (1959) 800.

[17] L. HEPPEL, P. ORTIZ AND S. OCHOA, *J. Biol. Chem.*, 229 (1957) 679.

[18] L. HEPPEL AND R. HILMOE, in S. COLOWICK AND N. KAPLAN, *Methods in Enzymology*, Vol. 2, New York (1955) 565.

[19] A. MICHELSON, L. SZABO AND A. TODD, *J. Chem. Soc.*, (1956) 1546.

[20] M. MAVER AND A. GRECO, *J. Natl. Cancer Inst.*, 17 (1956) 503.

[21] J. REIS, *Enzymologia*, 5 (1938) 251.

[22] A. KORNBERG AND W. PRICER, *J. Biol. Chem.*, 186 (1950) 557.

[23] L. HEPPEL AND R. HILMOE, *J. Biol. Chem.*, 188 (1951) 665.

[24] R. MARKHAM AND J. SMITH, *Biochem. J.*, 52 (1952) 552.

[25] H. LORING, F. CARPENTER AND P. ROLL, *J. Biol. Chem.*, 169 (1947) 601.

[26] G. SCHMIDT, R. CUBILES, N. ZOLLNER, L. HECHT, N. STRIKLER, K. SERAIDARIAN, M. SERAIDARIAN AND S. THANNHAUSER, *J. Biol. Chem.*, 192 (1951) 715.

[27] D. BROWN AND A. TODD, *J. Chem. Soc.*, (1953) 2040.

[28] H. MANDEL, R. MARKHAM AND R. MATTHEWS, *Biochim. et Biophys. Acta*, 24 (1957) 205.

[29] R. SINSHEIMER, *J. Biol. Chem.*, 215 (1955) 579.

[30] M. LASKOWSKI, *Ann. N.Y. Acad. Sci.*, 81 (1959) 776.

[31] J. POTTER, K. BROWN AND M. LASKOWSKI, *Biochim. et Biophys. Acta*, 9 (1952) 150.

[32] R. SINSHEIMER, *J. Biol. Chem.*, 208 (1954) 445.

[33] R. SINSHEIMER AND J. KOERNER, *Science*, 114 (1951) 42.

[34] L. CUNNINGHAM, B. CATLIN AND M. PRIVAT DE GARILHE, *J. Am. Chem. Soc.*, 78 (1956) 4642.

[35] U. LAURILA AND M. LASKOWSKI, *J. Biol. Chem.*, 228 (1957) 49.

[36] D. BROWN, D. MAGRATH AND A. TODD, *J. Chem. Soc.*, (1952) 2708.

[37] C. CARTER AND W. COHN, *Federation Proc.*, 8 (1949) 190.

[38] W. COHN, *J. Am. Chem. Soc.*, 72 (1950) 1471.

[39] W. COHN, *J. Am. Chem. Soc.*, 72 (1950) 2811.

[40] W. COHN, *J. Cellular Comp. Physiol.*, 38, Suppl. 1 (1951) 21.

[41] O. BAILLY AND J. GAUME, *Bull. soc. chim.*, 2 (1935) 354.

[42] D. BROWN AND A. TODD, *J. Chem. Soc.*, (1952) 52.

[43] R. MERRIFIELD AND D. WOOLLEY, *J. Biol. Chem.*, 197 (1952) 521.

[44] E. VOLKIN AND W. COHN, *Federation Proc.*, 11 (1952) 303.

[45] L. HEPPEL, R. MARKHAM AND R. HILMOE, *Nature*, 171 (1953) 1152.

[46] W. COHN AND E. VOLKIN, *Arch. Biochem. and Biophys.*, 35 (1952) 465.

[47] R. COX, A. JONES, G. MARSH, A. PEACOCKE, *Biochim. et Biophys. Acta*, 21 (1956) 576.

[48] W. FLETCHER, J. GULLAND AND D. JORDAN, *J. Chem. Soc.*, (1944) 33.

[49] R. MARKHAM AND J. SMITH, *Biochem. J.*, 52 (1952) 565.

[50] R. MARKHAM, R. MATTHEWS AND J. SMITH, *Nature*, 173 (1954) 537.

[51] K. REDDI AND C. KNIGHT, *Nature*, 180 (1957) 374.

[52] R. MATTHEWS AND J. SMITH, *Nature*, 180 (1957) 375.

[53] W. COHN, *Proc. Third Int. Congr. Biochem.*, Brussels, (1955) 152.

[54] E. CHARGAFF, B. MAGASANIK, E. VISCHER, C. GREEN, R. DONIGER AND D. ELSON, *J. Biol. Chem.*, 186 (1950) 51.

[55] D. ELSON AND E. CHARGAFF, *Phosphorus Metabolism*, 2 (1952) 329.

[56] D. ELSON AND E. CHARGAFF, *Biochim. et Biophys. Acta*, 17 (1955) 367.

[57] E. CHARGAFF, in W. MCELROY AND B. GLASS, *The Chemical Basis of Heredity*, Baltimore, 1957, 521.

[58] R. HURST, J. LITTLE AND G. BUTLER, *J. Biol. Chem.*, 188 (1951) 705.

[59] R. SINSHEIMER AND J. KOERNER, *J. Am. Chem. Soc.*, 74 (1952) 283.

[60] R. COX AND A. PEACOCKE, *J. Chem. Soc.*, (1956) 2499.

[61] C. HALL, *Ann. N.Y. Acad. Sci.*, 81 (1959) 723.

[62] E. CHARGAFF, in E. CHARGAFF AND J. DAVIDSON, *The Nucleic Acids*, Vol. 1, 1955, 307.

[63] R. SINSHEIMER, *J. Molec. Biol.*, 1 (1959) 43.

[64] A. BENDICH, H. PAHL, G. KORNGOLD, H. ROSENKRANTZ AND J. FRESCO, *J. Am. Chem. Soc.*, 80 (1958) 3949.

[65] D. DUNN AND J. SMITH, *Nature*, 175 (1955) 336.

[66] L. HEPPEL, P. ORTIZ AND S. OCHOA, *J. Biol. Chem.*, 229 (1957) 695.

[67] M. GRUNBERG-MANAGO, P. ORTIZ AND S. OCHOA, *Science*, 122 (1955) 907.

[68] S. OCHOA, *Federation Proc.*, 15 (1956) 832.

[69] S. OCHOA AND L. A. HEPPEL, in W. MCELROY AND B. GLASS, *The Chemical Basis of Heredity*, Baltimore, 1957, 615.

[70] L. A. HEPPEL, J. D. SMITH, P. ORTIZ AND S. OCHOA, *Federation Proc.*, 15 (1956) 273.

[71] L. HEPPEL, P. WHITFIELD AND R. MARKHAM, *Biochem. J.*, 60 (1955) 8.

[72] H. KAPLAN AND L. HEPPEL, *J. Biol. Chem.*, 222 (1956) 907.

[73] M. GRUNBERG-MANAGO, *Biokhimiia*, 23 (1959) 287.

[74] M. GRUNBERG-MANAGO AND J. WISNIEWSKI, *Compt. rend.*, 245 (1957) 750.

[75] A. MICHELSON, *J. Chem. Soc.*, (1959) 1371.

[76] A. MICHELSON, *Nature*, 181 (1958) 303.

[77] J. ADLER, I. LEHMAN, M. BESSMAN, E. SIMMS AND A. KORNBERG, *Proc. Natl. Acad. Sci.*, 44 (1958) 641.

[78] M. BESSMAN, I. LEHMAN, J. ADLER, S. ZIMMERMAN, E. SIMMS AND A. KORNBERG, *Proc. Natl. Acad. Sci.*, 44 (1958) 633.

[79] I. LEHMAN, S. ZIMMERMAN, J. ADLER, M. BESSMAN, E. SIMMS AND A. KORNBERG, *Proc. Natl., Acad. Sci.*, 44 (1958) 1191.

[80] M. BESSMAN, I. LEHMAN, E. SIMMS AND A. KORNBERG, *J. Biol. Chem.*, 233 (1958) 171.

[81] I. LEHMAN, M. BESSMAN, E. SIMMS AND A. KORNBERG, *J. Biol. Chem.*, 233 (1958) 163.

[82] I. LEHMAN, *Ann. N.Y. Acad. Sci.*, 81 (1959) 745.

[83] W. RAZZELL AND H. KHORANA, *J. Am. Chem. Soc.*, 80 (1958) 1770.

[84] J. HURWITZ, *J. Biol. Chem.*, 234 (1959) 2351.

Chapter 4

Assay and Purification of Polynucleotide-Synthesizing Enzymes

THE POLYNUCLEOTIDE PHOSPHORYLASES: ASSAY

An adequate means of assaying enzyme activity is, of course, basic to the development of a method of purification. In the case of polynucleotide phosphorylase, the over-all reaction catalyzed by the enzyme is usually described as follows[1-3]:

$$n \text{ XDP} \longleftrightarrow (\text{XMP})_n + n\text{P}_i \tag{1}$$

where XDP is any of the nucleoside diphosphates; $(\text{XMP})_n$ is the corresponding polymer; and P_i is the inorganic orthophosphate liberated. The variation with time of any of these may serve as a means of following the reaction.

Most assay methods currently in use have been based upon the approximation of the admittedly complex process by a single step mechanism of the above type. For practical purposes this practice appears to be adequate, and activities thereby measured have generally been found to be directly proportional to enzyme concentration over a reasonably wide range of values of the latter.

Nevertheless, the above expression clearly is an oversimplified representation of the actual process, which is almost certainly of a stepwise character. A more valid description of the events is as follows:

$$\text{XDP} + (\text{XMP})_n \longleftrightarrow (\text{XMP})_{n+1} + \text{P}_i \tag{2}$$

A rigorous kinetic treatment would have to take into account the possibility that the characteristic bimolecular rate constants for each stage may vary with the degree of polymerization of the polymer species. This is especially likely to be the case for the smaller polymeric species. In general the rate of formation of the species $(\text{XMP})_{n+1}$ will thus be a function of the concentrations of XDP and $(\text{XMP})_n$.

A consequence of the stepwise character of the mechanism is the failure of the observed over-all rate of polymer formation to obey simple kinetics under certain circumstances. Thus, if the reactivity of the polymer species increases with increasing values of n, it would be expected that the over-all rate would be autocatalytic in nature. This is, in fact, the explanation proposed by Mii and Ochoa[4] for the autocatalytic character of the over-all polymerization rate curves obtained with the purified enzyme of *A. vinelandii*, in the absence of primer.

A major difficulty, which considerably complicates the assay problem, arises from the existence of numerous cofactors which can modify the kinetics of the polymerization reaction to an important degree. These include the following:

a. polynucleotide activators (or primers). The role of these has been most extensively investigated in the case of the phosphorylase from *A. vinelandii.* Highly purified preparations of this enzyme which have been depleted of polynucleotide cofactors, show rate curves having a definite autocatalytic character. The addition of small amounts of the poly- or oligonucleotide corresponding to the polymer being synthesized serves to accelerate the over-all rate markedly and to abolish the autocatalytic nature of the rate curves. A primer requirement has also been reported for preparations of the phosphorylase from *M. lysodeikticus,* which have been subjected to tryptic digestion in the course of purification[5].

In cases where a definite primer requirement exists it is obviously desirable for practical assay purposes to select conditions so as to assure that the concentration of primer is not the effective rate limiting factor. This can be accomplished by adding a saturating amount of primer. The criteria for the attainment of this condition are the absence of an autocatalytic rate curve and the insensitivity of the rate to further addition of primer.

In the case of most crude enzyme preparations the accompanying polynucleotide contaminants are usually adequate to satisfy any primer requirement.

b. polynucleotide inhibitors. Several instances have been reported of the occurrence of poly- and oligonucleotides having definite inhibitory powers for polynucleotide phosphorylase[6]. These can not only alter the absolute activity of an enzyme preparation but can also modify its relative activity toward different substrates. The concentration of such inhibitors may be extremely small ($< 10^{-7} M$) and not detectable by any method other than the sensitivity of the enzyme to their presence. These effects have been reported only for the enzyme of *M. lysodeikticus*[6]. They have not been observed for the *A. vinelandii* enzyme.

In general, changes in the concentration of polynucleotide activators or inhibitors in the course of purification can often result in alterations in the measured specific activity which are unrelated to the actual fractional content of enzyme and can lead to false conclusions about the effectiveness of a particular procedure.

c. divalent cation activators. With the exception of the enzyme isolated from yeast by Grunberg-Manago[7], all enzymes detected so far require a divalent cation, of which Mg^{++} is generally the most effective and, in some instances, apparently the only metal which can act as a cofactor. There is an optimum concentration for the metal, beyond which the enzyme is inhibited. The range of optimum concentration depends upon several variables, including pH and substrate concentration. In addition, ionic strength plays an important role, particularly in abolishing the inhibition observed at high metal concentrations. This latter observation has been made only with enzyme preparations obtained from *M. lysodeikticus,* *B. subtilis,* and *B. megaterium*[6, 8]. The usual optimal concentration of Mg^{++} is of the order of $5 \cdot 10^{-4} M$.

d. pH and ionic strength. An alkaline pH is required for both polymerization and phosphorolysis, but the pH optimum, which is normally selected for assay, varies with the enzyme source from 7.4 for *E. coli* enzyme[3] and 8.1 for *A. vinelandii* enzyme[1] to above 9.5 for *M. lysodeikticus* enzyme[2], and with the conditions of the assay. In the case of the *M. lysodeikticus* enzyme the pH optimum is somewhat sensitive to Mg^{++} concentration and ionic strength.

Enzyme preparations from *M. lysodeikticus*, *B. subtilis*, and *B. megaterium* have been observed to require an optimum ionic strength of approximately 0.2 if KCl is used[8]. Completely salt-free enzyme preparations from these sources have been reported to be practically inactive toward the substrate unless the latter is in very high concentration[8]. The optimum salt concentration depends upon the pH, $[Mg^{++}]$, and the substrate concentration. The effect of salt is believed to be on the reactivity of the polymer, which must have most of its negatively charged phosphate groups masked by the shielding effect of the salt ions for the polymerization to take place[8]. A similar activating effect can, under similar conditions, be induced by the organic cation, acridine orange[9]. Other investigators have not confirmed these findings with preparations obtained from *A. vinelandii*[10] and possible reasons for this will be discussed elsewhere. Since the only effect of the salt is on the Michaelis constant for ADP, at sufficiently high substrate concentrations the activating effect of the salt disappears.

The usual enzyme assay is carried out with ADP or IDP, or with their corresponding polymers, if phosphorolysis is measured. ADP as a substrate for polymerization assays has the disadvantage of being readily dismutated with the adenylate kinases present in all polynucleotide phosphorylase preparations so far examined, except only the most highly purified. Against this disadvantage in the application of ADP is the lack of poly A susceptibility to hydrolysis by many nucleases, which are often present as contaminants. A second advantage of ADP is, of course, its relative cheapness in comparison with the other available nucleoside diphosphates.

A wide variety of assays of phosphorylase activity has been employed by the various groups of investigators active in the field of enzyme purification. The methods include the rate of polymer formation, the rate of ^{32}P-orthophosphate exchange with ADP, the rate of liberation of orthophosphate, the rate of polymer phosphorolysis, and the rate of incorporation of ADP into polymer.

Units of specific activity

Except in the case of conditions found with highly purified primer-requiring enzyme preparations or, as is more likely in many instances, with enzyme preparations containing inhibitors, the rate of polymerization is not affected by the amount of polymer added to the assay mixture. The rate of polymerization can be expressed as follows, in the absence of competing reactions:

$$d[ADP]/dt = -d[P_i]/dt = -d[polymer]/dt \qquad (3)$$

The observed relationship between [ADP] and the rate of polymerization approximates a Michaelis–Menten equation [15]:

$$d[ADP]/dt = \frac{V_{max}}{1 + K_m/[ADP]} \qquad (4)$$

Thus, one can determine an activity under standard conditions of substrate concentration in which the rate of polymerization is directly proportional to the substrate concentration ([ADP] small), or increases non-linearly with the substrate concentration ([ADP] intermediate), or is independent of ADP concentration ([ADP] large). Assays based on each of the three possible conditions have been described [1, 2].

As will be shown in the next chapter, both V_{max} and K_m may vary together or independently, depending upon the experimental conditions. By and large, however, the more sensitive parameter is K_m. For this reason it is probably a better procedure to base enzyme activities on a calculated V_{max}, as this is independent [8] of the value of K_m. Some of the factors found to influence K_m in the case of enzyme preparations from *M. lysodeikticus*, *B. subtilis*, and *B. megaterium* are ionic strength [8] and the presence of polynucleotide inhibitors and activators [6]. The effect of ionic strength on V_{max} is negligible and the effect of the activators and inhibitors is considerably less on V_{max} than on K_m. In contrast, Mg^{++} increases both K_m and V_{max} to about the same degree. Thus, it is of importance in comparing enzyme activities that the concentrations of the metal be the same, or that the different metal concentrations be accounted for in determining the respective activities.

The selection of enzyme units and specific activities has tended to be a rather haphazard process, which serves to add considerable confusion to the literature. The field of polynucleotide phosphorylase is no exception. Not only has the initial selection of the units and specific activities been entirely arbitrary, but the subsequent studies by other investigators have, for the most part, ignored the suggested standards introduced by the original investigators. One might account for this if the modifications were based on some more systematic approach to the problem, but, with few exceptions, the revisions are equally arbitrary.

The ultimate objective in any enzyme purification study is primarily the isolation of a homogeneous protein identified as being the enzyme in question. For this reason the concept of the specific activity of an enzyme preparation is introduced. It is proper, therefore, to consider the definition of the specific activity of the enzyme preparation and the choice of the units of enzyme activity in terms of this ultimate goal. In an increasing number of instances it is now possible to correlate the specific activity of a pure enzyme preparation with the molar concentration of the enzyme itself. Thus, the choice of enzyme units and the definition of specific activity are important if the mass of accumulated literature preceding the attainment of this goal is to be used intelligently.

References p. 125

In the following discussion we shall reinterpret the results given in the literature in terms of common units of time, volume, and concentration, *i.e.*, seconds, milliliters, and moles/liter. In the examples to be considered, the units of enzyme have been defined in terms of 15 minutes[1], 60 minutes[3], one minute[11], and 90 minutes[5]. A constant time interval of 1 minute or one second is preferable, depending upon the concentrations, or quantities of substrate, involved. We suggest that the unit of time be one second.

The standard concentrations for mass action equations are normally given as moles per liter. This corresponds to millimoles/ml or $1000 \times \mu$moles/ml. The latter quantity has been used extensively in biochemical studies and is, therefore, conceptually a more convenient form for many biochemists. However, failure of many investigators to specify concentrations when discussing a quantity of the dimensions of micromoles has often led to considerable confusion on the part of readers in interpreting the results. We suggest, therefore, that the volume be expressed in units of a milliliter and the quantities of substrate expressed as millimoles. Thus, it is a simple matter to convert these units of concentration to moles per liter without recourse to any conversion factors.

A unit of enzyme activity will be defined, therefore, as that amount in one ml of a reaction mixture which will catalyze the conversion of 1 millimole of substrate to product in one second, when substrate (XDP) is present in excess. One thousand units will, therefore, catalyze the conversion of one mole substrate in one second. It is important to note, however, that this definition of an enzyme unit assumes that regardless of the volume of the reaction mixture in the assay, the concentration of the substrate is constant. Moreover, the unit is actually based on a change in concentration, rather than quantity of substrate. Thus, if the reaction volume of the assay is 23 ml, the total number of units of enzyme in the reaction mixture is 23 times the rate of conversion of the substrate (in millimoles/ml · sec).

The above choice of units often leads to inconveniently small numbers for the usual levels of enzyme concentration. We shall, therefore, also introduce the supplementary definitions of a *milliunit* and a *microunit* of enzyme activity, which are equal to 10^{-3} and 10^{-6} times the unit as defined above.

The specification of conditions will be left open for the present. It is assumed that Mg^{++} concentration, pH, ionic strength, and primer concentration are optimal. The standard temperature will be taken as 37° C.

Specific activity is usually expressed in terms of the total weight of the enzyme preparation or of its protein content. In the latter case the biuret method can be used for determining protein content, if the fraction of polynucleotide material present is too high to make a measure of the total nitrogen content feasible. For more highly purified enzyme preparations in which the 280/260 ratio is greater than 0.5, the data of Warburg and Christian for mixtures of enolase and nucleic acid have been used by several investigators[1-3].

The standard weight of enzyme preparation, based on its protein content, will be taken as 1 g. The specific activity of the enzyme, is, however, a relative quantity which is independent of the amount of enzyme present in the assay:

$$\text{specific activity} = \text{units enzyme/g of protein}$$

In addition to units expressed in terms of the net amount of substrate conversion, it is also possible, in principle, to define an enzyme unit in terms of the per cent conversion, or half life of the substrate, provided the rate of substrate conversion follows a first order equation. This is not actually observed with polynucleotide phosphorylase in the entire time course of the reaction, although the rate may be proportional to the initial concentration of the substrate[11]. The advantage of this method of assay is the non-dependence of the rate constant on the initial substrate concentration, irrespective of the magnitude of the latter. For a classical first order reaction, both with respect to substrate concentration and time, the rate constant is the logarithm of the reciprocal of the time required for conversion of 50% of the substrate. Beers has suggested[11] that this same method may be used to calculate an enzyme unit for polynucleotide phosphorylase by determining the time required to convert 50% of ADP to the polymer, a figure which must be obtained by linear extrapolation of the rate curve. However, the sensitivity of the rate curve, both with respect to its magnitude and linearity, to ionic strength renders this method of specifying enzyme units less useful than the one discussed above.

Assay by inorganic phosphate liberation

The first assay based on polymerization was described by Grunberg-Manago et al.[1]. The parameter measured is the inorganic orthophosphate released from the nucleoside diphosphate in unit time. Either ADP or IDP are used as substrates. (Details of the various assays described in this chapter will be found in the Appendix). Under the conditions of the assay the rate of orthophosphate release is proportional to the enzyme concentration and is constant during the fifteen minutes of the reaction time, provided that substrate is present in excess. The release of phosphate can be followed by Fiske-Subbarow analysis.

A majority of the kinetic studies has been performed by means of this assay[8,9]. It is rapid and convenient and provides a high degree of precision. However, the release of orthophosphate is a feature of many phosphatase-catalyzed reactions and, therefore, lacks the specificity provided by other methods. Thus, if phosphatases are present as contaminants in the enzyme preparation, anomalously high apparent activities may be measured. In practice, the analysis for phosphate requires very careful standardization to be reliable, as is discussed in the appendix.

Assays based upon the rate of incorporation of nucleoside-diphosphate

The stoichiometry of the polymerization reaction is such that assays based upon the rate of disappearance of the nucleoside-diphosphate substrate and upon the rate of liberation of phosphate should, in principle, yield identical results. However,

References p. 125

as is the case with most enzyme assays in which the substrate is present in large excess, so that the rate has a constant value during the time of the assay, it is not feasible to measure directly the decrease in concentration of the substrate in nucleotide polymerization assays. For example, in the assay described above only a few per cent of the ADP is generally converted into the polymer. This means that a difference between two large numbers must be determined to give the fraction of ADP polymerized. This results in a large experimental error. It is, therefore, more feasible and accurate to measure the quantity of polymer synthesized during the assay time.

The simplest version of this type of assay involves a separation of the acid-soluble mononucleotides from the polymer by quantitative precipitation of the latter with non-ultraviolet-absorbing perchloric acid and an estimation of the polymer concentration by its absorption at 257 mμ, after being redissolved. Several precautions must be taken in the use of this assay. Crude enzyme preparations often contain a substantial amount of ethanol-soluble, ultraviolet-absorbing material, which will give a high blank if the material is not removed by washing with ethanol. Crude enzyme preparations containing a high concentration of acid-insoluble polynucleotide material will also give a large blank, which may reduce the precision of the method considerably.

A complication frequently encountered is either incomplete separation of the mononucleotides from the polymer or incomplete precipitation of the polymer. The former is corrected by repeated washing of the polymer with acid. The latter may require several modifications in the procedure, depending upon the reasons for the failure to recover all of the polymer. With more extensively purified enzyme preparations, the mass of precipitate contributed by the enzyme preparation decreases to a very small value. However, the errors from mechanical loss of material can be large. In addition, in the absence of adequate protein there is frequently a failure to precipitate the polymer completely. This can be compensated for by the addition of an inert protein at the end of the assay time. Extensive degradation of the polymer by contaminant nucleases may also reduce the quantity of polymer precipitated. Olmsted and Lowe[5] observed with trypsin-treated polynucleotide phosphorylase from *M. lysodeikticus* a marked decrease in the amount of polymer precipitated, after a given period of assay time, with increasing concentrations of enzyme. They attribute this artifact to the action of a nuclease on poly A. There are other mechanisms, however, which can produce artifacts in this assay, which are considered below.

The sensitivity of the ADP incorporation assay can be increased by the use of ^{14}C-labeled substrate. Littauer and Kornberg[3] describe such an assay with ADP-8-[14]C. The polymer is separated from the mononucleotide by acid precipitation after the addition of non-labeled *E. coli* RNA to facilitate the recovery of the polymer. From the specific activity of the substrate and the radioactivity of the polymer, the fraction of ADP converted to the polymer can be readily determined. This procedure is more cumbersome than the first one, but the large blank resulting from ultraviolet absorption by ethanol-soluble and acid-insoluble contaminants in the precipitate is not a factor.

Other methods in addition to precipitation have been used to separate the polymer from the substrate. One of these involves paper chromatographic separation with the Krebs–Hems [12] solvent system of isobutyric acid and ammonia in water. Highly polymerized polymeric material does not migrate with this system, but the nucleotides, AMP, ADP, and ATP, migrate from the origin in the order given. Indeed, it was by means of this solvent system that Grunberg-Manago and Ochoa [13] first detected a net synthesis of polynucleotide material. The nucleotide material is readily detected on paper chromatograms by its ability to quench the fluorescence of the filter paper induced by short wavelength ultraviolet radiation. Although the total quantities of substrate may be small in this type of assay, the concentration of substrate must be an order of magnitude higher than that used in other assays (0.01 M vs. 0.001 M).

The paper chromatographic method can be made quantitative in several ways. An early method consisted of using ADP$-8-$[14]C. The radioactivity at the origin of the paper is compared with that found at the ADP (and AMP and ATP, if myokinase is present) spot [11]. The ratio of total radioactivities at the two regions is a measure of the extent of incorporation of AMP into poly A. The radioactivity can be measured on the paper directly with reasonably good accuracy. In Fig. 15

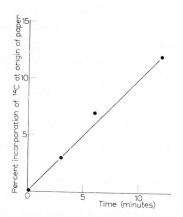

Fig. 15. A representative assay of polynucleotide phosphorylase [15]. The reaction is followed via the rate of incorporation of [14]C- labeled nucleotide into polymer, which remains at the origin of a paper chromatogram.

are given the results of such an assay, in which the extent of incorporation of ^{14}C at the origin was determined as a function of time. Olmsted and Lowe [5] have also used this method, although the results of such assays have not been reported.

It is also possible, of course, to elute the polymer from the origin of the paper with a solvent such as 0.1 N NH$_4$OH. The concentration of the polymer in a known volume is then determined by its ultraviolet absorption or by other methods. Hakim has used this method recently[14] in his study of the polynucleotide phosphorylase activity of human sperm extracts.

A variety of other methods is available for measuring the concentration of the polymer. Most of these require the separation of the polymer from the monomer species because of the common physical and chemical properties of the two. In addition to measuring the ultraviolet absorption of the polymer, one can also determine its organic phosphate content. This can be conveniently accomplished by digestion of the polymer with 70% perchloric acid and the use of one of several available colorimetric methods for determining the amount of inorganic phosphate in the digest[15].

Accurate determination of the concentration of the polymer can also be made by the use of the orcinol reagent[16]. This is specific for the purine polynucleotides and, therefore, cannot be used for poly C or for poly U. However, the procedure is reasonably sensitive and convenient. Its use has heretofore been restricted primarily to studies of phosphorolysis.

Because of the hypochromatic shift of the ultraviolet absorption spectrum of the nucleotide upon polymerization, accurate determinations of the concentration of polynucleotide by means of its ultraviolet absorption are often difficult. Part of this stems from the fact that the absorption is very sensitive to ionic strength, pH, and temperature. One can use the extinction coefficient reported by Warner[17] at 257 mμ, which is given in terms of the phosphorus content, but, as is pointed out by Warner, this value can vary by several per cent. from preparation to preparation. It is generally advisable, therefore, to hydrolyze the polymer with alkali to the isomeric mixture of adenylic acids a and b and determine the concentration of nucleotide from the known molar extinction coefficient of these substances (15,400).

When it is not practicable to separate the polymer from the monomer, two alternative methods are potentially available to measure the quantity of polymer formed. The first is based on the hypochromatic spectral shift of the nucleotide upon polymerization. With very low concentrations of ADP one can, in principle, follow the reaction by observing the drop in optical density at 257 mμ. However, this method is not very suitable for quantitative work and has not been used in polymerization assays. However, in the converse phosphorolysis reaction, in situations where the concentration of polymer is limiting, the increase in optical density with the extent of the reaction has proved to be a useful semi-quantitative method for following the reaction[16].

A second potential method is based on the reaction of dyes with polynucleotides[18]. Acridine orange can be used with considerable precision to titrate the nucleotide content of a polymer preparation, there being a one-to-one association of the dye with the polymer nucleotide units. This method has not actually been used as yet in polymerization assays to follow the increase in concentration of the polymer species.

Of particular importance in assays of this type for polynucleotide phosphorylase are the possible artifacts introduced by competing enzyme systems in the often crude enzyme preparations. These, in turn, may dictate the assay of choice. In view of the fact that we may expect considerable attention in the future to be devoted to the estimation of polynucleotide phosphorylase activity in an increasing number of organisms and tissues under both physiological and pathological conditions, it is well for us at this point to consider some of these artifacts in more detail. In general, there are two major enzyme systems which can interfere with polynucleotide phosphorylase assays based on the net synthesis of polymer: phosphatases and nucleases.

It may, in fact, be impossible to distinguish between the action of a phosphatase (with or without a kinase) and the combined action of a polynucleotide phosphorylase and a nuclease, since the final products of both systems are the same, i.e., inorganic orthophosphate and mononucleotides. Thus, a combination of a polynucleotide phosphorylase and a nuclease acting on the polymer gives the following sequence of reactions:

$$n(\text{XDP}) \rightarrow (\text{XMP})_n + n\text{P}_i \quad \text{(phosphorylase)}$$

$$(\text{XMP})_n \rightarrow n\text{XMP} \quad \text{(nuclease)}$$

The sum of these reactions is

$$n\text{XDP} \rightarrow n\text{XMP} + n\text{P}_i$$

which is indistinguishable from the products of the action of a nucleoside-diphosphate phosphatase.

On the other hand, a combination of a kinase and a phosphatase specific for the nucleoside-triphosphate (ATPase, for example) gives the same results:

$$2n\text{XDP} \rightarrow n\text{XTP} + n\text{XMP} \quad \text{(kinase)}$$

$$n\text{XTP} \rightarrow n\text{XDP} + n\text{P}_i \quad \text{(phosphatase)} \tag{5}$$

$$n\text{XDP} \rightarrow n\text{XMP} + n\text{P}_i \quad \text{(sum of reactions)}$$

These reactions occur in a variety of tissue extracts, particularly animal tissues. Preparations of polynucleotide phosphorylase from *M. lysodeikticus* generally contain both myokinase and ATPase. The yields of polymer may be particularly low if, through the action of myokinase, sufficient ATP is generated to permit substantial ATPase activity. On the other hand, little or no nuclease activity directed toward poly A has been observed in the more highly purified enzyme fractions from *M. lysodeikticus*[15].

The presence of excessive amounts of phosphatase, or of phosphatase plus kinase, thus introduces artifacts in both types of polymerization assay. They can render quantitative studies very difficult, or impossible, to perform. It is possible, however, to avoid the effects of these competing enzymes by following the phosphorolysis of a polymer (see below). This method was used by Hilmoe and Heppel[19] to detect polynucleotide phosphorylase activity in liver nuclei. It is probable that many of the studies with animal tissues, which contain high concentrations of kinases, phosphatases, and nucleases, will have to be based on phosphorolysis assays exclusively.

In contrast, nucleases alone do not actually interfere with the precision of the phosphate release assay, provided one can be certain, of course, that a nuclease is the only enzyme involved. The existence of a nuclease can be readily established by the action of the enzyme preparation on the polymer in the absence of orthophosphate. Since the purine polynucleotides are not attacked as readily by nucleases as are the pyrimidine polynucleotides, the problem of nucleases in enzyme assays has not proved to be as difficult as one might anticipate.

The myokinase-catalyzed reaction constitutes a competing system for the polynucleotide phosphorylase substrate. In practice, its effects are considerably less than might be anticipated from comparative studies of its effects on nucleoside diphosphate when triphosphate phosphatases are present. However, higher concentrations of myokinase will reduce the rate of the polymerization reaction, the maximum apparent inhibition occurring if the myokinase reaction reaches equilibrium promptly. The experience with enzyme preparations from *M. lysodeikticus* has generally revealed remarkably little effect of this contaminating enzyme on the polymerization reaction[8]. However, preincubation of the substrate, ADP, with added myokinase can reduce the rate of the polymerization reaction considerably.

If the influence of myokinase appears to be appreciable in the polymerization assays, it is theoretically possible to compensate for this effect by adding an excese of myokinase to the enzyme preparation or, preferably, by pretreating the substrate with myokinase to introduce a constant and reproducible per cent. change in the concentration of ADP (if triphosphate phosphatases are absent). If the myokinase is sufficient to maintain this equilibrium during the course of the polymerization, then one should still obtain a constant proportionality between the observed rate of polymerization and the concentration of the phosphorylase enzyme.

Alternatively, one can add an excess of ATP to the ADP to depress the myokinase reaction. Littauer and Kornberg[3] have described an assay based on the coupling of myokinase with polynucleotide phosphorylase in the presence of an excess of ^{14}C-labeled ATP. The ratio of ATP to ADP was approximately 4 : 1. Thus, if the myokinase maintained an equilibrium concentration ratio throughout the polymerization reaction, the actual concentration of ADP would be depressed by only a small percentage. The extent of polymer formation was determined by measurements of the radioactivity of the acid-insoluble material. Under the conditions of the assay there was good proportionality between the extent of ^{14}C incorporation and the concentration of polynucleotide phosphorylase.

Alternatively, the synthesis of poly A has also been followed by incubating a mixture of ^{14}C-labeled AMP and unlabeled ATP[11] in the presence of myokinase and polynucleotide phosphorylase. The specific activity of the polymer is, of course, one half that of the AMP. It is essential, of course, in using coupled enzyme systems of this kind to ascertain positively that the concentration of the coupled enzyme is not limiting the reaction. This, in turn, suggests the possibility that a myokinase assay could be developed, which is based on the limiting step of the myokinase reaction in the presence of excess polynucleotide phosphorylase, which would polymerize the ADP as fast as it is formed.

Assays based on phosphorolysis of the polymer

Phosphorolysis has been studied primarily as an indicator of the mechanism and specificity of the polynucleotide phosphorylase-catalyzed reaction rather than as a potential method for assaying enzyme activity[20]. However, in many respects, phosphorolysis provides a less equivocal measure of the specificity and quantity of polynucleotide phosphorylase activity than do the assays based on polymerization. The assay is not complicated by the action of phosphatases or kinases. It has thus been used successfully in detecting the enzyme in mammalian tissue[19]. The substrate of choice for routine assays has been poly A, primarily because of the availability of large quantities of the polymer and the lack of susceptibility of poly A to hydrolysis by most nucleases.

Grunberg-Manago et al., described the first assay procedures for following phosphorolysis. One of these is based on measurements of the rate of incorporation of ^{32}P-labeled orthophosphate into the organic phosphate fraction, i.e., ADP or IDP. The other is based on the rate of incorporation of unlabeled inorganic orthophosphate into the organic phosphate fraction. For ^{32}P assays, the inorganic phosphate is extracted from the mixture with isobutanol, leaving in the aqueous phase the organic-bound phosphate. Singer[21] modified the procedure by adsorbing the organic phosphate onto Norite A charcoal and determining the radioactivity of the charcoal. Earlier, Littauer and Kornberg used the Norite separation in their ^{32}P-phosphate exchange assay. With unlabeled inorganic phosphate it is, of course, necessary to obtain a complete separation of the nucleoside-diphosphate synthesized from the polymer. Hilmoe and Heppel[19] used this technique to identify a polynucleotide phosphorylase in liver nuclei. Hendley and Beers[16] have also used this method extensively in kinetic studies of phosphorolysis.

Quantitative estimation of the nucleoside-diphosphate produced can be accomplished by the same techniques as are described above for the polymer, i.e., ultraviolet absorption, organic phosphate content, and the orcinol reaction (for purines). Ochoa and Heppel[20] have devised a method based on the procedure of Kornberg and Pricer[22] for determining the nucleoside-diphosphate concentration.

The disappearance of the polymer has also been used as a basis for an enzyme assay. Littauer and Kornberg[3] used [14]-C-labeled poly A for the substrate and measured the radioactivity of the perchloric acid-insoluble material after phosphorolysis. Hendley and Beers[16] followed the disappearance of the polymer under conditions in which the inorganic orthophosphate was present in great excess and the concentration of the polymer was low. This method is particularly adaptable to the use of ultraviolet absorption measurements of the polymer concentration.

A major problem presented by this variant of the assay based upon phosphorolysis is the frequent failure of the residual polymer to precipitate completely after it has been extensively degraded. The oligonucleotides are never acid soluble to the degree that a di- or trinucleotide is and, therefore, the fragments of polymer precipitated are usually rather large. The colloidal suspension of this material in an acid solution can, however, introduce serious errors. These can be partially or completely avoided by the addition of an inert protein such as casein[16] prior to the addition of the acid to the reaction mixture.

The kinetics of phosphorolysis can also be followed by paper chromatographic methods. The analysis for the products of phosphorolysis of large polymers presents the same problems as are described above for the case of the polymerization reaction. However, if oligonucleotides containing two to ten monomers are used as substrates, solvent systems designed to separate the homologous series of polymers are available. A useful solvent system for this purpose is the isobutyric acid-ammonia-water system of Krebs and Hems[12]. Paper electrophoresis has also been used successfully[21]. Mention has been made in Chapter 2 of the solvent systems used for cellulose chromatography of oligonucleotides. Elution by lithium acetate from ECTEOLA[23] provides a reasonably good separation of the oligonucleotides containing up to 6 members.

The rate of phosphorolysis of a polymer such as poly A provides an excellent measure of the polynucleotide phosphorylase activity. The rate of release of nucleoside-diphosphate remains constant for a considerable fraction of the reaction time if substrate is present in excess[16] and shows a constant proportionality to the enzyme concentration. The effects of inhibitors and activators appear to be similar for the phosphorolysis and polymerization reactions, *i.e.*, their effects can be partially circumvented by the methods described earlier. Unlike the polymerization reaction in which the concentration of polymer molecules cannot be controlled and is, therefore, an unknown variable which must be evaluated empirically, phosphorolysis can be made to vary as a function of the known amount of polymer present initially. Some variation in the rate of phosphorolysis has been observed with increasing chain lengths of the oligonucleotides[21]. In general, it can be stated that the initial rate of phosphorolysis is more or less independent of the particular poly A preparation used, as long as the total concentration of nucleotide material is the same, and the initial degree of polymerization is not too small.

As yet no units have been suggested for an assay based on phosphorolysis. Since the phosphorolysis reaction is schematically similar to polymerization (inorganic orthophosphate replacing ADP in attacking the polymer), an identical system of units and specific activities can be used for both polymerization and phosphorolysis assays. Accordingly, a unit of enzyme activity for phosphorolysis will be defined as that amount in one ml which will catalyze the incorporation of 1 millimole of inorganic phosphate into one millimole of ADP in one second, when both polymer and phosphate are present in large excess. As will be seen below, the units for phosphorolysis are similar to those used for the phosphate exchange assay, which as it is usually carried out, is essentially a phosphorolysis measurement. Milli- and microunits are also defined as before.

Assay by means of ^{32}P-phosphate exchange

The third major type of enzyme assay is based on the observation that, at chemical equilibrium, there is a rapid exchange between inorganic phosphate and the terminal phosphate group of the nucleoside-diphosphate. This exchange reaction can be followed by using ^{32}P-labeled inorganic phosphate or ADP. Up to the present, only the former has been used.

The mechanism of exchange can be visualized by the following scheme, where P is unlabeled phosphate and P* is ^{32}P-labeled phosphate. We will ignore for the moment the role of the enzyme.

$$\text{XPP} + (\text{XMP})_n \rightleftharpoons (\text{XMP})_{n+1} + \text{P}_i \qquad \text{(polymerization)}$$

$$\overset{*}{\text{P}}_i + (\text{XMP})_{n+1} \rightleftharpoons (\text{XMP})_n + \text{XPP}^* \qquad \text{(phosphorolysis)} \qquad (6)$$

$$\overset{*}{\text{P}}_i + \text{XPP} \rightleftharpoons \text{P}_i + \text{XPP}^* \qquad \text{(sum of reactions)}$$

As this scheme is given, the labeled orthophosphate in the exchange with ADP arises as a result of its attack on the polymer, not ADP.

Although an alternative mechanism has been proposed [24], we shall for the moment assume that the model cited above is correct. Under equilibrium conditions the *total* concentrations of phosphate and of nucleoside-diphosphate are constant. The amount of polymer present is also constant. There is no net synthesis of polymer once chemical equilibrium has been attained. Although we have no direct information, it appears likely that the degree of polymerization of any polymer present is low, probably not exceeding the oligonucleotide level.

If this mechanism is correct, the polymer may, in fact, be regarded as a kind of catalyst. The question of whether it exists only as a transient complex with the enzyme must be left open for the present. For assay purposes it is clearly advantageous to have the initial concentrations of ADP and P_i as close to the equilibrium ratio as possible, in order to avoid a transient state.

The extent of incorporation of inorganic ^{32}P-labeled orthophosphate into ADP is determined as follows: The initial radioactivity in the reaction mixture is confined to the inorganic orthophosphate with a value, expressed in counts per minute (c.p.m.), of R_T. At the end of the assay period a fraction of the radioactivity is incorporated into the terminal phosphate position of ADP as organic phosphate with a radioactivity of R_A. The residual radioactivity in the inorganic orthophosphate is R_P. Thus,

$$R_T = R_A + R_P \tag{7}$$

and the fraction of inorganic phosphate incorporated into ADP is

$$R_A/R_T = 1 - R_P/R_T \tag{8}$$

It follows, therefore, that the quantity of orthophosphate converted is

$$R_A\,[P_1]/R_T = R_A/(S.A.)_P \tag{9}$$

where $[P_1]$ is the concentration of inorganic orthophosphate and $(S.A.)_P$ is the initial specific radioactivity of the labeled orthophosphate.

The use of this assay method is, of course, considerably simplified if both ADP and P_1 are present in sufficient excess so that concentration of labeled phosphate may be regarded as constant during the period of assay. This implies that both the depletion of the labeled phosphate reservoir by the phosphorolysis reaction, and its dilution via the production of unlabeled phosphate by the reverse polymerization reaction, proceed to an insufficient extent to alter its concentration appreciably. If this is not the case, an appropriate correction must be applied. The stoichiometry of the exchange at chemical equilibrium requires that, for each atom of ^{32}P incorporated into ADP, the specific radioactivity of the orthophosphate be decreased by one ^{32}P atom, while its total concentration remains unchanged.

There is as yet little direct information about the concentration and degree of polymerization of the polymer species under representative assay conditions. If the view that the polymer is an essential intermediate in the exchange reaction is correct, considerations similar to those discussed by Boyer[25] suggest that a definite correspondence between the exchange rate and the concentration of polymer should exist.

Olmsted[24] has proposed an alternative mechanism which postulates the formation of an intermediate activated AMP complex, which can subsequently be attacked by either inorganic phosphate or the polymer. According to this model the polymer is not necessary for an exchange and would not be expected to influence the exchange rate. However, there is as yet no conclusive evidence either for or against this mechanism. Fortunately, this uncertainty does not vitiate the usefulness of the assay.

The first exchange assay was described by Grunberg-Manago et al.[1]. Under the conditions of their assay the ratio of ADP to P_1 was 0.69 (2.5 micromoles of ADP and 3.6 micromoles of P_1 in 1 ml of reaction mixture). The equilibrium of the reaction approached via polynucleotide synthesis corresponds[1] to an ADP/P_1 ratio of approximately 0.67 to 0.5. Thus, the exchange assay conditions of these investigators approximated equilibrium conditions. Their unit of enzyme was defined as the amount of enzyme in 1 ml which will catalyze the incorporation of one micromole of inorganic orthophosphate into ADP in 15 minutes at 30°. Under the conditions of the assay the rate of incorporation was found to be linearly proportional to the enzyme concentration.

The method used by Grunberg-Manago and co-workers to calculate the extent of orthophosphate incorporation involved a modification of equation (9):

$$\text{micromoles of } P_i \text{ incorporated} = R_A [P_i]/R_T + R_A [ADP]/R_T \tag{10}$$

The addition of the term, $R_A [ADP]/R_T$, was apparently made in an attempt to compensate for the dilution effect of the unlabeled orthophosphate of ADP upon the radioactivity of the inorganic phosphate. The right-hand side of equation 10 is $\{1 + [ADP]/[P_i]\}$ times larger than that of equation (9). The authors point out that this expression is only an approximation. It probably amounts to an overcorrection. Since the addition of the second factor amounts to, in fact, multiplication by a proportionality constant, the proportionality between the calculated extent of orthophosphate incorporation based on equation (10) and the concentration of the enzyme remains constant. With the substrate concentrations used by Grunberg-Manago et al., the enzyme unit based on equation (10) is thus 1.69 times larger than the enzyme unit based on equation (9).

The experimental phosphate exchange enzyme unit, based on equation 10, was from 2.5 to 2.8 times larger than the polymerization assay unit[1], a fact which has been interpreted by Olmsted[24] to indicate that the polymer is not involved in the exchange assay. Allowing for a maximum possible error of 1.69 in the magnitude of the computed exchange assay unit obtained using the equation of Grunberg-Manago et al.[1], the minimum discrepancy between the two enzyme units is 1.48 to 1.69. It is also quite possible that the initial ratio of ADP/P_i was too low, resulting in a net phosphorolysis and a high "exchange", or that competing enzymes catalyzed the exchange reaction[26].

Littauer and Kornberg[3] have also devised an exchange assay based on the incorporation of inorganic orthophosphate into ADP. In their assay with E. coli

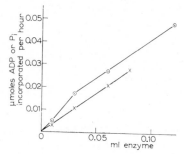

Fig. 16. A comparison of two assay methods for the polynucleotide phosphorylase of E. coli[3]. × exchange assay; ⊙ nucleoside diphosphate incorporation.

polynucleotide phosphorylase preparations, the ratio of ADP to P_i was 1.53 ($8 \cdot 10^{-4}$ M ADP, $5.2 \cdot 10^{-4}$ M P_i), a value considerably larger than that used in the assay of Grunberg-Manago *et al.*[1]. This difference cannot be accounted for by any difference in the position of equilibrium under the two assay conditions, since neither pH nor temperature influences this value significantly in the range of these assays. Fig. 16 gives the results of this assay applied to a crude preparation of *E. coli* enzyme. For comparison the results obtained by the polymerization assay are also included. The conditions of assay, except for the concentrations of substrate and enzyme, are the same. The authors obtained for the ratio [exchange assay/polymerization assay], a value of 2.0 with crude enzyme preparations. With purification, however, this value dropped to 0.435 and was restored to 1.68 by the addition of a heat stable factor obtained from a protamine extract of the enzyme. The effect of the activator is on the exchange rate.

The ^{32}P-exchange assay has several obvious advantages. Errors arising from the difficulty of separating the polymer quantitatively are circumvented. The inorganic phosphate and nucleoside-diphosphate are readily separable. The measurements themselves are rapid and precise, although somewhat more elaborate equipment is required than in the case of the purely chemical assays.

PURIFICATION AND PROPERTIES

The phosphorylase of Azotobacter vinelandii

The first polynucleotide phosphorylase to be extensively purified was isolated from *Azotobacter vinelandii* by Grunberg-Manago, Ortiz and Ochoa[1]. The original procedure began with the extraction with 0.15 M KCl of fresh cells which had been ruptured either sonically, or by grinding with alumina.

The initial extract, after centrifugal clarification, was dialyzed versus 0.01 M phosphate, pH 7.0. It was then fractionated by the addition of $(NH_4)_2 SO_4$ to 0.35 saturation. The precipitate was centrifuged off and the $(NH_4)_2 SO_4$ concentration of the supernatant raised to 0.46 saturation. The precipitate appearing at this stage, which contained the polynucleotide phosphorylase activity, was redissolved in 0.01 M phosphate, pH 7.4, and dialyzed *versus* solvent.

The pH of the dialyzed solution was adjusted to 5.8. Successive additions of calcium phosphate gel were then made. After each addition of gel, the mixture was stirred and then centrifuged. The recovered gel was eluted with 0.1 M phosphate, pH 6, and the eluates recombined. About 76 per cent of the total activity was recovered in the combined eluate.

After dialysis *versus* 0.01 M phosphate, pH 7.4, the combined eluate was fractionated with $(NH_4)_2 SO_4$. The second fraction, which appeared between 0.45 and 0.55 saturation, contained most of the activity and had a specific activity of 24 milliunits/g.

TABLE 6

PURIFICATION OF *A. vinelandii* ENZYME[1]

Step	Volume (ml)	Total activity (milliunits)	Amount of protein (mg)	Specific activity milliunits/g
Dialyzed extract	376	2	3450	0.6
(NH₂)₃ SO₄ (0.35–0.46)	95	2	810	2.4
Ca₂(PO₃)₄ gel eluate	58	1.6	142	12
(NH₂)₃ SO₄ (0.45–0.55)	5	1.1	45	24

It was subsequently found that a product of higher activity could be obtained by adding a Zn–ethanol precipitation step prior to the selective absorption by calcium phosphate gel. In this manner preparations with a specific activity of 53 milliunits/g could be obtained[27]. More recently, it has been reported that specific activities as high as 330 milliunits/g could be obtained by protamine fractionation of the final product of the earlier procedure[4].

Tests of activity at various stages of purification indicated that the relative activity toward the five nucleoside-diphosphates remained essentially unchanged throughout the process. This strongly suggested that only a single enzyme was present.

The enzyme was found to retain activity for long periods when stored in the frozen state at −18° C. In solution a fairly rapid loss of activity occurred. Heating for five minutes at 60° C irreversibly destroyed all activity.

The optimum pH for ^{32}P-exchange was in the vicinity of 8.1. A broader optimum, from pH 7.5 to pH 9 was observed for the forward polymerization reaction. The requirement for Mg^{++} was absolute.

The polynucleotide phosphorylase from *Azotobacter* is the sole enzyme of this class for which a primer requirement has conclusively been shown to exist. It was found by Mii and Ochoa[4] that highly purified preparations of this enzyme showed a definite lag phase in the polymerization of ADP, IDP, CDP, and UDP, which could be overcome by the addition of RNA or certain of the biosynthetic polymers. Some degree of specificity was observed. Thus the synthesis of poly C is accelerated by poly C, but inhibited by poly A or poly U. Poly A and poly U served as primers for their own synthesis but inhibited the polymerization of the other nucleoside-diphosphates. In contrast, poly C functioned as a primer for the polymerization of all three nucleoside-diphosphates.

These observations were paralleled by the finding of Singer *et al.*[28] that 5'-oligo-nucleotides could also catalyze the polymerization and were incorporated into the growing polymer. Priming activity was pronounced for dinucleotides, but did not occur for monucleotides.

Specificity requirements appeared to be somewhat relaxed in the case of the oligonucleotides. Thus the trinucleotide adenylyl-5',3'-adenylyl-5',3'-adenosine-

5'-phosphate was found to prime polymerization of both ADP and UDP. Furthermore, the 3'-terminal trinucleotide adenylyl-3',5'-adenylyl-3',5'-uridine-3'-phosphate accelerated the polymerization of ADP and UDP, despite the non-availability of a 3'-hydroxyl, which prevented its incorporation into the polymer.

The 5'-terminal triadenylic acid also served as a primer for the polymerization of GDP, which is not ordinarily polymerized by this enzyme. As many as nine GMP units have been added to the primer in this manner.

Singer[29] has studied the phosphorolysis of oligonucleotides by the *Azotobacter* enzyme. Only oligonucleotides containing three or more nucleoside units were phosphorolyzed. Dinucleotides and dinucleoside-monophosphates were not attacked.

Tri- and tetranucleotides with a terminal 5'-phosphomonoester group were found to be readily phosphorolyzed. In contrast, oligonucleotides with a terminal 3'-phosphomonoester group were invariably resistant. This latter observation probably partially explains the resistance of degraded RNA samples to phosphorolysis.

That there is no requirement for a terminal 5'-phosphomonoester group was shown by the observation that trinucleoside-diphosphates and tetranucleoside-triphosphates, which have no terminal phosphate, are phosphorolyzed at rates comparable to those of the 5'-oligonucleotides[29].

The phosphorylase of A. faecalis

Brummond, Staehelin and Ochoa[26] have described the preparation of a polynucleotide phosphorylase from *A. faecalis*.

Washed cells of *A. faecalis* suspended in water were ruptured sonically, and centrifuged. The supernatant was fractionated with $(NH_4)_2SO_4$. The fraction appearing between 0.4 and 0.5 saturation was collected, redissolved, and dialyzed *versus* 0.01 M phosphate, pH 7.

The pH of the dialyzed solution was adjusted to 5.1. Calcium phosphate gel was added, recovered by centrifugation, and then eluted with 0.1 M phosphate, pH 6.0.

After overnight dialysis against 0.1 M phosphate, pH 7.4, the calcium phosphate eluate was refractionated with $(NH_4)_2SO_4$. The fraction appearing between 0.45 and 0.55 saturation was collected, redissolved, and dialyzed *versus* 0.01 M phosphate, pH 7, as before.

A final adsorption and elution from calcium phosphate gel was then made. The product, after dialysis, was stored in the frozen state.

The specific activity increased only tenfold in the course of the purification. The final product had a specific activity of 10 microunits/g based on the exchange assay.

The *A. faecalis* enzyme appears to have properties at least roughly similar to those of the *Azotobacter* enzyme. It has been found to catalyze the polymerization of ADP, IDP, and CTP. As yet, no primer requirement has been reported.

The phosphorylase of E. coli

Littauer and Kornberg recently described the isolation of a polynucleotide phosphorylase from extracts of *E. coli*. Cells of *E. coli* strain B were harvested at the end of the logarithmic growth phase and ruptured sonically.

To the sonic extract was added $MnCl_2$ to a molarity of 0.05. After clarification of the solution by centrifugation, an enzyme-containing fraction was precipitated by the addition of protamine sulfate to a concentration of 0.1%.

The protamine fraction was eluted with 0.05 M phosphate, pH 7.5. After clarification, the supernatant was dialyzed *versus* 0.9 per cent KCl, and its pH subsequently adjusted to 5.5. An active fraction was then separated by adding $ZnCl_2$ to a molarity of 0.002, clarifying, and then adding ethanol in a stepwise manner to a final volume fraction of 0.15 at $-2°$ C.

The Zn-ethanol precipitate was redissolved and then reprecipitated from 0.003 M $ZnCl_2$, 9 per cent ethanol (by volume) at pH 5.5 and $-2°$ C.

Alternatively, the first Zn–ethanol precipitate could be further purified by starch column electrophoresis. The enzyme preparations, as obtained by either procedure, were fairly stable in the frozen state, but showed a rapid decay in activity when in solution.

A considerable variation in the d_{280}/d_{260} ratio was observed for different preparations. The usual range of values was 1.5–1.75. All preparations probably contained a high proportion of inactive material.

The most purified preparations showed a marginal amount of ribonuclease and adenylate kinase activity. Deoxyribonuclease activity was wholly absent.

The specific activity, based on the polymerization assay, using ADP, increased from 0.12 milliunits/g for the crude sonic extract to 7.6 milliunits/g for the final ethanol fraction. This corresponded to a 70-fold purification. The turnover number of the final product was 667 moles ADP per 10^5 g protein per minute.

These enzyme preparations were able to synthesize high molecular weight polymers of AMP, CMP, and UMP, as well as a copolymer of all four ribonucleotides. Only a marginal polymerizing activity toward GDP was observed.

The synthetic polynucleotides and undegraded preparations of TMV and yeast RNA were readily phosphorolyzed. The ^{32}P-exchange reaction between inorganic phosphate and nucleoside diphosphate was also catalyzed by this enzyme.

The only evidence obtained for an activator requirement was the enhancement of the rate of the ^{32}P-exchange reaction with ADP catalyzed by the purified material by the addition of a heat-stable factor, which was isolated from the crude sonic extract. The exchange reactions for the other nucleoside-diphosphates and the polymerization reactions for all monomers were not influenced by this factor.

An interesting observation in the data of Littauer and Kornberg (Table 7) is the apparent increase in *total* enzyme activity during the early stages of purification. If we assume that the initial activities reflect the influence of inhibitors and take the eluate as representing a true measure of enzyme activity, then the actual degree

TABLE 7

PURIFICATION OF *E. Coli* ENZYME[3]

Step	Microunits per ml	Total microunits	Protein (mg/ml)	Specific activity (milliunits/g)
Sonic extract	.83	517	6.9	0.12
Protamine eluate	2.7	544	0.88	3.1
First Zn–ethanol fraction	3.6	242	0.76	4.7
Second Zn–ethanol fraction	1.3	89	0.17	7.6

of purification is reduced to less than 3-fold. This emphasizes the problems encountered in purification studies at present. Similar results have been observed in the purification of *M. lysodeikticus* polynucleotide phosphorylase[15].

The polynucleotide phosphorylase of M. lysodeikticus*

As in the case of the *E. coli* enzyme, the phosphorylase of *M. lysodeikticus* has yet to be obtained in a state approaching purity. The findings which have emerged from the purification studies carried out so far have a number of features which have not been observed with the other phosphorylases and which tend to complicate the evaluation of any purification scheme.

The most important of these is the existence of both activators and inhibitors, which are as yet incompletely characterized[15]. These can occur in impure enzyme preparations. Their presence can lead to false conclusions on the effectiveness of a particular purification method. Those cofactors of either type which have been identified appear to be of a nucleotide or polynucleotide nature, although the possibility that compounds of an altogether different nature may be effective cannot be excluded. As no parallel to these observations has been reported in the case of the other phosphorylases, it is possible that their activity is limited to the *M. lysodeikticus* enzyme.

The impure character of the enzyme preparations obtained so far and the uncertain contribution of the activators and inhibitors have precluded a final decision as to whether a primer requirement exists for this phosphorylase. The activation effects which have been observed cannot be attributed unequivocally to the presence of primers, in view of the possibility that the "activators" may be merely countering the effects of inhibitors. If this is the case, it would be expected that the ratio of the two in an impure enzyme preparation would have an important influence on its activity.

Our present understanding of the structure and mode of action of the above-mentioned activators and inhibitors is still very incomplete. Activators appear

---

* This section summarizes findings of Beers[6, 8, 9, 15, 16].

for the most part to be either nucleotides or small oligonucleotides, in view of their free dialyzability against water or salt solutions. Indeed this has been the usual method of demonstrating their existence. Thus, substances which can act as activators have been detected in dialysates of *M. lysodeikticus* and *B. subtilis*, dialysates of yeast RNA which has been degraded by alkali or by ribonuclease, and even in impure commercial samples of nucleoside diphosphates[6,9,15].

The inhibitors, on the other hand, have been uniformly shown to be non-dialyzable and generally acid-insoluble. Substances with inhibitory activity have been found in the non-dialyzable fraction of chemical or enzymatic digests of RNA. It has been suggested[6] that the inhibitors are 3′-terminal polynucleotides. Both activators and inhibitors appear to occur in crude preparations of the *M. lysodeikticus* enzyme[15].

It is at present impossible to specify further the properties of these cofactors. A characteristic difference between the two is the relative rapidity with which the activators stimulate polymerization immediately after addition[15]. In contrast, the inhibitors generally require a period of pre-incubation with the enzyme, prior to addition of the substrate, if inhibition is to attain its maximum extent.

Of paramount importance for the successful preparation of polynucleotide phosphorylase from *M. lysodeikticus*, either for subsequent purification steps or for the synthesis of polynucleotide material, is the choice of the proper conditions for the extraction of the enzyme from the cells[2]. The *M. lysodeikticus* cells are readily lysed by the enzyme, lysozyme, which is found in egg white and is available commercially as a crystalline enzyme. It has been found that many of the soluble enzymes can be removed preferentially by *controlled* lysis, leaving in the insoluble cell debris a major portion of the RNA and DNA. The details of this technique are described in the Appendix. The essential requirements include: a 5–10% suspension of cells in 0.5% NaCl, buffered between pH 7 and 8.5, and held between 32° and 40°. The concentration of lysozyme added should be sufficient to produce complete lysis of the cell wall in from 10 to 15 minutes, without any significant lysis of the protoplasts. If these requirements are rigorously met, an aqueous extract of the cells can be obtained which contains the bulk of the polynucleotide phosphorylase and a minimal quantity of polynucleotide material.

The quality of the preparation of cells used is, of course, important. They may be acetone-dried, lyophilized, frozen wet, or used when freshly harvested. The cells should be harvested from a surface culture or, preferably, from a submerged culture[2]. In the latter case, the pH should be alkaline at the time of harvest.

After lysis is complete, the cell mass is brought to 30% saturation with ammonium sulfate and centrifuged. The addition of ammonium sulfate blocks further destruction of the cell structure, particularly of the protoplasts, which contain the bulk of the polynucleotide material and the ribonuclease, and facilitates the separation of the soluble fraction from the gelatinous residue. The clear brown supernatant is then brought to 65% saturation with ammonium sulfate to precipitate a fraction containing most of the enzyme.

The turnover number of the enzyme preparation at this stage, as determined from the estimated V_{max} in $1.3 \cdot 10^{-3}$ M $MgCl_2$ at pH 9.0 and 37°, is usually in the vicinity of 40 moles of ADP incorporated into polymer per minute per 10^5 grams of protein. Assuming that all of the enzyme has been extracted from the cells, the turnover number per 10^5 grams of cells is approximately 4. In routine synthesis of poly A it has been found that one gram of cells yields roughly enough enzyme to synthesize 1 gram of polymer in approximately 12 hours (0.5% ADP).

The Michaelis constant of the enzyme at this stage of purification, at optimum salt concentration, is usually small, i.e., less than 10^{-3} M. However, it can vary considerably with different enzyme preparations and may be as high as $2 \cdot 10^{-3}$ M or as low as $5 \cdot 10^{-4}$ M. Moreover, in addition to the variations occurring for different preparations of enzyme, any contaminants present in the particular preparation of ADP can also cause variations in the apparent Michaelis constant. Unfortunately these variations in K_m are accompanied by changes in the maximum velocity constant and in the corresponding turnover number.

Dialysis of the crude enzyme at this state of purification against either distilled water or buffer results in a pronounced change in the kinetic constants, the magnitude and direction of which depend in part on the extent of dialysis[15]. In general, the Michaelis constant increases and the V_{max} or turnover number first increases and then decreases[15]. The latter effect is apparently accompanied by an irreversible loss of enzyme activity, which may possibly be associated with the removal of some unknown protecting substance. Allowing the enzyme to stand in the buffer without dialysis, under otherwise identical conditions, results in no significant change in the enzyme activity. Dialysis presumably removes, among other things, a portion of the nucleotides and smaller oligonucleotides. The 280 mμ/260 mμ ratio may increase upon dialysis from an original value of 0.9 to 1.0.

Of course, one of the variables which can be responsible for a change in the Michaelis constant is the ionic strength[8]. The loss in enzyme activity under standard assay conditions, without the addition of KCl and at low substrate concentration, is often complete after dialysis versus water.

Adding KCl restores a major portion of the activity. Yet, even after making allowances for this variable, the change in the properties of the enzyme after dialysis at this stage remains substantial.

A second marked change in the enzyme preparation after dialysis is the acquired sensitivity of the enzyme to activators, presumably of a nucleotide or oligonucleotide nature, which can be isolated from commercial sources of ADP and from crude enzyme dialysates[15]. These substances increase both the Michaelis constant and the maximum velocity constant of the dialyzed enzyme, but have little or no effect on the crude ammonium sulfate fraction. Thus, in their presence the specific activity of the enzyme may increase by a factor of two or more, i.e., the total enzyme activity may be greater than that measured in the original crude enzyme preparation[15]. It is uncertain whether these substances are true activators, or whether they merely counter the effect of inhibitors.

A second ammonium sulfate fractionation, between 0.43 and 0.57 saturation at pH 8.0, results in no major changes in the specific or total activity of the enzyme preparation, although the preparation, strangely enough, no longer shows any response to the addition of the activators mentioned above. Dialysis does not restore the stimulating action of the activators[15]. At this point the 280 mμ/260 mμ ratio may be as high as 1.3–1.4.

Subsequent fractionation of the enzyme preparation with acetone at –15° yields a preparation with a 280 mμ/260 mμ ratio often as high as 1.65. This material regains an appreciable sensitivity toward the influence of activators. A similar preparation with a high 280 mμ/260 mμ ratio can be obtained by successive treatments of the enzyme with Norite A charcoal. The latter treatment increases the Michaelis constant and, depending upon the number of successive treatments with charcoal, first increases and then decreases the specific activity of the enzyme. The turnover number of such preparations is usually in the vicinity of 150 to 200.

It is obvious from the above discussion that the purification of the polynucleotide phosphorylase of *M. lysodeikticus* has in no way approached a stage suitable for an examination of the enzyme properties as they relate to the role of primers and other cofactors, which may control the activity or specificity of the enzyme. At best we can describe the problem of purification and list some of the factors which must be eliminated or allowed for in any interpretation of purification work.

The purification steps employed for preferential removal of inert protein also preferentially remove nucleotide derivatives. Since the dialyzable and non-dialyzable nucleotide materials of the crude enzyme appear to contain the activators and inhibitors, respectively, the effect of dialysis may be primarily on the ratio and concentration of these two components. Thus, the dialyzed preparations would be expected to show a loss of specific activity and an increase in the Michaelis constant in the presence of inhibitors and activators may possibly arise from a more complicated process than simple competitive inhibition.

Norite A adsorption appears to remove the activators preferentially, as is indicated by the increased sensitivity of the enzyme preparation to the subsequent addition of activators[15]. Acetone fractionation does the same. It is probable, though the evidence is by no means conclusive, that the ratio of inhibitors to activators increases with each purification step. Since the activators have been shown to be effective in reversing inhibition by polynucleotide material, demonstration of their activating effect on an enzyme preparation, irrespective of whether they are incorporated into the polymer, does not establish proof for an absolute primer requirement.

Two additional changes in *M. lysodeikticus* polynucleotide phosphorylase also occur during the purification. The first is a progressive loss of stability, especially after the 280 mμ/260 mμ ratio exceeds 1.6. This makes additional purification steps difficult to carry out. Electrophoresis on paper results in a total loss of activity which cannot be restored by reconstitution of the original mixture applied to the paper. Similar losses occur after chromatography on cellulose columns.

Organic solvents have very little effect on the enzyme existing in crude form, as is illustrated by the failure of 25% acetone solutions at 37° to cause any significant loss in enzyme activity, even after three hours. This step can be used to denature preferentially some of the inert protein. The resultant is a gel-like product, to which is adsorbed the active enzyme. By elution at high pH with KCl one can obtain a preparation with a high 280 mμ/260 mμ ratio and a low adenylate kinase activity. Indeed, this has been, until recently, the only method used successfully for the preparation of an adenylate kinase-free enzyme preparation. Similar results can be obtained with ethanol, but the yields are generally much lower.

In contrast to the stability of the crude preparation to organic solvents, the more highly purified material, i.e., with high 280 mμ/260 mμ ratios, shows a marked sensitivity to the action of organic solvents, even at –15°.

The instability of M. lysodeikticus polynucleotide phosphorylase after several purification steps has also been observed with other enzyme preparations. Littauer and Kornberg[3] observed that the E. coli enzyme, when diluted in a glycylglycine buffer at pH 7.4, underwent a rapid and irreversible loss in activity. Olmsted and Lowe[5] have also reported a marked instability of their purified preparations of M. lysodeikticus enzyme. The extensively purified preparations from A. vinelandii have also been reported to be very unstable and rapidly destroyed during further purification[10].

The reasons for the instability are not clear, although a common factor associated with instability is a high degree of purification, with respect to both the specific activity and the 280 mμ/260 mμ ratio. One obvious possibility is the loss of a stabilizer. Evidence for such a stabilizer in preparations of the enzyme from E. coli responsible for the polymerization of polydeoxyribonucleotides has been obtained by Lehmann et al.[30]. It is presumed to be DNA. Similar stabilizers of polynucleotide phosphorylase have not been positively identified, but it is possible that the substrate of this reaction for both polymerization and phosphorolysis, i.e., the polynucleotide, is, in fact, a stabilizer of the enzyme. However, direct evidence for this is lacking. The addition of poly A, or of nucleic acid fractions from M. lysodeikticus, does not increase, to any significant degree, the stability of the enzyme.

A second major change occurring in the properties of M. lysodeikticus polynucleotide phosphorylase during purification is the variation in relative activity of the enzyme toward different nucleoside diphosphates. This phenomenon may well be associated with the variation in the ratio and concentration of the activators and inhibitors present in the enzyme preparation. It is rather remarkable that the preparations of A. vinelandii, through the various purification steps, have failed to show any variation in the ratio of activities of the enzyme toward the different substrates[27]. However, the assays were performed either by the exchange assay or with high substrate concentrations, which might tend to minimize any differences.

In the case of the polynucleotide phosphorylase of M. lysodeikticus, the kinetic constants, K_m and V_m, vary with the substrate and with the inhibitor or activator present. In general, crude preparations of the enzyme show as much as a two-fold greater rate with CDP than with ADP. However, after one or two purification steps, this ratio may be reversed. In contrast, the effect of the activators becomes much more marked with CDP than with ADP. Moreover, the polymerization of CDP is very sensitive to the inhibiting action of polynucleotide material and can be completely abolished by concentrations of inhibitory polymer which have relatively little effect on the polymerization of poly A. This phenomenon may be of importance in gaining an understanding of the data recently published by Olmsted and Lowe[5].

Olmsted and Lowe[5] have recently published a method for purifying a polynucleotide phosphorylase of *M. lysodeikticus*, which they claim is specific for ADP and inactive to CDP. They have, therefore, raised the important question of multiple *versus* single enzymes in this micro-organism. On the basis of the kinetic data presented they draw the conclusion that there is either more than one enzyme or more than one site on a single enzyme, each enzyme or site being specific for a particular nucleotide.

The purification steps of Olmsted and Lowe include a 30 to 180 minute lysis of the cells, at pH 8.1 in 1 to 2% NaCl at a concentration of approximately 2.5% (dry wt.). The lysis is allowed to progress beyond the stage recommended above and it is apparent from the description of the end product that the bulk of the protoplast material has been destroyed, yielding a highly viscous preparation in which the RNA and DNA have been *solubilized*. Unfortunately, no data have been published regarding the 280 mμ/260 mμ ratios during the subsequent purification steps. However, this is of relatively small importance in view of the extremely low concentrations of cofactors of a polynucleotide nature which can produce an appreciable effect on the enzyme.

The second step involves fractionation with ethanol at $-15°$, which frequently yields an insoluble preparation (See above). The third step consists of *solubilization* of the insoluble material by tryptic digestion. This is a rather unfortunate step to include because of the uncertain effects trypsin may have on the enzyme itself. It is of interest to note, however, that trypsin destroyed the myokinase activity of the preparation. Other enzymes have also been used by these workers in this step, including cellulase, hyaluronidase, papain, etc. Each preparation was believed to exert its action by virtue of a contaminating protease.

The fourth and fifth steps include a second alcohol and a second ammonium sulfate fractionation. The final product, which was active solely with ADP, had a turnover number ranging from 1.1 to 20.2, compared with an approximate value of 0.1 with the first alcohol precipitate. These turnover values were based on a specific activity which was determined with 3.3 mM to 5 mM ADP without the addition of KCl. The actual turnover number based on V_{max} may, therefore, be considerably higher.

The trypsin digestion step of the above procedure certainly amounts to a rather drastic treatment. Since it is at this step that activity toward nucleotides other than ADP is lost, any conclusion on the occurrence of multiple enzymes (or multiple sites) is probably premature. Certainly, the possibility that trypsin digestion could alter a single enzyme (or site) in such a way as to modify its specificity has not yet been excluded. A somewhat more compelling proof would be the actual resolution of the hypothetical mixture of enzymes into fractions of different specificity by a milder procedure. The low specific activity of the final preparations of Olmsted and Lowe makes it questionable whether the use of the term *purified* is justified.

A practical asset of preparations of the *M. lysodeikticus* enzyme are their frequent ability to produce polynucleotides of remarkably high degrees of polymerization. This property, which probably reflects the absence of nucleases, makes this enzyme system of particular value for the synthesis of polymers for physical studies.

We have gone into considerable detail in this Chapter to stress some of the major problems presented by polynucleotide phosphorylase assays and purification and have, therefore, presented a rather pessimistic picture of the accomplishments obtained so far in this field. This is necessary because as yet none of the major questions relating to the mechanism of action of this enzyme or its biological activity have been given unequivocal answers by the studies published so far. The initial enthusiasm inspired by the apparent simplicity of this system has given way to a more humble approach and a recognition of its complicated nature. A cardinal, though frequently forgotten, rule in enzymology studies is the statement that kinetics can usually provide no proof of a given mechanism and, indeed, may often provide misleading conclusions. This follows from the obvious but also frequently forgotten fact that the observed kinetics are generally a function of both known and unknown variables. The latter constitute the major problem in this field today. It is possible that the examination of the influence of nucleotide derivatives acting as activators and inhibitors may eventually increase our understanding of the mechanism of action of this enzyme. But our present state of knowledge and its confusion should caution us from making any major hypothesis at this stage to *explain* the mechanism of action or the specificity of this enzyme.

In summary, what is known of the properties of polynucleotide phosphorylase, which show variations with the degree and method of purification as well as with the source of the enzyme, include the following: (*a*) Primer requirement apparently exists in *A. vinelandii* after extensive purification, for preparations containing up to 3% nucleotide material. The primer, depending upon its nature, may or may not be incorporated into the polymer[4]. The exchange reaction is also stimulated. (*b*) Primer requirement does not exist in *E. coli* preparations, even for those with 280 mμ/ 260 mμ ratios[3] as large as 1.75. However, the exchange assay is stimulated by material which presumably contains nucleotide compounds. (*c*) A primer requirement has not definitely been shown to exist in *M. lysodeikticus* preparations. However, addition of various preparations of polynucleotides to this enzyme can result in a substantial inhibition, which can be reversed by the addition of suitable nucleotide or oligonucleotide cofactors.

phosphorolysis reaction with *M. lysodeikticus* preparations[5] is approximately 8.5. For the exchange reaction the pH optimum of the *A. vinelandii* enzyme[2] is 8.1 and for the *E. coli* enzyme[3] 7.4.

Since there are no ionizable groups of the substrate (ADP) with pK values in this region it appears likely that the effect of pH is primarily upon the enzyme.

The position of the pH optimum of the polynucleotide phosphorylase of *M. lysodeikticus* varies in a complicated manner with several experimental parameters, including ionic strength and Mg^{++} concentration[4, 6, 7]. As an illustration, the removal of electrolyte by dialysis *versus* distilled water can reduce the pH optimum of a crude ammonium sulfate fraction of the enzyme from above pH 10 to pH 7.5, provided that the Mg^{++} concentration is held constant during the assay (Fig. 17). However, as Fig. 17 shows, a reduction in Mg^{++} concentration under the conditions of assay of the dialyzed preparation can restore the position of the optimum to above pH 10.

The effect of dialysis *versus* water upon the pH optimum appears to be a consequence solely of the reduction of ionic strength rather than the loss of a dialyzable cofactor. Thus, the addition of electrolyte to the dialyzed preparation serves to restore the position of the pH optimum to its original high value, even in the presence of high concentrations of Mg^{++}, as Fig. 18 shows.

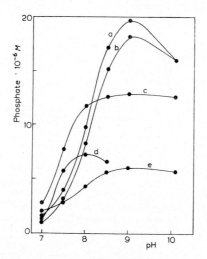

Fig. 18. pH-activity curves[4]. A volume of 2.5 ml of reaction mixture contained 7.2 · 10^{-4} M ADP, 0.1 M tris. Reaction time 20 min. Temp. 37°. Rate recorded as moles of orthophosphate released per liter of reaction mixture per minute. Curves: a 0.2 M KCl, 2.3 · 10^{-4} M MgCl$_2$; b 0.1 M KCl, 2.3 · 10^{-4} M MgCl$_2$; c 0.1 M KCl, 1.15 · 10^{-3} M MgCl$_2$; d no KCl, 1.15 · 10^{-3} M MgCl$_2$; e, no KCl, 2.3 · 10^{-4} M MgCl$_2$.

The situation is further complicated by a dependence of the pH optimum upon the concentration of substrate. For a given Mg^{++} concentration, an increase of substrate concentration tends to increase the value of the optimal pH, possibly as a consequence of the ability of substrate to bind Mg^{++}.

In summary, an increase in Mg^{++} concentration tends to shift the position of the optimum pH range to lower values. A decrease in ionic strength enhances the sensitivity to Mg^{++}. These relationships are paralleled by those holding for the phosphorolysis reaction[5]. It appears likely that the influence of these variables upon the system is via the enzyme–polymer relationship. Other evidence for this surmise will be given below.

The pH has no demonstrable effect on the equilibrium of the reaction[8] between pH 7 and 9. One might anticipate this from the fact that with the exception of the inorganic orthophosphate, none of the reactants in the system undergoes any change in the transition from pH 7.0 to 9.0.

Characteristic of many phosphorylase-catalyzed reactions is the requirement for a divalent cation. Magnesium is the most active of the series of metals studied. However, Mn^{++}, Ba^{++}, Ca^{++}[4] and Zn^{++}[9] can serve as less effective activators in this system. All metals show a characteristic optimum concentration, beyond which they inhibit the reaction. This inhibition is more pronounced in the polymerization than in the phosphorolysis reactions. Fig. 19 illustrates the type of Mg^{++}-activity

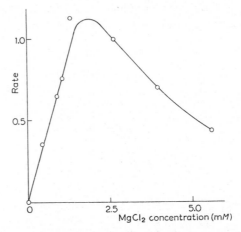

Fig. 19. Variation of rate of synthesis of poly A with MgCl$_2$ concentration. Rate given as optical-density increment in 10 min (see text for details)[4].

curve one obtains with polynucleotide phosphorylase from *M. lysodeikticus* in a low ionic strength assay. The requirement for the metal is absolute. At low Mg^{++} concentrations the rate of polymerization is directly proportional to the concentration of the metal.

The optimum concentration of Mg^{++} depends upon several variables in the assay system. The first of these, as indicated above, is the pH. It is clear from Fig. 17 that by increasing the ionic strength, the optimum concentration of Mg^{++} also increases. Fig. 20 illustrates this in curves d (no salt) and b (0.4 *M* KCl).

Indeed, at high concentrations of salt the inhibitory effects of the metal are abolished.

A third variable in the relationship with Mg^{++} is the concentration of the substrate. Increasing the substrate concentration increases the Mg^{++} optimum concentration, as illustrated by a comparison of curves d ($7.2 \cdot 10^{-4}$ M ADP) and c ($1.44 \cdot 10^{-3}$ M ADP) in Fig. 20. This effect has also been reported for other enzyme preparations. Littauer and Kornberg[3] report an optimum ADP: Mg^{++} mole ratio of 1.5 for *E. coli* polynucleotide phosphorylase at pH 7.4. Singer *et al.*[10], report an optimum UDP: Mg^{++} and ADP: Mg^{++} ratio of 2.0 for the highly

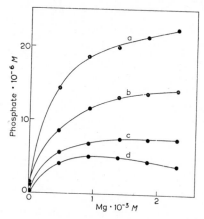

Fig. 20. Activation by Mg^{++} at various concentrations of KCl and ADP[7]. A volume of 2.5 ml of reaction mixture contained 0.1 M tris, pH 9.0. Reaction time 20 min. Temp. 37°. Rate recorded as moles of orthophosphate released per liter of reaction mixture per minute. Curves: a 0.4 M KCl, $1.44 \cdot 10^{-3}$ M ADP; b 0.4 M KCl, $7.2 \cdot 10^{-4}$ M ADP; c no KCl, $1.44 \cdot 10^{-3}$ M ADP; d no KCl, $7.2 \cdot 10^{-4}$ M ADP.

purified *A. vinelandii* enzyme preparations which show a lag in the polymerization reaction at pH 8.3. For *M. lysodeikticus* enzyme preparations under similar assay conditions (no salt added) at pH 8.0 the optimum ADP: Mg^{++} ratio is approximately 1.6. However, this ratio is not constant and decreases with increasing substrate concentration.

The attention given to the significance of the substrate: Mg^{++} ratios[3] may not be justified in view of the fact that the reactive species of the substrate may not be a magnesium–substrate complex.

A fourth, as yet little understood, variable influencing the effect of Mg^{++} is the effects of activators and inhibitors of the oligo- and poly-nucleotide class. The addition of poly A to the reaction mixture with *M. lysodeikticus* polynucleotide phosphorylase increases the optimum Mg^{++} concentration[9], presumably by virtue of its Mg^{++} binding property. However, this effect is variable and may disappear if the polymer and enzyme are *preincubated* together for several minutes before the addition of the substrate. Inhibition by degraded RNA from yeast does not appear

The maximum velocity constant for the polymerization of ADP by *M. lysodeikticus* polynucleotide phosphorylase is not influenced by the ionic strength, but it is increased by increasing magnesium concentration (Tables 8 and 9). One consequence of this insensitivity to ionic strength is the reduction of the activating effect of salt at high substrate concentration.

Comparable variations in the Michaelis constant and maximum velocity constant occur in the phosphorolysis reaction as the ionic strength and Mg^{++} concentration are varied. These effects are summarized in Tables 10 and 11, in which the concentration of the polymer is the variable.

TABLE 10

VARIATION OF K_m FOR POLY A WITH (Mg^{++})[5]

$Mg^{++} \cdot 10^4 M$	0.5	2.0	8.0
$K_{MR} \cdot 10^5$	3.1	12.0	18.6
V_m(rel.)	3.0	8.6	13.3

0.1 M tris, pH 8.5, 37° C

TABLE 11

VARIATION OF K_m FOR POLY A WITH KCl[5]

KCl M	0.021	0.042	0.083	0.35	0.45
$K_{MR} \cdot 10^5$	26	9.0	4.2	5.3*	7.7*
V_m(rel.)	106	103	100	100*	96*

* Normalized values from another experiment.

0.1 M tris, pH 8.5, 1.7×10^{-3} M Mg^{++}, 37° C

The similar effects of ionic strength and Mg^{++} on both polymerization and phosphorolysis of poly A suggest that the underlying determinant in this system is the reactivity of the polymer. This is not unexpected in view of the highly charged nature of the polymer. Presumably the ionic strength serves to shield these charges. Part of the effect of Mg^{++}, particularly at low ionic strength, may be a consequence of its ability to neutralize the negative charges. Another possible example is the activation effect of acridine orange, an organic cation[9].

The Michaelis constant and maximum velocity constant for orthophosphate in

TABLE 12

VARIATION OF K_m FOR PHOSPHATE WITH IONIC STRENGTH[5]

Ionic strength	0.031	0.056	0.186
$K_{MP} \cdot 10^4$	6.0	5.8	6.8
V_m(rel.)	92	117	304

pH 8.5, 1.0×10^{-3} M Mg^{++}, 37° C

the phosphorolysis reaction with *M. lysodeikticus* polynucleotide phosphorylase do not show the same variation and insensitivity, respectively, with ionic strength. As illustrated by the data in Table 12, the Michaelis constant is independent of the ionic strength, whereas the maximum velocity constant increases continuously with ionic strength.

Discussions of the kinetic constants, V_{max} and K_m, should be prefaced by a comment on the kind of substrate-activity curve obtained in either polymerization or phosphorolysis. Under extreme conditions, particularly with high magnesium concentration, the substrate-activity curve does not obey the Michaelis-Menten equation. One illustration of this is given in Fig. 22. Four substrate-activity curves are given in which the Mg^{++} and KCl concentrations have been varied. At high magnesium concentrations, in the absence of added KCl, the rate is exponential with respect to the substrate concentration, an illustration of the ability of the

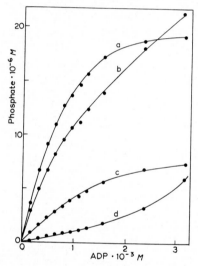

Fig. 22. Rate of polymerization of ADP as a function of ADP concentration[7]. A volume of 2.5 ml of reaction mixture contained 0.1 M tris, pH 9.0. Reaction time 20 mins. Temp. 37°. Rate recorded as moles of orthophosphate released per liter of reaction mixture per minute. Curves: a 2.3 · 10^{-4} M MgCl$_2$, 0.2 M KCl; b 2.3 · 10^{-3} M MgCl$_2$; c 2.3 · 10^{-4} M MgCl$_2$, no KCl; d 2.3 · 10^{-3} M MgCl$_2$, no KCl.

substrate to reverse Mg^{++} inhibition. Similar deviations from the Michaelis-Menton equation can be observed in the presence of inhibitors such as polynucleotides and cationic dyes[9,17].

Thus, it is not an infrequent observation to find that the data of a particular experiment fail to fit a linear curve of a Lineweaver-Burk plot. In phosphorolysis the data tend to deviate rather consistently at low substrate concentrations[5]. The mechanism for this is not clear, but it is possible that the coexistence of either inhibitors or activators or both may in some instances produce the aberrant results.

or replaced by inhibition. Of course, the effect of added salt will also depend upon the initial ionic strength of the assay mixture.

In addition, the pH is critical. This is illustrated in Fig. 18. At pH 7.0, increasing the KCl concentration from 0.0 to 0.1 M decreases the rate of polymerization, wheras at pH 9, the addition of KCl stimulates the reaction strikingly. Most of the assays with *A. vinelandii* enzyme preparations have been performed at or above pH 8.0.

SITES OF REACTION FOR THE FORMATION AND PHOSPHOROLYSIS OF POLYMERS

The formation of polymers might conceivably occur by one of several mechanisms, including a condensation of monomers, a linear addition of polymer to polymer, or an addition of monomer to polymer. Structural studies upon the biosynthetic polyribonucleotides, as discussed in Chapter 3, have indicated that only linear polymers are formed by the action of polynucleotide phosphorylase. In the case of phosphorolysis of the polymers, there exist the alternative possibilities of a random splitting or of a stepwise attack originating at the chain termini.

The kinetics which have been described in the preceding section are entirely consistent with a simple sequential addition of monomer units to pre-existing polymers or dimers. There is no evidence for the occurrence of polymer to polymer addition, which would be reflected not by a change in the total mass of polymer synthesized but by an increase in the average degree of polymerization of the polymer species. The failure to demonstrate any increase in the average molecular weight after equilibrium has been attained with respect to the conversion of mono-mer is evidence that polymer to polymer addition probably does not occur[17]. In contrast, the average molecular weight normally decreases after equilibrium has been attained.

Some inferential evidence for monomer to polymer addition is the invariance of the equilibrium ratio of ADP to P_i to the total concentration of polymer[8]. Thus, at equilibrium attained through either the polymerization of ADP or the phos-phorolysis of poly A, the addition of poly A does not alter the $ADP : P_i$ ratio. This is consistent with the equilibrium expression:

$$\frac{[P_i]\,[poly\,A]_n}{[ADP]\,[poly\,A]_{n-1}} = K$$

If the distribution of the concentrations of the polymer species at equilibrium is constant, then

$$[poly\,A]_n \cong [poly\,A]_{n-1} \text{ and } K = [P_i]/[ADP]$$

The available kinetic data upon the phosphorolysis reaction appear to provide fairly convincing evidence against the occurrence of random scission of the polymer to any important degree. In contrast to the enzymatic or alkaline hydro-lysis of poly A, which shows a definite time lag with regard to the appearance of the monomer species, the phosphorolysis of poly A displays no time lag, and the monomer and polymer species coexist at all stages of the reaction. Furthermore, the only product obtained in appreciable quantity by the phosphorolysis of high molecular weight poly A is the monomer. This is again in contrast to the cases of alkaline and enzymatic hydrolysis, which yield a variety of oligonucleotide intermediates.

A definitive answer to the question of the mechanism of polymerization and phosphorolysis has been given by the elegant studies of Heppel's group upon oligonucleotides of known structure. Before citing their results, it is well to describe briefly some of the methods and principles developed for the synthesis of specific oligonucleotides. Prior to the availability of polynucleotide phosphorylase, it was possible to obtain specific oligonucleotide only by the laborious process of partial degradation of RNA and isolation by ionic exchange and paper chromatographic means.

Homologous series of 5'-oligonucleotides, represented by pApA, pApApA, pApApApA, etc., are prepared by the hydrolysis of poly A by a phosphodiesterase obtained from guinea pig liver nuclei or a nuclease isolated from *A. vinelandii*[10] which splits the $C_{3'}-O$ bond of the phosphodiester linkage randomly along the chain. The oligonucleotides are separated by paper chromatography or ion exchange (See appendix). The isomer of pApA, ApAp, has been synthesized from ApApUp, a product of pancreatic ribonuclease digestion of an AU polymer. After removal of the $C_{3'}$-phosphate group with phosphomonoesterase, the uridine group is removed by periodate oxidation[10].

Mention has been made of the use of phosphomonoesterase for the removal of the $C_{3'}$-phosphate group. The same enzyme may also be used for the removal of the $C_{5'}$-phosphate group to yield the series ApA, ApApA, ApApApA, etc.

The synthesis of the mixed oligonucleotides, such as pApApUp, *i.e.*, mixtures containing a pyrimidine and a purine base, can be accomplished by the successive or simultaneous action of polynucleotide phosphorylase and low concentrations of ribonuclease on a mixture of ADP and UDP or a specific oligonucleotide of ADP, *i.e.*, pApA or pApApA, etc., and UDP. Synthesis of an AU polymer by polynucleotide phosphorylase is followed by the degradation of the polymer by pancreatic ribonuclease. All the pyrimidine-pyrimidine phosphodiester bonds are hydrolyzed, *i.e.*, p-Py-p-Py. In addition, the pyrimidine-purine bond p-Py-p-Pu is also hydrolyzed. However, the purine-pyrimidine bond is not hydrolyzed, *i.e.* p-Pu-p-Py. Consequently, a polymer with the structure pApApUpUpApA, yields after hydrolysis by pancreatic ribonuclease the oligonucleotide, pApApUp, the dinucleoside, ApA, and the nucleotide, Up.

The yields of these compounds can be made much more quantitative if the purine fraction of the oligonucleotide is introduced not as ADP but as a specific oligonucleotide, *i.e.*, pApA or pApApA. The polymerization of poly U in the presence of these compounds begins on the free $C_{3'}$-OH group of the oligonucleotides. Thus, if the reaction with polynucleotide phosphorylase is carried out in the presence of pancreatic ribonuclease, the products of the reaction consist primarily of pApApUp and Up.

substrates ADP, CDP, and UDP, and that the ratio of the exchange assay and polymerization assay activities remain constant.

Littauer and Kornberg[3] also observed no variation in the ratios of the activities of the *E. coli* enzyme preparations toward the different substrates as a result of the successive purification procedures.

More recent data published in a review by Singer *et al.*[25], indicate, however, that the activity of the enzyme toward CDP increases relative to the other substrates.

With *Micrococcus lysodeikticus* polynucleotide phosphorylase, these relative rates do not remain constant but vary with the degree and manner of purification. These variations led Olmsted[26] to postulate the presence of more than one polynucleotide phosphorylase enzyme (or site), each specific for a particular nucleoside diphosphate.

The situation, of course, is complicated by the unknown effects of activators and inhibitors in the enzyme preparations. Briefly, through the purification procedures employed (see Chapter 4) an enzyme preparation has been obtained from *M. lysodeikticus* which shows a disproportionately high ratio of the ADP/CDP polymerization rates. Moreover, the polymerization of poly A is stimulated by the addition of poly A, whereas the polymerization of poly C is not stimulated by the addition of poly C. Finally, a variety of proteases, inhibitors and other ions inhibit preferentially the polymerization of poly C and have a comparatively slight effect on the polymerization of poly A. These observations are taken as an indication of at least two polynucleotide phosphorylase enzymes specific for ADP and CDP, respectively.

The conclusions of Olmsted and Lowe can be questioned on several grounds, chief of which is the failure to consider seriously the relative effects of activators and inhibitors on the specificity of the enzyme toward a given substrate. We shall return to this point later after a consideration of the role of primers in the initiation of the polymerization reaction.

Role of primers

The first evidence for primer requirements in a polynucleotide phosphorylase-catalyzed polymerization reaction was reported by Mii and Ochoa[24] with a highly purified *A. vinelandii* enzyme preparation. This enzyme had an estimated 3% nucleotide material in it, a turnover number of approximately 3500 for poly A synthesis from 0.06 *M* ADP. The specific activity and the ultracentrifuge studies indicate a significant degree of purification. From the latter it is estimated that the enzyme is 80% purified.

With the substrate, UDP, there is a significant lag in the rate of polymerization which is gradually overcome as the extent of the reaction progresses. This lag does not occur with the crude enzyme preparations. It is abolished by the addition of yeast RNA, poly AGUC, and *Azotobacter* RNA. Similar lags are observed with the synthesis of poly C and poly A as well as poly AGUC. The latter is "primed" by yeast RNA, poly AGUC, and *Azotobacter* RNA. "Self-priming", the explanation for the autocatalytic shape of the rate curve, also occurs with addition of the polymer being synthesized.

Considerable specificity was observed in the priming action of the various polymers. Some activate, some have no effect and others actually inhibit. The mechanism of inhibition of poly A synthesis by poly U and *vice versa* has been discussed above and may not be related to the inhibitory effects observed with other polymer-substrate relationships.

Singer, Heppel and Hilmoe[19] extended these studies further with oligonucleotides as primers. Thus, with the smaller oligonucleotides, the reciprocal inhibitory relationship between poly A and poly U was not observed. The oligonucleotides, pApA and pApApA, abolished the lag in the polymerization of poly A completely. They also abolished the lag in the polymerization of poly U, but more importantly, as described previously, the adenylic acid oligonucleotide is incorporated into the poly U molecules.

Other evidence for a true priming action of the oligonucleotides includes the following[19]. Synthesis of poly A in the presence of ^{32}P-labeled oligonucleotides resulted in the incorporation of the radioactivity into the acid-insoluble polymer. The oligonucleotide disappears during the polymerization, as shown by paper chromatography, and is replaced by the acid-insoluble material with an R_F value of zero, corresponding to that of the polymer. During the intermediate phases of the polymerization reaction, the short chain oligonucleotides are replaced by intermediate chains of longer length.

The specificity observed by these investigators was more restrictive than that of Mii and Ochoa. Poly A synthesis was primed by poly A and poly AU, poly U by poly U and poly AU, poly I by poly I and poly AU by poly AU.

These studies strongly suggested that polynucleotide phosphorylase requires a primer to initiate the polymerization reaction. If such is the case, this enzyme behaves similarly to glycogen phosphorylase. There are two aspects of this problem to be kept in mind, however, in evaluating the data. The first, briefly referred to in Chapter 4, is the general fallacy of using kinetic data to establish a partial mechanism. The presence of a lag in the rate of a polymerization reaction can be accounted for by several mechanisms which do not include a primer requirement. The second is the obvious fact that the primers employed are, in fact, substrates in the polymerization reaction. Therefore, the fact that they stimulate the reaction and are incorporated into the final product does not establish them as primers *required* either relatively or absolutely for the synthesis of the polymers. Unfortunately the task of resolving this problem lies near the border of impossibility. A valid solution requires an absolute correlation between the polymerization reaction and the concentration of primer. Technically, this is going to be very difficult to achieve.

Further studies on the primer requirements of *A. vinelandii* polynucleotide phosphorylase have been made by Heppel's group[10], the results of which serve to

OLIGO- AND POLY-NUCLEOTIDE ACTIVATORS AND INHIBITORS*

The ability of polyribonucleotide to inhibit phosphorolysis of a polynucleotide was first demonstrated by Grunberg-Manago et al.[2], in a series of experiments designed to examine the specificity of the enzyme from *A. vinelandii*. The phosphorolysis of poly A was inhibited by as much as 75% by a preparation of *A. vinelandii* RNA.

Later Singer[20], in her studies on the site of phosphorolytic attack, observed that the $C_{3'}$-phosphate ended oligonucleotides inhibited the phosphorolysis of the $C_{3'}$-OH ended polymers to a slight extent.

Subsequently, Hendley and Beers[16] reported that alkaline degraded poly A, RNAase-treated poly AU, and commercial yeast RNA inhibit not only the phosphorolysis of poly A but also its polymerization by the *M. lysodeikticus* enzyme. The latter finding was of particular importance and provided a possible clue to the reasons for the variations in properties of polynucleotide phosphorylase prepared from different micro-organisms and of different stages of purification.

Studies of the kinetics of inhibition by the various polynucleotide inhibitors revealed the presence of an autocatalytic time curve[11] in the polymerization of ADP (Fig. 26). Moreover, the inhibition and the autocatalytic nature of the rate curve could be partially or completely abolished by the addition of either poly A

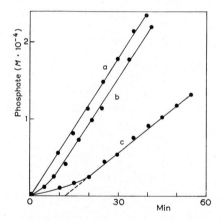

Fig. 26. Effect of yeast and *B. subtilis* ribonucleic acids on the polymerization of polynucleotide phosphorylase[11]. Reaction mixture consisted of polynucleotide phosphorylase 113 from *M. lysodeikticus*, 0.017 M tris (hydroxymethylamino) methane buffer (pH 9.0), $1.7 \cdot 10^{-4}$ M magnesium chloride, 0.2 M potassium chloride, $7 \cdot 10^{-4}$ M adenosine diphosphate. Mixture was incubated at 37° for 30 min. with inhibitors and/or activators before the addition of adenosine diphosphate. Curve *a*, control; curve *b* $1.8 \cdot 10^{-7}$ M yeast ribonucleic acid, $1.8 \cdot 10^{-4}$ M *B. subtilis* ribonucleic acid.; curve *c*, $1.8 \cdot 10^{-7}$ yeast ribonucleic acid. Rate recorded as moles of inorganic phosphate liberated per liter of reaction mixture.

---

* Unless otherwise indicated, the results cited in this section were obtained in the laboratory of R. Beers.

or a variety of nucleotide derivatives dialyzable at low salt concentrations. Subsequent studies[17] have revealed the following characteristics of the inhibitory phenomena.

All polynucleotide *inhibitors* have so far been found to be non-dialyzable and, therefore, must have a reasonable molecular weight. They have been prepared from alkaline-degraded poly A, RNAase-degraded *B. subtilis* RNA, and have been detected in commercial sources of yeast RNA. In addition, they have been found in various enzyme fractions of *M. lysodeikticus* and *B. subtilis*.

The inhibition by these polynucleotides requires a definite period of "preincubation" with the enzyme, reaching a maximum and constant extent of inhibition[11] after 15 to 30 min.

The degree of inhibition is difficult to measure because of the autocatalytic nature of the polymerization reaction in the presence of these inhibitors. However, the extent of inhibition is dependent upon both the kind of polynucleotide inhibitor and the polymer being synthesized. Thus, with yeast RNA, although it inhibits polymerization of ADP at extremely low concentrations, *i.e.* 10^{-7} M total nucleotide concentration, the extent of inhibition does not reach 100% at high RNA concentrations. Instead a plateau is reached. In contrast, alkaline-degraded poly A may inhibit the polymerization of ADP by 100%.

The extent of inhibition is most marked with the synthesis of poly C, a fact which may have a significant bearing on the interpretation given by Olmsted and Lowe[27] to the apparent specificity of various polynucleotide phosphorylases. Indeed, at appropriate concentrations of yeast RNA, the inhibition of poly A synthesis may be only a few per cent, whereas that[17] of poly C may be 100%.

The shape of the autocatalyic curve and the extent of the reversal of inhibition during the polymerization of the polymer depend upon the inhibiting polynucleotide. Yeast RNA inhibition is not reversed completely during the polymerization of poly A, nor, in fact, does added poly A completely reverse the inhibition by yeast RNA. In contrast, the inhibition by alkaline-degraded poly A is completely reversed during the polymerization and is also completely reversed by the addition[17] of poly A.

One important effect of the polynucleotide inhibitors is the reduction of the salt activating effects. With yeast RNA the salt-activity curve is almost flat. If the enzyme is not preincubated with the polynucleotide material, the shape of the activity curve may become inverted (see below).

The extent of inhibition of *M. lysodeikticus* and *B. subtilis* polynucleotide phosphorylase depends upon the state of purification of the enzyme. Moreover, the quantity of inhibitor required is reduced considerably as the quantity of polynucleotide material in the enzyme preparation is reduced. Thus, *B. subtilis* polynucleotide phosphorylase with an 280 mμ/260 mμ ratio of 0.5 is relatively insensitive to the inhibitory action of yeast RNA, whereas after extensive treatment of the enzyme with Norite A charcoal the enzyme becomes markedly sensitive to the action of yeast RNA. In the case of *M. lysodeikticus* polynucleotide phosphorylase,

distribution of oligonucleotides when incubated with the enzyme under conditions of equilibrium or even in the absence of detectable quantities of orthophosphate. Smaller molecules are increased in length at the expense of the larger ones. This provides an explanation for the drop in viscosity of poly A after the equilibrium has been reached (Fig. 23). The fallacy of using weight average data to establish the primer synthesizing ability of the enzyme is shown also in comparisons of different preparations of poly A. Although it has been found that the weight average is larger with high ADP/enzyme ratios for a given enzyme preparation, there is no correlation between different enzyme preparations. Thus, the material synthesized by *A. vinelandii* preparations[2] requires up to 24 h for completion. The weight average molecular weights are of the order of 10^5. In contrast, material synthesized by *M. lysodeikticus* preparations[4] require only two or three hours for completion. Nevertheless, the weight average molecular weights are of the order of 10^6. Nor is it possible even with *M. lysodeikticus* preparations to predict the average molecular weight from the activity of the enzyme preparation. Frequently, the most crude enzyme preparation will give the highest molecular weight polymers.

REFERENCES

[1] S. OCHOA, *Special Publications, N.Y. Acad. Sc.*, V (1957) 191.
[2] M. GRUNBERG-MANAGO, P. ORTIZ AND S. OCHOA, *Biochim. et Biophys. Acta*, 20 (1956) 269.
[3] U. LITTAUER AND A. KORNBERG, *J. Biol. Chem.*, 226 (1957) 1077.
[4] R. BEERS JR., *Biochem. J.*, 66 (1957) 686.
[5] D. HENDLEY AND R. BEERS JR., unpublished.
[6] R. BEERS JR., *Nature*, 180 (1957) 246.
[7] R. BEERS JR., *Arch. Biochem. Biophys.*, 75 (1958) 497.
[8] D. HENDLEY AND R. BEERS JR., *Fed. Proc.*, 17 (1958) 240.
[9] R. BEERS JR., *J. Biol. Chem.*, 235 (1960) 726.
[10] M. SINGER, L. HEPPEL AND R. HILMOE, *J. Biol. Chem.*, 235 (1960) 738.
[11] R. BEERS JR., *Nature*, 183 (1959) 1335.
[12] H. LINEWEAVER AND D. BURK, *J. Am. Chem. Soc.*, 56 (1934) 658.
[13] R. SIMHA AND I. ZIMMERMAN (in the press).
[14] S. OCHOA, personal communication.
[15] L. HEPPEL, personal communication.
[16] D. HENDLEY AND R. BEERS, *Fed. Proc.*, 18 (1959) 245.
[17] R. BEERS JR., unpublished.
[18] M. SINGER, R. HILMOE AND L. HEPPEL, *J. Biol. Chem.*, 235 (1960) 751.
[19] M. SINGER, L. HEPPEL AND R. HILMOE, *Biochem. Biophys. Acta*, 26 (1957) 445.
[20] M. SINGER, *J. Biol. Chem.*, 232 (1958) 211.
[21] D. BRUMMOND, M. STAEHELIN AND S. OCHOA, *J. Biol. Chem.*, 225 (1957) 835.
[22] B. GRIFFIN, A. TODD AND A. RICH, *Proc. Natl. Acad. Sci.*, 44 (1958) 1123.
[23] S. OCHOA, *Arch. Biochem. Biophys.*, 69 (1957) 119.
[24] S. MII AND S. OCHOA, *Biochim. et Biophys. Acta*, 26 (1957) 445.
[25] M. SINGER, L. HEPPEL, R. HILMOE, S. OCHOA AND S. MII, *Proc. 3rd Can. Cancer Conf.*, (1959) p. 41.
[26] P. OLMSTED, *Biochim. et Biophys. Acta*, 27 (1958) 222.
[27] P. OLMSTED AND G. LOWE, *J. Biol. Chem.*, 234 (1959) 2971.
[28] R. BEERS JR., *Ann. N. Y. Acad. Sci.*, 81 (1959) 645.
[29] L. HEPPEL, M. SINGER AND R. HILMOE, *Ann. N. Y. Acad. Sci.*, 81 (1959) 635.
[30] M. SINGER, R. HILMOE AND M. GRUNBERG-MANAGO, see ref. 29.
[31] J. FRESCO AND P. DOTY, *J. Am. Chem. Soc.*, 79 (1957) 3928.
[32] L. HEPPEL, P. ORTIZ AND S. OCHOA, *J. Biol. Chem.*, 229 (1957) 695.

As usual, an unambiguous prediction of the sign of the birefringence can be made only for two limiting extremes, to which no real system corresponds exactly. If the system consists of a uniform pile of flat disks arrayed perpendicularly to the fiber axis then, when viewed with light which vibrates perpendicularly to the fiber axis and hence parallel to the disks, the effective dielectric constant will be of the form corresponding to a system of electrical condensers in parallel:

$$\varepsilon_\perp = \varepsilon v + \varepsilon_0 v_0 \tag{1}$$

where ε, ε_0 are the dielectric constants of the disks and the medium, respectively, and v, v_0 are the corresponding volume fractions. The volume fractions will be proportional to the relative thickness of the disks and the medium in which they are immersed, as the system is assumed to have a uniform cross-section.

When viewed by light oscillating parallel to the fiber axis the system will be analogous to a set of condensers in series. Hence we have for $\varepsilon_{//}$:

$$\frac{1}{\varepsilon_{//}} = \frac{v}{\varepsilon} + \frac{v_0}{\varepsilon_0} \tag{2}$$

As the dielectric constant may be replaced by the square of the refractive index, we have upon combining:

$$n_{//}^2 - n_\perp^2 = -\frac{v \, v_0 \left(n^2 - n_0^2\right)^2}{v_0 \, n^2 + v \, n_0^2} \tag{3}$$

From the form of the right hand side of equation (3) it is obvious that $n_{//}^2 - n_\perp^2$ and hence $n_{//} - n_\perp^2$ must always be negative in sign, irrespective of the magnitudes of n and n_0. As $n_{//} - n_\perp$ may be equated with $n_e - n_o$, the birefringence will always be negative in sign.

The other extreme consists of a system of thin rods oriented parallel to the fiber axis. When viewed with light oscillating parallel to the fiber axis such a system should again correspond to an arrangement of parallel condensers with ε given, as before, by:

$$\varepsilon_{//} = v\varepsilon + v_0 \, \varepsilon_0 \tag{4}$$

The case of light vibrating perpendicularly to the fiber axis is less obvious. However, Wiener[4,5] has shown that:

$$\varepsilon_\perp = \varepsilon_0 \frac{(v+1) \, \varepsilon + v_0 \, \varepsilon_0}{(v+1) \, \varepsilon_0 + v_0 \, \varepsilon} \tag{5}$$

Upon combination of equations (4) and (5) we finally obtain:

$$n_{//}^2 - n_\perp^2 = \frac{v \, v_0 \left(n_0^2 - n^2\right)^2}{(v+1) \, n_0^2 + v_0 \, n^2} \tag{6}$$

Hence the sign of the birefringence is always positive in this case. It is to be noted that equations (3) and (6) both predict that the birefringence should vanish when the system is immersed in a medium of the same refractive index. This has been amply verified in practice and provides a means for differentiating between intrinsic and form birefringence, as the former does not vanish for any refractive index of the medium[6].

There is a limit to the extent to which so crude an argument can be pushed. However, to anticipate, it would be expected that, in the absence of any preferential orientation of the planar bases, singly stranded polynucleotides would be positively birefringent when in an extended state. The observation of negative birefringence is clearly suggestive of a stacking of planar purine and pyrimidine bases perpendicularly to the fiber axis. The negative birefringence of DNA is part of the evidence commonly cited in support of its currently accepted structure.

Measurements of the birefringence of oriented macromolecules may be made directly upon dry fibers, using a polarizing microscope[1,2]. The birefringence often persists in solution if the particles are sufficiently oriented by means of a velocity gradient or an electric field. The former case corresponds to the familiar technique of streaming birefringence, detailed discussion of which is beyond the scope of this book. A thorough discussion may be found in the excellent review by Cerf and Scheraga[7].

In brief, the method depends upon the orientation of asymmetric macromolecules by a velocity gradient produced by placing the solution in the annular space between two cylinders, one of which rotates while the other is stationary. Such a system may for practical purposes be regarded as like a uniaxial crystal. If the solution is placed vertically between two crossed Nicols and illuminated from below with parallel light, the induced birefringence causes the solution to appear bright when viewed from above except in the region of a dark cross, the cross of isocline. The smaller of the angles between the arms of the cross of isocline and the planes of transmission of the Nicols is called the extinction angle, ψ.

The value of the extinction angle is a function of the velocity gradient and the rotary diffusion coefficient of the dissolved particles. In order to make the relationship explicit, some assumption of the shape of the molecules must be made. Peterlin and Stuart have developed the theory for the case of prolate ellipsoids of revolution[8,9]. For the limit of small ratios of velocity gradient to rotary diffusion constant, they find:

$$\psi = \frac{\pi}{4} - \frac{\alpha}{12} = \frac{\pi}{4} - \frac{G}{12\theta} + \cdots \qquad 7$$

where G = velocity gradient

θ = rotary diffusion constant

$$\alpha = \frac{G}{\theta}$$

It was recognized quite early, in the case of the naturally occurring nucleic acids, that the ultraviolet spectrum of the intact polymer did not correspond to that predicted upon summation of the expected contributions of the bases[15-23]. The discrepancy was in the direction of decreased absorbency and was disconcertingly large, amounting to as much as 40% for both DNA and RNA. Furthermore, this effect, which has been called hypochromism, was found to be pronouncedly dependent upon both the medium and the prior treatment of the sample[15-24].

Because of their varying water content, the molar absorbencies of nucleic acids cannot be reliably based upon weight. The usual procedure has been to derive a molar absorbency ε_p, based on one gram atom of phosphorus per liter. As nucleic acids contain one phosphorus atom per base, ε_p corresponds to a mean absorbency per mole of nucleotide.

The published values of ε_p show wide variation for native nucleic acids, ranging from $6 \cdot 10^3$ to $8 \cdot 10^3$ for DNA and from $7 \cdot 10^3$ to $1 \cdot 10^4$ for RNA. Enzymatic or alkaline degradation has been shown to produce invariably a decrease in hypochromism[20-23].

The molar absorbency of nucleic acids has been known for some time to be dependent upon such parameters as pH, ionic strength, and temperature[15, 24]. The variation generally shows no particular correlation with that expected for a mixture of nucleotides in the correct proportions.

Thomas found that the exposure of DNA to very low ionic strengths ($< 10^{-3}$) resulted in a partially irreversible increase in absorbency[16, 24]. Shack et al.[18, 19], working with DNA which had been initially dissolved in water, found that the addition of electrolyte resulted in an increase in absorbency, divalent cations being much more effective than monovalent. The ionic history of a particular sample of DNA is thus very important with regard to its absorbency. It has, in fact, been suggested that the ε_p of a preparation (at neutral pH and ionic strength greater than 10^{-3}) is a good index of its degree of denaturation.

In harmony with this view it has been found that the exposure of native DNA to extremes of pH results in an incompletely reversible increase in ε_p. If the sample has previously been exposed to very low ionic strengths the pH dependence of absorbency is greatly diminished. Similarly the exposure of DNA to elevated temperatures produces a partially irreversible increase in absorbency.

In general the appearance of irreversible changes in ε_p for DNA appears to parallel the onset of a disruption of the secondary structure, as judged by other criteria. This will be discussed in detail in Chapter 7. There is thus considerable ground for the belief that the degree of hypochromism is dependent upon the nature of the secondary structure and the degree of ordering.

A quantitative treatment of the hypochromatic effect for polynucleotides is not yet available. Roughly speaking, it has generally been regarded as arising from the *stacking* of the bases in an array perpendicular to the fiber axis. From the extent that such stacking reflects the ordered fine structure of the polynucleotide, it would be expected that alterations in the secondary structure would be reflected by changes in the degree of hypochromism. It would, in particular, be anticipaedt that an organization of the nucleotide bases into an ordered array would permit more efficient stacking and hence a greater hypochromatic effect than a purely random arrangement. This supposition has been the basis for many speculations about the helical content of the several polynucleotide systems.

Why stacking should result in hypochromism is still not very clear. It may result from the interaction of the π electrons of the bases to produce mutually altered resonance forms or it may reflect simply the optical inhomogeneity of the ordered array.

With regard to interpretations of the hypochromatic effect, a timely note of caution has been sounded by the work of Michelson upon the ultraviolet spectra of synthetic purine and pyrimidine oligonucleotides[,25]. It was found by this worker that the hypochromatic effect was quite important even for purine dinucleo-tides and was as high as 30% for trinucleotides. As the existence of any hydrogen bonded structure is virtually precluded for such small systems, these results indicate that the existence of such a structure is not necessarily a prerequisite for the occur-rence of an important degree of hypochromism.

In the present inadequate state of the theory variations in hypochromism are probably best regarded as a purely empirical index of the relative extent of forma-tion of an ordered structure.

Among the most interesting developments in the study of biosynthetic polynucleo-tides has been the discovery of several instances in which two different relatively unorganized polynucleotides interact stoichiometrically to form an ordered helical complex[26-28]. These will be discussed in detail in the subsequent chapter. Such interactions have invariably been found to be reflected by an increase in hypo-chromism. The best-studied example is the poly A plus poly U interaction[26].

It has been shown by Felsenfeld[29] that definite inferences may be made of the mechanism of an interaction of this kind from the form of the ultraviolet spectral mixing curves alone. The analysis of Felsenfeld is quite independent of any assumptions about the detailed structure of the complex species and would apply equally well to a helical or a purely linear aggregate. The treatment is confined to the case of the interaction of two different singly stranded polymers to form a doubly stranded complex. It would, however, apply equally well to the addition of a third strand by a doubly stranded complex. Three assumptions are essential to the argument:

a. Each monomer unit of a given polymer molecule can form a linkage with one and only one complementary monomer unit of a polymer of the second type. This clearly fits the polynucleotide cases, on which our interest is centered, provided that the current ideas of the manner of linkage are valid.

b. The intrinsic equilibrium constant for bonding between two complementary monomer units is very large so that the reaction essentially goes to completion. This assumption likewise appears to be valid for the cases of interest at sufficiently high ionic strength, as we shall see in the next chapter.

(d) The formation of linkages is irreversible. Polymers A and B are monodisperse with $n >> m$. Overlapping of bound B chains cannot occur. This case differs from (c) only in the prohibition of overlapping.

This latter proviso means that when the final segment of one bound B strand is separated from the initial segment of an adjacent strand by fewer than m A units, a third B strand cannot be inserted between them. Thus imperfections in the doubly stranded complex species will have the form of unoccupied gaps.

In this case the predicted mixing curve is linear and V-shaped, but has a minimum at a value of x_B less than 0.50.

In general it can be stated that the only case likely to be encountered in practice for which a linear mixing curve with a sharp minimum at $x_B = 0.50$ is predicted is case (a), which postulates complete reversibility and no restrictions upon the number of A and B molecules which can combine.

The detailed derivations of the theoretical mixing curves discussed above will be summarized in the following section, which can be skipped by the reader without interrupting the continuity.

Derivation of theoretical mixing curves [29]

The various cases treated by Felsenfeld are discussed below. Case (a) is omitted, being fairly obvious. In each case combination occurs between a polymer of type A, of degree of polymerization n, and a polymer of type B, of degree of polymerization m.

(b) The formation of linkages is reversible, but each A chain can bind only one B chain. If the distribution of A and B chain lengths is heterogeneous, we can assume a series of equilibrium constants of the following form:

$$[A_n B_m] = K n^\alpha m^\beta [A_n][B_m] \tag{11}$$

Then
$$[A_n] = A_n^0 - \Sigma_m [A_n B_m]; \quad [B_m] = B_m^0 - \Sigma_n [A_n B_m] \tag{12}$$

where $A_n^0, B_m^0 = $ *total* concentrations of species A_n and B_m

Also
$$\Sigma_m [A_n B_m] = K n^\alpha [A_n] \Sigma_m m^\beta [B_m]$$

$$\Sigma_n [A_n B_m] = K m^\beta [B_m] \Sigma_n n^\alpha [A_n] \tag{13}$$

If we let $c_{1\beta} = \Sigma_m m^\beta [B_m]$ and $c_{2\alpha} = \Sigma_n n^\alpha [A_n]$

then
$$[A_n] = \frac{A_n^0}{1 + K n^\alpha c_{1\beta}}; \quad [B_m] = \frac{B_m^0}{1 + K m^\beta c_{2\alpha}} \tag{14}$$

If the number of A strands is greater than the number of B strands so that $c_{2\alpha}$ is not equal to zero, we then have for very large values of K:

$$[A_n \, B_m] = \frac{K \, A_n^0 \, B_m^0 \, n^\alpha \, m^\beta}{(1 + Kn^\alpha \, c_{1\beta})(1 + Km^\beta \, c_{2\alpha})}$$

$$\simeq \frac{A_n^0 \, B_m^0 \, n^\alpha}{c_{2\alpha}(1 + Kn^\alpha \, c_{1\beta})} \tag{15}$$

$$(\text{as } Km^\beta \, c_{2\alpha} >> 1)$$

The total number of bonds formed is

$$\nu = \Sigma_n \, \underset{n<m}{\Sigma_m} \, n[A_n \, B_m] + \Sigma_n \, \underset{n>m}{\Sigma_m} \, m \, [A_n \, B_m] \tag{16}$$

Since the process is reversible each complex of one A strand with one B strand will attain the energetically favored state for which the maximum number of bonds is formed. This will be equal to either n or m, whichever is smaller.

For the special case where $\alpha = \beta = 0$, we may write for c_{20} and c_{10}

$$c_{20} = \frac{1}{1 + Kc_{10}} \, \Sigma_n \, A_n^0 = \frac{A_t}{1 + Kc_{10}} \tag{17}$$

$$c_{10} = \frac{\Sigma_m \, B_m^0}{Kc_{20}} = \frac{B_t}{Kc_{20}} \, (\text{as } Kc_{20} >> 1) \tag{18}$$

where A_t, B_t are the total number of A and B molecules added. From equations (15), (16) and (17)

$$\nu = \Sigma_n \, \underset{n<m}{\Sigma_m} \, \frac{n \, A_n^0 \, B_m^0}{c_{20}(1 + Kc_{10})} + \Sigma_n \, \underset{n>m}{\Sigma_m} \, \frac{m \, A_n^0 \, B_m^0}{c_{20}(1 + Kc_{10})} \tag{19}$$

$$= \frac{1}{A_t} \, \{ \Sigma_n \, \underset{n<m}{\Sigma_m} \, n \, A_n^0 \, B_m^0 + \Sigma_n \, \underset{n>m}{\Sigma_m} \, m \, A_n^0 \, B_m^0 \}$$

$$= \frac{1}{A_t} \, (A_t B_t) \, (\Sigma_n \, \Sigma_m \, n x_{An} x_{Bm} + \Sigma_n \, \Sigma_m \, m x_{An} x_{Bm}) = H \, B_t$$

where X_{An}, X_{Bm} are the fractions of species A and B which are n and m units long. H is a function which depends upon the form of the distribution of chain lengths only and is independent of A_t and B_t.

Thus, when A_t is greater than B_t, ν is directly proportional to B_t and hence the fraction of all units which are bonded is proportional to X_B. When B_t is greater than A_t, the analysis is exactly similar, so that in this region $\nu' = H \, A_t$ and the fraction of bonded units is proportional to $1 - X_B$. The intersection of the two straight lines occurs at $v=v'$, when $A_t=B_t$; or at a mole fraction of B monomer units equal to $\overline{m}/\overline{m}+\overline{n}$, where $\overline{n}$ and $\overline{m}$ are the number average values of n and m. Hence the mixing curve in this case consists of two straight lines interacting at $X_B=\overline{m}/\overline{m}+\overline{n}$.

Thus the imposition upon case (a) of the restriction that each complex species may contain no more than one strand each of A and B has the effect of displacing the minimum of the V-shaped mixing curve from $X_B=0.50$, unless of course $\overline{n}$ is equal to $\overline{m}$.

If α or β is not equal to zero a somewhat more involved analysis shows that v is not linear in A_t and hence that the mixing curve is no longer linear[29].

(c) The formation of linkages is irreversible. Polymers A and B are monodisperse with $n \gg m$. (The analysis is, of course, identical when $m \gg n$). Overlapping of the bound B strands is permitted, so that structures of the type shown in Fig. 32c can occur.

In this case the occurrence of double thicknesses of B strands in the regions of overlap prevents the maximum number of linkages from being formed. We require first the probability of finding an interval of length i when k B chains are randomly attached to a single A. Unless the interval i between the points of attachment of two adjacent B terminal segments is greater than m A units, overlapping must occur.

The statistical problem is equivalent to the familiar one of finding the probability of occurrence of a segment of length greater than m upon random scission of a chain of n units in $(k-1)$ places.

For segments which do not involve an end unit of the A chain the probability of occurrence of an i-mer upon random scission of the A chain in $(k-1)$ places is given by:

$$p_i'=\frac{S}{N}\left(1-\frac{S-1}{N-1}\right)\cdots\left(1-\frac{S-1}{N-i+1}\right)\left(\frac{S-1}{N-i}\right) \tag{20}$$

$$=S(S-1)\frac{(N-S)!(N-i-1)!}{(N-S-i+1)!N!}\equiv S(S-1)\theta$$

where S, $N=k-1$, $n-1$, respectively. The probability for the case in which an end unit is involved is given by:

$$p_i''=\left(1-\frac{S}{N}\right)\left(1-\frac{S}{N-1}\right)\cdots\left(1-\frac{S}{N-i+2}\right)\left(\frac{S}{N-i+1}\right)=S(N-i)\theta \tag{21}$$

By combining (20) and (21) we obtain for the total probability of occurrence of an i-mer:

$$p_i=(N-i)\,p_i'+2p_i''=S\,(S+1)\,(N-i)\theta \tag{22}$$

The function p_i gives the average number of spaces of length i separating the points of attachment of two B chains. (If the two are adjacent, $i=1$.) The total number of such spaces of length greater than m is given by:

$$Q_s = 1 + S - \sum_{i=1}^{m} p_i \tag{23}$$

The total number of occupied sites on the A chain is equal to

$$mQ_s + \sum_{i=1}^{m} i\, p_i$$

Thus the fraction of B sites which is involved in bonding to A sites rather than in mutual overlapping is

$$f_s = \frac{mQ_s + \sum_{i=1}^{m} i\, p_i}{m\,(S+1)} \tag{24}$$

When every B chain is combined with an A chain the mole fraction of B monomer units is given by:

$$X_B = \frac{m(S+1)}{m(S+1) + N + 1} \tag{25}$$

All of the B chains will be combined when empty spaces on the A chain are available. This will be the case if Q_s is equal to or greater than unity. The corresponding value of S (S_c) represents the critical value of this parameter and effectively determines, through equation (25), the saturation value of X_B, which in turn fixes the minimum of the mixing curve. The parameter S_c may be computed from equations (22) and (23), setting $Q_s = 1$.

If N and S are large numbers a considerable simplification becomes possible. In this case equation (22) reduces to:

$$p_i \cong \frac{S^2}{N} \left[1 - \frac{S}{N} \right]^{i-1} \tag{26}$$

and (24) becomes:

$$f_s = \frac{N}{mS} \left\{ 1 - \left(1 - \frac{S}{N} \right)^m \right\} \tag{27}$$

The preceding relationships suffice for the computation of the mixing curve when $S < S_c$. The fraction of all monomer units which are bonded is equal to $2 X_B f_s$. At mole fractions of B monomer units greater than $X_{B,C}$ (the value of X_B when $S = S_c$), f_s is equal to

$$\frac{f_{s,c}\, X_{B,c}\, (1 - X_B)}{X_B\, (1 - X_{B,c})}$$

where $f_{s,c}$ is the value of f_s when $S = S_c$.

References p. 184/185

Thus the complete mixing curve is readily computible. The approximate forms given by equations (26) and (27) appear to be adequate when n and m are greater than about 10. Computation shows that for case (c) the predicted mixing curve is rounded with a minimum at a mole fraction of B equal to 0.50 (Fig. 33). The form of the mixing curve is almost independent of m and n when n/m is greater than about 10.

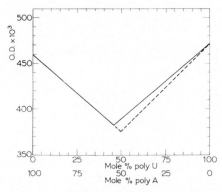

Fig. 34. An example of mixing curves predicted for case (a) (dotted line) and case (d) (solid line) for a poly A plus poly U system of total molarity 4.6 ·10⁻⁵. The experimental value for the maximum hypochromism is used[28].

(d) The formation of linkages is irreversible. Polymers A and B are monodisperse with $n >> m$. Overlapping of bound B chains cannot occur.

In this case the total number of empty sites on the A chain is equal to $n-mk$. However, these will not be available for further binding of B chains unless they are part of a sequence of length greater than m, because of the prohibition of overlapping.

The statistical problem is similar to that of case (c) and is equivalent to computing the probability of occurrence of an i-mer when a chain $(n-mk)$ units long is ruptured in $(k-1)$ places. The total number of sequences of empty A sites of length greater than m is given by

$$Q_s = S + 1 - \sum_{i=1}^{m} p_i \qquad (28)$$

The parameter p_i is still given by equation (22) with N replaced by $N-m(S+1)$.

At a critical value of $S(S_c)$ Q_s will be equal to unity. At larger values of S, Q_s will be less than unity, indicating that no more B chains can be accommodated. S_c thus determines the saturation point of the A chains and hence the position of the minimum in the mixing curve. The number of bonded B sites per A chain is mk. At mole fractions of B less than that corresponding to the critical value of S, all the B chains will be bound.

The critical mole fraction of B is given by

$$X_{B,c} = \frac{m(S_c+1)}{m(S_c+1)+n}$$

At mole fractions of B less than $X_{B,c}$ the fraction of B sites which are bonded is unity. The number of bonds formed, ν, is directly proportional to X_B. The fraction of all monomer units which are bonded is equal to $2X_B$.

At mole fractions of B greater than $X_{B,c}$ the fraction of all monomer units which are bonded is equal to

$$\frac{2X_{B,c}(X_B-1)}{X_{B,c}-1}$$

The mixing curve predicted for case (d) is V-shaped with a sharp minimum at $X_{B,c}$. The value of $X_{B,c}$ is less than 0.50.

HYDRODYNAMIC METHODS

The discussion of the hydrodynamic methods will be confined here to sedimentation and viscosity. As in the case of the other macromolecular systems, the application of these techniques to polynucleotides is generally made with the hope of gaining information on the polydispersity, the average molecular weight, and the molecular shape.

The difficulties involved in obtaining an accurate picture of the distribution of sedimentation coefficients for a polynucleotide system remained incompletely appreciated until relatively recent times. As with other thread-like polymers, the problem is complicated by the profound dependence of sedimentation coefficient upon concentration, especially for samples of high molecular weight. The generally observed decrease in sedimentation coefficient with increasing concentration has the effect of pronouncedly distorting and sharpening the concentration gradient in the vicinity of the boundary. This tends to mask the usually high degree of polydispersity.

In general both the concentration dependence of sedimentation rate and the degree of boundary sharpening are particularly important for the more rigid and extended polynucleotides. An extreme example is furnished by solutions of thymus DNA at concentrations of 1 g/l or greater. Under these conditions the sedimentation diagram, as viewed by schlieren optics, consists of a single very sharp line with no appreciable boundary spreading, despite the high degree of heterogeneity actually characteristic of this system.

Thus the extrapolation of sedimentation data to infinite dilution becomes of paramount importance if the true distribution of sedimentation coefficients is to be obtained. With ordinary schlieren optics it is difficult to extend measurements to concentrations much below 1 g/l. Because of this restriction the high polydispersity of thymus DNA long went unrecognized.

However, the very strong ultraviolet absorption characteristic of all polynucleotides has permitted a revival, in the case of these systems, of the older technique of following sedimentation through the use of optical density as a measure of concentration, rather than refractive index[30-32]. This method permits the extension of measurements to concentrations as low as 0.01 g/l, thereby circumventing the boundary sharpening effects dominant at higher concentrations, as this concentration is sufficiently low to be effectively equivalent to infinite dilution.

The relatively low density gradients produced by sedimentation at such extreme dilutions raise, of course, the possibility that convection might be a problem. However, the demonstrated invariance with time of the corrected concentration distribution function indicates that errors from this source are probably not important.

With regard to instrumental problems, absorption systems are probably the simplest of all the optical methods which have been used in conjunction with the ultracentrifuge. However, the as yet incomplete resolution of several technical difficulties renders this technique somewhat less precise than either the schlieren or interferometric systems.

The high selectivity of ultraviolet absorption, as compared with the methods based on refractive index, is both an asset and a disadvantage. Thus the presence of concentration gradients of supporting electrolyte causes no difficulty. On the other hand, if the sample contains molecules of varying absorbency, as in the case of a heterodisperse mixture of DNA's differing in base composition or in extent of denaturation, the apparent distribution will, of course, be biased by this factor.

For polynucleotides of reasonably high molecular weight ($> 10^5$) diffusion is negligible and it is possible to convert the experimental curves of concentration *versus* distance directly to integral plots of the distribution of sedimentation coefficients by correcting for radial dilution and transforming the abscissa to a scale of sedimentation coefficients. The radial dilution correction is made by multiplying the ordinate by $(x/x_m)^2$, where x and x_m are the radial distances at a given point in the cell and at the meniscus, respectively. The conversion of the abscissa to a sedimentation scale may be done from the relationship[32]:

$$s = \text{sedimentation coefficient} = \frac{1}{\omega^2 t} \ln \frac{x}{x_m} \text{ where } \omega = \text{angular velocity and } t = \text{time.}$$

The resulting integral plots show essentially the fraction of material with sedimentation coefficient less than a certain value. By differentiating the integral plots a more informative plot of

$$\frac{1}{c} \frac{dc}{ds}$$

may be obtained, where c is the weight concentration.

In principle, average values of the molecular weight of polynucleotide samples can be determined by a combination of sedimentation and diffusion data through the use of the Svedberg equation[32]:

$$M = \frac{RT s_0}{D_0(1 - \bar{v}\varrho)} \tag{29}$$

where M = molecular weight, s_0 = sedimentation coefficient at infinite dilution, D_0 = diffusion coefficient at infinite dilution, $\bar{v}$ = partial specific volume, ϱ = solvent density.

However, sedimentation-diffusion is rarely the method of choice for most polynucleotide systems. For polynucleotides of high molecular weight it is difficult to make an unambiguous extrapolation of diffusion coefficient to infinite dilution. For lower molecular weight preparations this difficulty is less apparent. However, the method suffers from the disadvantage of not yielding a simply defined average molecular weight. This drawback is not important in the case of systems for which fairly sharp fractions are obtainable, but it is severe in the case of polynucleotides for which an adequate means of fractionation with respect to molecular weight has yet to be developed.

For polynucleotide preparations whose mean molecular weight is not too high (less than about $5 \cdot 10^5$) a more satisfactory means of molecular weight determination is by the Archibald method, which is a variant of sedimentation equilibrium[32, 33]. This has its origin in the theoretical considerations of transient states by Archibald[33], who concluded that molecular weights should be determinable from the concentration distribution in the vicinity of the meniscus and bottom of the cell. This holds true at any time, irrespective of whether true sedimentation equilibrium throughout the cell has been attained, provided that solute is still present at the meniscus.

The method depends upon the measurement of values of dc/dx and c at the meniscus and preferably at the bottom of the cell as well. The accurate determination of these quantities requires a particularly well aligned optical system. The essential requirement of a narrow base line (for schlieren optics) is attained by the use of a phase plate. Measurements at the base of the cell are made possible by the use of a layer of inert organic solvent, which is denser than water and immiscible in it.

There are, of course, several different experimental methods of obtaining c and dc/dx. The bulk of the work so far has utilized the schlieren optical system which gives dc/dx directly. Concentration is determined by integration of the gradient. An alternative approach is to use an interferometric technique, which yields c as a function of x and requires differentiation to produce curves of the concentration gradient. Schachman has discussed the problems involved in each case[32].

The basic equation relating average molecular weight to the concentration distribution at the meniscus is, for ideal conditions:

$$M_w = \frac{RT}{(1 - \bar{v}\varrho)\omega^2} \frac{(dc/dx)_m}{x_m \, c_m} \tag{30}$$

where M_w = weight average molecular weight, ω = angular velocity, c_m = weight concentration at the meniscus, x_m = radial distance at the meniscus from the axis of rotation, $(dc/dx)_m$ = concentration gradient at the meniscus.

A completely analogous expression holds for the base of the cell. In practice it is usually most convenient to confine measurements to sufficiently short sedimentation times so that a concentration plateau occurs in the cell. Under these conditions we have:

at the meniscus:
$$c_m = c_0 - \frac{1}{x_m^2} \int_{x_m}^{x} x^2 \frac{dc}{dx} dx$$

at the base:
$$c_b = c_0 + \frac{1}{x_b^2} \int_{x}^{x_b} x^2 \frac{dc}{dx} dx$$

where c_0 = initial (uniform) concentration. The integral is evaluated graphically from a point in the plateau region to the meniscus or base. The quantity c_0 is usually obtained in arbitrary units by making a separate determination with the synthetic boundary cell.

Equation (30) holds for ideal conditions. For real systems an extrapolation of apparent molecular weight to zero concentration is usually necessary.

It should be recognized that, as sedimentation progresses, there will be a continuous alteration in the composition as well as the total concentration at the meniscus and base. The larger molecules will be preferentially removed from the meniscus region and added to the base zone. Thus, for a heterodisperse system, the apparent values of molecular weight will drift downward with time at the meniscus and upward at the base. In principle an extrapolation to zero time is required to obtain the weight average molecular weight characteristic of the original solution. However, if the speed of rotation has been suitably chosen, the variation with time is usually sufficiently gradual so that the extrapolation to zero time presents little difficulty.

The method has several distinct advantages:

(a) It requires only one kind of measurement.

(b) A well-defined weight average value of molecular weight is obtainable.

(c) Information on the heterogeneity of the system is obtained directly. The chief source of experimental error arises from difficulties in measuring $(dc/dx)_m$ and $(dc/dx)_b$ precisely. This is usually done by extrapolation. Schachman[32] has discussed some of the problems this involves.

With increasing molecular weight the use of the Archibald method becomes more difficult. In order to use the method at all it must be possible to find speeds which are low enough so that the concentration gradients at the top and bottom of the cell remain reasonably flat for an appreciable length of time, but still high enough so that a stable system and accurate speed control are possible. Deviations from ideality also become progressively more important with increasing molecular weight. In practice, the extreme upper limit of molecular weight which permits application of this method is probably in the vicinity of 10^6.

Still another method of obtaining average molecular weights, which does not suffer from the above restriction, is by a combination of sedimentation and viscosity data. As its use requires some knowledge of the average *shape* of the molecules we will defer its discussion until later in the chapter.

The question of determining the molecular shape in solution of a polynucleotide system has still not been solved completely, partially because of the difficulty of defining the problem. As will be discussed in the following chapter, the natural and synthetic polynucleotides so far examined range in properties from flexible random coils to structures approaching in rigidity a perfect helix. The available theories dealing with the hydrodynamic properties of macromolecules are as yet insufficiently refined to permit a prediction of properties for all gradations of flexibility. Thus, for the many systems which fall in a category intermediate to the two extremes, it is at present impossible to make a quantitative correlation of hydrodynamic behavior with the shape and dimensions of the molecule as determined by light scattering.

Let us consider first the flexible coil extreme. It is useful to examine first the hypothetical case of a chain consisting of n linkages of length l joined in linear sequence, with no restrictions at all upon the successive bond angles. The latter may thus range over all values from π to 0 with equal probability. In this case the problem of finding the probability of a given value of r, the separation of the ends, reduces to the familiar random flight problem in statistics.

In the three dimensional case $W(r)\,dr$, which is the probability that the separation of chain ends has a value in the range $r + dr$ irrespective of direction, is given by [34-37].

$$W(r)\,dr = (\beta/\pi^{1/2})^3\, e^{-\beta^2\, r^2}\, 4\pi r^2\, dr \tag{31}$$

where
$$\beta = \left(\frac{3}{2nl^2}\right)^{1/2}$$

The most probable value of r corresponds to the maximum of $W(r)$ and is equal to $1/\beta$. A more useful parameter is the *root mean square* value of r, which is given by:

$$(\overline{r^2})^{1/2} = (3/2\,\beta^2)^{1/2} \tag{32}$$
$$= n^{1/2}l$$

Thus, in this hypothetical limiting case, the *root mean square* end-to-end distance varies as $n^{1/2}$.

Equation (31) is actually an approximation valid when the ratio of r to the maximum fully extended length is not too large. The deviation from equation (31) is negligible when $r/r_{max} < 0.3$.

The links of a real polymer chain will not, of course, be joined by universal joints but by bonds forming fixed valence angles. If rotation is unrestricted equation (32) may be replaced by:

$$\bar{r^2} = nl^2 \frac{1 - \cos\theta}{1 + \cos\theta} \tag{33}$$

where θ is the bond angle. In dealing with processes involving the linear translation of a polymer chain thru solvent, such as viscous flow or sedimentation, it is convenient to introduce a model resembling a string of beads joined by frictionless links. Toward the periphery of the coil the flow of solvent is almost unhindered. As the center is approached the bead density increases, as does the degree of retardation of solvent flow[34].

For a random coil approximated by this model the following relationship between the frictional coefficient, f, and $(\bar{r^2})^{1/2}$ has been derived[38]:

$$f/\eta_0 = P(\bar{r^2})^{1/2} \tag{34}$$

where η_0 = solvent viscosity and P is a universal constant. In the case of intrinsic viscosity the following expression has been obtained for this model[39]:

$$[\eta] = \Phi(\bar{r^2})^{3/2}/M \tag{35}$$

where Φ is another universal constant. For a homologous series of randomly coiled polymers $\bar{r^2}$ is directly proportional to M and hence (in an ideal solvent)

$$[\eta] = KM^{1/2} \tag{36}$$

The sedimentation coefficient of a polymer at infinite dilution is given by[40]:

$$S_0 = M(1 - \varrho\bar{v})/N_0 f \tag{37}$$

where $\bar{v}$ is the partial specific volume and ϱ is the solvent density. Upon combining equations (34), (35), and (37) we have:

$$S_0[\eta]^{1/3} M^{-2/3} = \Phi^{1/3} P^{-1} (1 - \bar{V}\varrho)/\eta_0 N_0 \tag{38}$$

This relationship between S_0, $[\eta]$, and M should hold for all polymer systems corresponding to the random coil model. The invariance of $\Phi^{1/3} P^{-1}$ with these three parameters is a good test for this model. In practice $\Phi^{1/3} P^{-1}$ has proved to be almost constant for a wide range of polymer systems, with an average value close to $2.5 \cdot 10^6$.

Equation (38) thus provides a means of obtaining molecular weights from sedimentation and viscosity data alone. It is useful for polynucleotide systems of high molecular weight, for which the other hydrodynamic methods are inadequate.

However, the method suffers from the disadvantage of not giving a well-defined average value of molecular weight. This tends to limit its usefulness for polydisperse systems.

The use of equation (38) requires values of intrinsic viscosity which have been extrapolated to zero shear gradient. As the viscosity of polynucleotide solutions is frequently non-Newtonian, it is necessary to make measurements of viscosity at several shear gradients, using a multibulb capillary viscometer, to obtain a valid extrapolation to zero shear.

Finally it must be emphasized that the applicability of equation (38) is limited to macromolecules having the overall shape characteristics of random coils. Its use for rod-like particles will result in severe errors.

For the variation of S_0 with M we have, from (32), (34), and (37):

$$S_0 = KM^{1/2}$$

Let us now consider the other extreme of a completely rigid rod of length L. If the rod is approximated by a prolate ellipsoid of axial ratio J, Perrin's equations give for the frictional ratio[41]:

$$\frac{f}{f_0} = \frac{J^{2/3}(1-1/J^2)^{1/2}}{\ln[J+J(1-1/J^2)^{1/2}]} \tag{39}$$

For the intrinsic viscosity we have, from Simha[42]:

$$[\eta] = \frac{J^2}{15(\ln 2J - 3/2)} + \frac{J^2}{5(\ln 2J - 1/2)} + \frac{14}{15} \tag{40}$$

Alternatively, for a linear array of spherical beads of diameter b which are rigidly joined we have the Kirkwood–Auer equation[43]:

$$b\,[\eta] = \frac{24\,J^2\,\bar{v}}{9000 \ln J} \tag{41}$$

For a homologous series of rigid asymmetric molecules of constant minor axis, J is directly proportional to M. If the axial ratio is high we may write from equation (40) or equation (41):

$$[\eta] \cong K\,M^2 \tag{42}$$

Thus the intrinsic viscosity should vary roughly as the square of the molecular weight in the limit of complete rigidity. Nishihara and Doty[44] have examined the molecular weight dependence of the intrinsic viscosity of a homologous series of soluble collagen sonicates and found the relationship:

$$[\eta] = K\,M^{1.80} \tag{43}$$

As the available evidence indicates that this system indeed behaves as rigid rod-like particles, it is probably justified to place the upper limit of the exponent of M in the $[\eta]$ *versus* M relationship in the range 1.8–2.0 for rigid rods.

By combining equations (37) and (39) and introducing the definition of f_0

$$f_0 = 6\pi\eta_0(3M\bar{v}/4\pi N_0)^{1/3}$$

we obtain approximately for a homologous series of prolate ellipsoids of constant minor axis and axial ratio greater than about 10:

$$S_0 = K \ln 2J$$
or
$$S_0 = K \ln K'M \tag{44}$$

where K, K' are constants. This corresponds to a much more gradual variation of S_0 with M than in the random coil case. The measurements of Doty and Nishihara show for rod-like collagen sonicates:

$$S_0 \cong K M^{0.20} \tag{45}$$

No exact theoretical treatment is as yet available for the case of systems intermediate to the rod and coil extremes. At present the exponential variation of S_0 and $[\eta]$ with M is probably best regarded as a semi-empirical index of the degree of extension. The limits for randomly coiled molecules may be set roughly as

$$S_0 = K M^{0.33-0.50} \tag{46}$$

$$[\eta] = K M^{0.50-1.0} \tag{47}$$

An alternative approach to the problem of characterizing the molecular domain of particles of indeterminant shape is provided by the treatment of Scheraga and Mandelkern[45]. These workers have introduced the concept of the hydrodynamically equivalent ellipsoid. By this is meant a hypothetical impermeable, unsolvated, and rigid ellipsoid of revolution whose hydrodynamic properties would be equivalent to those of the actual system.

By combining the classical expressions for the frictional coefficient and the intrinsic viscosity of ellipsoids of revolution in terms of their axial ratios, Scheraga and Mandelkern were able to define a new parameter β as:

$$\beta \equiv N_0 S_0 [\eta]^{1/3} \eta_0 / M^{2/3}(1 - \bar{v}\varrho) \tag{48}$$

The convenience of β lies in its invariance with respect to molecular weight and solvation. Thus β may be tabulated as a function of axial ratio alone. For prolate ellipsoids of revolution, β ranges from $2.12 \cdot 10^6$ ($J=1$) to $3.2 \cdot 10^6$ ($J=100$).

This method is more useful for the relatively compact globular proteins than for coiled macromolecules of large molecular domain. In the latter case the equivalent ellipsoid will usually bear no particular relationship to the actual shape of the molecule. Even in this case, however, β retains some value as a concise quasi-empirical index of hydrodynamic properties.

In addition to providing information on the size and shape factor of polynucleotides, ultracentrifugal measurements may also be used to obtain their mean density and density distribution. Meselson, Stahl, and Vinograd[46] have recently described an interesting variant of the sedimentation-equilibrium method in which a density gradient is set up within the cell by the use of $8M$ cesium chloride as a solvent. At sufficiently high speeds of rotation, the redistribution of the concentration of CsCl under the influence of the centrifugal field results in the attainment of a range of densities which spans the usual density of polynucleotides.

When a polynucleotide is present as a solute, centrifugation under these conditions results in both sedimentation and flotation. At equilibrium the polynucleotide will be collected in a band at the zone of the cell where its density and the density of the medium are equal. Measurements are usually made at extreme dilutions of polynucleotide and the process is normally followed by ultraviolet absorption.

The breadth of the band is dependent upon several factors, including the molecular weight of the polynucleotide species and its heterogeneity with regard to density. If the distribution of densities is continuous and single-peaked, heterogeneity of density will be reflected by a broadening of the polynucleotide band. If the density distribution is bimodal, the distribution of concentrations at equilibrium will also be bimodal, and, in extreme cases, an actual resolution into two bands can occur.

This technique has the often crucial advantage of permitting the use of very small quantities of material. One example of its application is the resolution of mixtures of normal and 5-bromouracil-containing phage DNA. In this case the difference in densities is such that two distinct bands appear. In general density differences of less than 0.001 g/cm³ may be detected.

If the polymer is homogeneous in density, the sharpening of the band is opposed only by its thermal motion. Under these circumstances it has been shown that the molecular weight is related to the breadth of the band by

$$M = RT/\bar{v}\left(\frac{d\varrho}{dr}\right)_{r_b} \omega^2 r_b \sigma^2$$

where

$$\left(\frac{d\varrho}{dr}\right)_{r_b}$$

is the density gradient at the radial distance, r_b, of the center of the band and σ^2 is the variance of the concentration distribution[46]. In the absence of any density heterogeneity the distribution of concentration is Gaussian.

The usual presence of density heterogeneity in the case of natural DNA and RNA renders this technique of limited value as a means of determining molecular weight. Under these circumstances the values obtained will be essentially lower limits.

LIGHT SCATTERING

The scattering of light by small independent particles has been fairly well understood for many years. Because of the polarizability of its electrons, such a particle will behave as an oscillating dipole when exposed to a periodically varying electric and magnetic field, such as occurs in a beam of light. From the basic theory of electromagnetism such an oscillating dipole must emit, or scatter, radiation in all directions.

If the scattering particles are completely independent the intensity of their scattered light will be additive and hence directly proportional to the number of particles in unit volume. At the other extreme a completely ordered system, such as a perfect crystal at absolute zero, will scatter no light, as a result of complete destructive interference of light dispersed from the different scattering centers. Ordinary solutions will usually represent an intermediate case.

From the theory of fluctuations we may write for the scattering, in excess of that of the solvent, for a solution of isotropic particles which have no dimension comparable in magnitude to the wavelength of the incident light[47-50]:

$$R_\theta = \frac{2\pi^2 n_0^2 (dn/dc)^2 RTM}{N_0 \lambda^4 (\delta\mu/\delta c)_{T,P}} = \frac{KRTM}{(\delta\mu/\delta c)_{T,P}} \tag{49}$$

Here R_θ, the reduced intensity, equals

$$\frac{i_\theta r^2}{I_0(1+\cos^2\theta)}$$

where i_θ is the excess intensity of scattered light detected at a distance r from the scattering volume; θ is the angle of the scattered to the incident ray; I_0 is the intensity of the incident ray; N_0 is Avogadro's number; λ is the wavelength *in vacuo*; n_0 and dn/dc are the refractive index of the solvent and the slope corresponding to the (linear) variation of the refractive index of the solution with solute concentration (c), respectively; R is the gas constant; T is the absolute temperature; M the molecular weight of solute; and μ is the chemical potential of the solute.

For the above case of small isotropic particles, R_θ is independent of θ and it is sufficient to confine measurements of scattered light to only one angle, usually $90°$. Our primary interest is usually to obtain M. Intuitively it would appear that this can be done by making some kind of extrapolation to concentrations sufficiently low so that the solute particles are effectively independent kinetic units. The chemical potential of solute is given by:

$$\mu = \mu^0 + RT \ln \gamma m \tag{50}$$

where γ is the activity coefficient of solute, m is its molality, and μ^0 is its standard chemical potential. Thus introducing (50) into (49) we have:

$$K \frac{C}{R_{90^\circ}} = \frac{1}{M} + \frac{1}{M} \left(\frac{\delta \ln \gamma}{\delta \ln c} \right)_{T,P} \tag{51}$$

It is easy to show that the second term on the right hand side of (51) may be expressed in terms of a virial-like expansion so that

$$K \frac{c}{R_{90^\circ}} = \frac{1}{M} + A_2 c + A_3 c^2 + \dots \tag{52}$$

It may be shown from the dependence of osmotic pressure upon the chemical potential of the solute that A_2 is equal to twice the corresponding second virial coefficient for the reduced osmotic pressure expansion.

Thus,

$$\frac{\pi}{cRT} = \frac{1}{M} + Bc + Cc^2 + \dots \tag{53}$$

where π = osmotic pressure

$$A_2 = 2B$$

In normal practice $K \cdot c/R_{90}^\circ$ is determined as a function of concentration for solutions so dilute that only the first two terms are important. Hence equation (52) furnishes a guide for the extrapolation of $K \cdot c/R_{90}^\circ$ to zero concentration. The reciprocal of the intercept yields the molecular weight of a monodisperse solute directly.

It may be noted that K contains the factor dn/dc, or the refractive index increment. For the usual range of solute concentrations ($< 2\%$) $(n - n_o)$ is invariably linear in c so that dn/dc may be regarded as a constant.

Equation (53) is valid only when the longest dimension of the scattering particle is less than about one-tenth the wavelength of the incident light, as it was derived subject to the assumption that all the light scattered from each particle was in phase. For larger molecules the possibility of destructive interference of light scattered from different parts of the same molecule arises. Thus R_θ will no longer be independent of θ. The nature of its variation with θ will depend upon the shape, dimensions, and polydispersity of the solute system.

An analysis of this internal interference problem requires several simplifying assumptions. These include a parallel and monochromatic incident beam, the absence of secondary scattering, randomly oriented and isotropic solute particles, and a solution sufficiently dilute so that the solute molecules may be regarded as independent scattering units.

It is convenient to define a particle scattering factor P_θ as follows[51]:

$$R_\theta = KcMP_\theta \text{ (at infinite dilution)} \tag{54}$$

The quantity P_θ contains the angular dependence of R_θ. The derivation of P_θ for a given system involves the summation of all the waves from the scattering points in the molecule with due account to their phase. It has been shown that this kind of analysis leads to the following, quite general, expression[52] for P_θ:

$$P_\theta = \frac{1}{N^2} \sum_n^N \sum_m^N \frac{\sin h\, r_{nm}}{h\, r_{nm}} \tag{55}$$

Here r_{nm} is the scalar separation of the two scattering centers n and m; h is equal to

$$\frac{4\pi}{\lambda'} \sin \frac{\theta}{2}$$

N is the total number of scattering centers; and λ' is the wavelength in the medium. The summation is carried out over all pairs of scattering centers.

The above expression may be placed in more tractable form by introducing $F(r)$, which is equal to the number of pairs of scattering elements separated by distance r, and by replacing summation by integration. Thus[53]:

$$P_\theta = \frac{1}{N^2} \int_0^{r\,\text{max}} F(r) \frac{\sin hr}{hr}\, dr \tag{56}$$

At this point the problem of the dependence of $F(r)$ and hence of $P\theta$ upon particle shape arises. We will first mention the well-known results for three simple shapes.

(a) thin, uniform rigid rods. In this case the number of scattering subelement pairs separated by a distance r is independent of linear position within the rod. $F(r)dr$ is equal to $2\sigma^2(L-r)\,dr$ where $\sigma = N/L$. Introducing this into equation (56) and integrating we obtain finally[53, 54]

$$P_\theta = \frac{1}{X} \int_0^{2X} \frac{\sin w}{w}\, dw - \left(\frac{\sin X}{X}\right)^2 \tag{57}$$

where

$$X = 2\pi \frac{L}{\lambda'} \sin \frac{\theta}{2} = \frac{hL}{2}$$

(b) spherical particles. For this case P_θ has the form [53]:

$$P_\theta = 9 \left(\frac{\sin X' - X' \cos x}{x^3}\right)^2 \tag{58}$$

where

$$X' = hR$$

$$R = \text{radius}$$

(c) random coils. When the distribution of separations of two subelements situated in different parts of the chain is Gaussian, P_θ has been shown to have the form[53, 54]:

$$P_\theta = \frac{2}{Y^2}(Y - 1 + e^{-Y}) \tag{59}$$

where $$Y = h^2 \bar{r}^2/6$$

$$\bar{r}^2 = \text{mean square end-to-end separation}$$

In the present connection our interest is, of course, centered upon cases (a) and (c). In both cases P_θ^{-1} can be expressed as either of two power series expansions[55]. The first of these holds for small values of X:

$$P_\theta^{-1}, \text{rods} = 1 + \frac{X^2}{9} + \dots \quad (X \text{ small})$$

$$\tag{60}$$

$$P_\theta^{-1}, \text{coils} = 1 + \frac{Y}{3} + \dots \quad (Y \text{ small})$$

Alternatively P_θ^{-1} may be expanded in a form valid for its asymtotic range[55].

$$P_\theta^{-1}, \text{coils} = \frac{Y}{2} + \frac{1}{2} + \dots \quad (Y \text{ large})$$

$$\tag{61}$$

$$P_\theta^{-1}, \text{rods} = \frac{2X}{\pi} + \frac{2}{\pi^2} + \dots \quad (X \text{ large})$$

Equations (60) and (61) may be placed in a more general form which is valid for any particle shape by introducing a new parameter, the radius of gyration, R_G, which is defined as the weighted mean distance of subelements from the center of mass. Thus:

$$R_G^2 = \frac{1}{N}\Sigma_i \, n_i \, r_i^2 \tag{62}$$

where n_i is the number of subelements at a distance r_i from the center of mass. For rods $R_G^2 = L^2/12$ and for coils $R_G^2 = \bar{r}^2/6$. Upon introducing these into equation (60), they both assume the form:

$$P_\theta^{-1} = 1 + \frac{h^2 R_G^2}{3} - \dots \tag{63}$$

Thus the initial term in the expansion and hence the limiting slope of P_θ^{-1} as a function of $\sin^2 \theta/2$ depends upon the radius of gyration only. In general the radius of gyration is the only shape parameter which can be obtained unambiguously from light scattering. The variation of P_θ with $h^2 R_G^2$ is shown in Fig. 35.

The technique of extrapolating light scattering data to obtain unambiguous values of molecular weight and radius of gyration should now be obvious. Since P_θ^{-1} may be expressed as a power series expansion in $\sin^2(\theta/2)$ while c/R_θ may be expanded in terms of concentration, we may write from equations (52) and (54), to a good approximation:

$$\frac{Kc}{R_\theta} = \frac{P_\theta^{-1}}{M} + A_2c \qquad (64)$$

The limiting value of $K \cdot c/R_\theta$ at zero angle and zero concentration gives the reciprocal of the molecular weight. From the limiting slope, multiplied by M, of $K \cdot c/R_\theta$ as a function of $\sin^2(\theta/2)$ at zero concentration, the radius of gyration is obtained. Thus

$$M \cdot (\text{limiting slope}) = \frac{16}{3}\pi^2 \frac{R_G^2}{\lambda'^2}$$

It has become customary to extrapolate data to zero angle and zero concentration simultaneously by plotting $K \cdot c/R_\theta$ as a function of $\sin^2(\theta/2) + kc$, where k is a convenient constant. The resultant two dimensional grids are generally known as Zimm plots, after their originator.

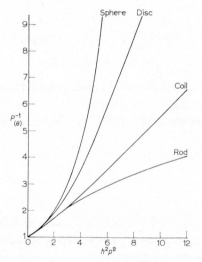

Fig. 35. The variation of the reciprocal scattering factor with $h^2R_G^2$ for particles of various shapes[53]. ϱ is equivalent to our R_G.

If the geometric shape of the particle is independently known, R_G may be converted into a more meaningful dimension, such as length or root mean square end-to-end separation. If measurements are carried out over a wide range of angles, P_θ may be obtained as a function of $\sin^2 \theta/2$.

The discussion has so far been confined to monodisperse systems. In the case of polydisperse systems, average values of the parameters M and R_G will be obtained.

It may be shown that, irrespective of the particle shape or the form of the distribution of molecular weights, the average molecular weight obtained by extrapolation to $\theta = 0$ always corresponds to the weight-average defined as follows:

$$M_w = \Sigma_i \, n_i \, M_i^2 / \Sigma_i \, n_i \, M_i = \Sigma_i \, c_i \, M_i / \Sigma_i \, c_i \tag{65}$$

where $n_i =$ the number of molecules of molecular weight M_i. In the case of the radius of gyration a different kind of average is obtained. Thus it may be shown[53]:

$$R_G^2 = \Sigma_i \, c_i \, M_i \, R_{G,i}^2 / M_w \, \Sigma_i \, c_i \tag{66}$$

This clearly weights the contribution of the larger particles more heavily than does the weight average molecular weight. For a clearer picture of the dependence upon molecular weight distribution the relationship between $R_{G,i}$ and M_i may be introduced explicitly.

For rods $R_{G,i} = k \, M_i$

and $R_G^2 = k^2 \, \Sigma_i \, c_i \, M_i^3 / \Sigma_i \, c_i M_i$

For coils $R_{G,i}^2 = k' \, M_i$ $\qquad\qquad\qquad$ (67)

and $R_G^2 = k' \, \Sigma_i \, c_i \, M_i^2 / \Sigma_i \, c_i \, M_i$

Let us turn now to the question of the complete form of P_θ including the higher terms in $\sin^2 \theta/2$. In general it may be stated that the form of P_θ will depend both upon the particle shape and the polydispersity. It is usually very difficult to resolve the two.

In the case of polymer systems which fall unequivocally into the random coil class the form of P_θ has been correlated directly with the molecular weight distribution by introducing an explicit expression for the latter. Zimm[56] has made use of a single-peaked distribution function of the form

$$\frac{c_i}{\Sigma_i c_i} = \left(\frac{z+1}{M_w} \right)^{z+1} \frac{M_i^z}{Z!} e^{-(z+1) \, M_i / M_w} \tag{68}$$

The breadth of the distribution is characterized by the parameter z. Zimm has made computations of P_θ as a function of $h^2 R_G^2$ for varying values of z. In general the shape of the curves of P_θ versus $h^2 R_G^2$ is insufficiently sensitive to variations in z to permit use of light scattering as a practical means of measuring polydispersity.

However, two cases are of particular interest. The case of $z = \infty$ corresponds to a monodisperse system for which P_θ has its usual form. The other case of interest is that of $z = 1$. It has been shown that this corresponds to the so-called *random distribution* for which

$$M_z : M_w : M_n = 3 : 2 : 1 \left(M_z = \frac{\Sigma \, c_i \, M_i^2}{\Sigma \, c_i \, M_i} \right)$$

In this case P_θ has the particularly simple form[56]:

$$P_\theta = 1 - Y_w/(2 + Y_w); \quad P_\theta^{-1} = 1 + Y_w/2 \tag{69}$$

Here Y_w is the *weight average* value of Y. P_θ^{-1} and hence the limiting values of $K \cdot c/R_\theta$ are linear in Y_w and thus in $\sin^2(\theta/2)$. This case is of especial importance because most unfractionated polymer samples appear, in practice, to have a molecular weight distribution not greatly different from this one. The occurrence of this type of distribution is always convenient, as the linear variation of P_θ^{-1} with $\sin^2(\theta/2)$ permits an unambiguous extrapolation of $K \cdot c/R_\theta$ to zero angle.

In many cases the polymer studied does not fall exactly into either the random coil or the rigid rod category. This will be so for *stiff* coils whose extension is sufficiently great to make the Gaussian distribution of subelement separations a poor approximation, but which are too coiled to be regarded as rigid rods. From the work of Treloar[59] upon aliphatic chains the boundary between true random coils and stiff coils may be roughly set at extensions such that the (root mean square) end-to-end separation is one third the contour length. For extensions less than this the Gaussian distribution provides an accurate description of the physical properties of the system and its light scattering behavior may be interpreted on the random coil model.

For extensions greater than this limit the Gaussian distribution becomes a progressively poorer approximation. In order to account for the dependence of the form of P_θ upon shape it is necessary to introduce a new parameter characterizing the coil stiffness. Perhaps the most convenient choice is the *persistence length* introduced by Porod[57,58].

If the chain is visualized as made of a large number of linear links, each of length l, which are joined end to end, and whose mutual orientations are incompletely independent, the persistence length may be defined as the summation of the projections of all the links on the direction of the first link. If the number of links is very large:

$$a \equiv \text{persistence length} = l/(1 - \cos a)$$

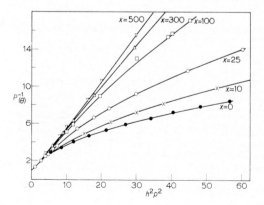

Fig. 36. Reciprocal scattering factors for coils of varying degrees of stiffness (taken from ref.[53]). ϱ is the radius of gyration and is equivalent to our R_g. X is a parameter characterizing the stiffness and is equal to the ratio of the contour length to the persistence length.

where cos α is the average value of the cosine of the angle between links. This parameter suffices to describe a continuous gradation of stiffness. For Gaussian coils, cos $\alpha = 0$ and $a = l$. For rigid rods cos $\alpha = 1$ and $a = L$. Values of P_θ have been computed for monodisperse stiff coils as a function of cos α (Fig. 36). In the case of polydisperse stiff coils the value of R_G^2 obtained corresponds to a relatively complicated average. Thus Geiduschek and Holtzer[53] have shown that, if the persistence length can be regarded as independent of molecular weight:

$$R_G^2 = \frac{a}{3} \text{ const. } M_z - a^2 + \frac{2a^3}{\text{const. } M_w} + \ldots \ldots \tag{70}$$

When both polydispersity and stiffness are present as complicating factors, the problem of accounting for the form of P_θ in detail may be regarded as practically hopeless.

Returning to the case of true random coils, the reader may recall that P_θ^{-1} may be expanded in a form valid for the asymtote (equation 59) at large values of Y. If the polydispersity is such that $z \neq 1$, P_θ^{-1} as a function of $h^2 R_G^2$ will exhibit curvature either upward ($z > 1$) or downward ($z < 1$). The range of angles corresponding to asymptotic behavior depends of course upon the magnitude of R_G. If the radius of gyration is in the range 600 Å–1000 Å both the limiting and the asymptotic regions of P_θ^{-1} will correspond to experimentally accessible angular regions. It is important to note that if R_G is sufficiently large, *only* the asymptotic region will normally be observed.

In view of the above it is obviously important to know the meaning of the apparent intercept obtained by extrapolation of the asymptotic portion of the curve of $K \cdot c/R_\theta$ versus $\sin^2 (\theta/2)$ to zero angle. For polydisperse systems[55] of random coils it may be shown that:

$$\left(K\frac{c}{R_\theta} \right)_{c=0} = \frac{1}{2 M_n} + \frac{h^2 (R_G^2)_n}{2 M_n} + \ldots \quad h^2 R_G^2 \gg 1 \tag{71}$$

Thus the apparent intercept obtained by extrapolation of the asymtotic curve leads to a molecular weight equal to twice the number-average value. Similarly the angular slope yields a *number average* radius of gyration. If, as is often the case, the data extrapolated correspond neither to the true limiting region nor to the asymptotic region, the molecular weight computed will not represent a well-defined average.

In conclusion it is well to point out that the relations cited in this section are explicitly for the case of isotropic particles. If the molecules are sufficiently anisotropic important corrections become, in principle, necessary[60]. However, as a concrete example of this effect has yet to be observed, at least among biological macromolecules, no attempt will be made to discuss this factor here.

OPTICAL ROTATION

In the last few years it has come to be generally recognized that the helical content of polypeptides and polynucleotides makes an important contribution to their optical rotatory properties, with regard to both the sign and magnitude of the specific rotation and the nature of its wavelength dispersion.

Neither the theory nor the application of this technique can be said to be in as advanced a state for the polynucleotide case as for that of polypeptides. Indeed its extensive application to polynucleotides is a quite recent development.

We will confine ourselves here to the purely empirical grounding for the use of this measurement to obtain a measure of the helical content of polynucleotides[61]. The optical activity of the mononucleotides is entirely a consequence of their pentose content, as none of the bases has a center of asymmetry. The specific rotations ($[a]_D$) of the nucleoside monophosphates are clustered about $0°$ and are less than about $10°$ in magnitude. Furthermore, their specific rotations are almost independent of temperature.

The specific rotation of the one polynucleotide, poly U, which is believed to have zero helical content, is quite small ($-8°$) and close to that of the monomer[61]. Furthermore, its specific rotation is invariant to the temperature and to the presence of various denaturing agents.

A very different picture is presented by the polynucleotides which are known to possess a high helical content. The native DNA and the equimolar poly A plus poly U complex, both of which exist as nearly perfect right-handed helical duplexes, have values of $[a]_D$ at $22°$ C of $126°$ and $300°$, respectively. Moreover, the magnitude of the positive rotation is very sensitive to agents, such as high temperatures or high concentrations of urea, which would be expected to disrupt the hydrogen bonding which stabilizes the helical structure. Thus at $90°$ C the value of $[a]_D$ for the A + U system falls to a value close to zero. As will be discussed in the next chapter, the loss of dextrorotation closely parallels the fall in helical content, as judged by other criteria.

The similarity of these observations to those reported earlier for the a-helical polypeptide case reinforces the conclusion that the magnitude of positive rotation for polynucleotides is closely correlated with their helical content.

As yet it is not possible to make the correlation quantitative. It would appear from the results so far that the maximum contribution to $[a]_D$ of the helical structure in the case of polyribonucleotides is about $300°$. In the case of DNA the figure is much lower, about $100°$. This may reflect the difference in the pentose constituents.

DIRECT β-RAY COUNTING

Levinthal and Thomas have recently introduced an elegant new method of measuring the size of ^{32}P-labeled DNA by direct β-ray counting[62]. The method depends upon incorporating the radioactive DNA, in molecularly dispersed form, in an electron-sensitive photographic emulsion; developing; and counting with a micro-scope the tracks or rays produced by each particle. The individual particles appear as stars, from which the rays emanate.

Application of this technique has largely been confined to the DNA from bacteriophage, in particular that from T-coliphage. Labeling of the phage DNA is achieved by allowing the coliphage to infect and replicate in bacteria which have been grown in media containing ^{32}P-labeled phosphate. After lysis of the bacteria and recovery of the phage, their radioactive DNA may be liberated by osmotic shock. A solution of the labeled DNA is then mixed with melted emulsion (such as Ilford G – 5) and the mixture spread on slides and allowed to harden. The β-ray tracks begin to register as soon as the emulsion is sufficiently dry.

After storage for a suitable interval the slides are developed and observed microscopically. The information desired is the number of stars per unit volume of the original solution and the distribution of tracks among the star-forming particles. The former quantity is computable by including in the original solution a known concentration of polystyrene latex spheres, which serve as indicator parti-cles. The ratio of stars to indicator particles yields the concentration of stars directly.

The application of the method depends upon the entirely reasonable assumption of uniform labeling of the DNA. If this is the case, the average number of rays in the stars produced by a particular class of particles should be proportional to the number of ^{32}P atoms each particle contains. This, in turn, is proportional to the total number of phosphorus atoms per particle and hence to the size of the particle, provided that the particles are of uniform composition.

If the system of particles is monodisperse the distribution of rays per star will be of the Poisson form, given by[62]:

$$P(\bar{r},r) = e^{-\bar{r}} \bar{r}^{r}/r!$$

   = fraction of stars having r rays when there is an average of r rays per star.

If the distribution of star sizes can be fitted with a function of this kind, it is highly probable that the particles are uniform in size and degree of labeling[62].

In practice, the average number of rays per particle is converted to the mean number of ^{32}P atoms per particle by dividing by the known fraction of ^{32}P atoms which have decayed during the exposure. The number of ^{32}P atoms is corrected to zero time, which is normally taken as the time of phage growth.

By a comparison of the mean star sizes produced by intact and by disintegrated phage, the ratio of the average size of their effective DNA molecular units to the total DNA content of the organism may be measured.

This technique can yield only relative molecular sizes and cannot, of course, differentiate between true DNA molecular units and aggregates of these held together by protein or other ligaments. In general it will be the method of choice only when special factors, such as a paucity of material, render the use of the more conventional techniques inconvenient.

REFERENCES

[1] G. OSTER, in G. OSTER AND A. POLLISTER, *Physical Techniques in Biological Research*, Vol. 1, New York, 1955, p. 439.

[2] T. GIBB, *Optical Methods of Chemical Analysis*, New York, 1942.

[3] J. ROBERTSON, *Introduction to Physical Optics*, New York, 1941.

[4] O. WIENER, *Abh. sachs. Ges. Wiss.*, 33 (1912) 507.

[5] O. WIENER, *Kolloidchem. Beih.*, 23 (1926) 189.

[6] W. BRAGG, *Proc. Roy. Soc. (London) A*, 106 (1924) 346.

[7] R. CERF AND H. SCHERAGA, *Chem. Rev.*, 51 (1952) 185.

[8] A. PETERLIN, *Z. Physik.*, 111 (1938) 232.

[9] A. PETERLIN AND H. STUART, *Z. Physik.*, 112 (1939) 1, 129.

[10] H. SCHERAGA, *Arch. Biochem. Biophys.*, 33 (1951) 277.

[11] H. SCHERAGA, J. EDSALL AND J. GADD, *J. Chem. Phys.*, 19 (1951) 1101.

[12] F. PERRIN, *J. phys. radium*, 5 (1934) 497.

[13] J. LOOFBOUROUGH, *Revs. Mod. Phys.*, 12 (1940) 320.

[14] G. BEAVEN, E. HOLIDAY AND E. JOHNSON, in E. CHARGAFF AND J. DAVIDSON, *The Nucleic Acids*, Vol. 1, New York, 1955, p. 493.

[15] L. CAVALIERI, *J. Am. Chem. Soc.*, 74 (1952) 1242.

[16] R. THOMAS, *Bull. soc. chim. biol.*, 35 (1953) 609.

[17] P. LAWLEY, *Ph.D. Thesis*, Nottingham University, 1953.

[18] J. SHACK, R. JENKINS AND J. THOMPSETT, *J. Biol. Chem.*, 198 (1952) 85.

[19] J. SHACK, R. JENKINS AND J. THOMPSETT, *J. Biol. Chem.*, 203 (1953) 373.

[20] M. KUNITZ, *J. Biol. Chem.*, 164 (1946) 563.

[21] M. KUNITZ, *J. Gen. Physiol.*, 33 (1950) 349.

[22] K. TSUBOI, *Biochim. et Biophys. Acta*, 6 (1950) 202.

[23] B. MAGASANIK AND E. CHARGAFF, *Biochim. et Biophys. Acta*, 7 (1951) 396.

[24] R. THOMAS, *Biochim. et Biophys. Acta*, 14 (1954) 231.

[25] A. MICHELSON, *J. Chem. Soc.*, (1959) 1371.

[26] G. FELSENFELD, D. DAVIES AND A. RICH, *J. Am. Chem. Soc.*, 79 (1957) 2023.

[27] A. RICH, *Nature*, 181 (1958) 521.

[28] D. DAVIES AND A. RICH, *J. Am. Chem. Soc.*, 80 (1958) 1003.

[29] G. FELSENFELD, *Biochim. et Biophys. Acta*, 29 (1958) 133.

[30] K. SHOOTER AND J. BUTLER, *Trans. Faraday Soc.*, 52 (1956) 734.

[31] V. SCHUMAKER AND H. SCHACHMAN, *Biochim. et Biophys. Acta*, 23 (1957) 628.

[32] H. SCHACHMAN, *Ultracentrifugation in Biology*, New York, 1959.

[33] W. ARCHIBALD, *J. Phys. and Colloid Chem.*, 51 (1947) 1204.

[34] P. FLORY, *Principles of Polymer Chemistry*, Ithaca, 1953.

[35] E. GUTH AND H. MARK, *Mh. Chem.*, 65 (1934) 93.

[36] W. KUHN, *Kolloidzschr.*, 68 (1934) 2.

[37] A. ALEXANDER AND P. JOHNSON, *Colloid Science*, Oxford, 1949.

[38] P. FLORY, *J. Chem. Phys.*, 17 (1949) 303.

[39] P. FLORY AND T. FOX, *J. Am. Chem. Soc.*, 73 (1951) 1904.

[40] T. SVEDBERG AND K. PEDERSEN, *The Ultracentrifuge*, Oxford, 1940.

[41] F. PERRIN, *J. Phys. Rad.*, [7] 7 (1936) 1.

[42] R. SIMHA, *J. Phys. Chem.*, 44 (1940) 25.

[43] J. KIRKWOOD AND P. AUER, *J. Chem. Phys.*, 19 (1951) 281.

[44] T. NISHIHARA AND P. DOTY, *Proc. Natl. Acad. Sci.*, 44 (1958) 411.

[45] H. SCHERAGA AND L. MANDELKERN, *J. Am. Chem. Soc.*, 75 (1953) 179.

[46] M. MESELSON, F. STAHL AND J. VINOGRAD, *Proc. Natl. Acad. Sci.*, 43 (1957) 581.

[47] P. DEBYE, *J. Phys. Chem.*, 51 (1947) 18.

[48] A. EINSTEIN, *Ann. Physik*, 33 (1910) 1275.

[49] M. FIXMAN, *J. Chem. Phys.*, 23 (1955) 2074.

[50] P. DOTY AND J. EDSALL, *Advances in Protein Chem.*, 6 (1951) 35.

[51] P. DOTY AND R. STEINER, *J. Chem. Phys.*, 18 (1950) 1211.

[52] P. DEBYE, *Ann. Physik*, 46 (1915) 809.

[53] E. GEIDUSCHEK AND A. HOLTZER, *Advances in Biological and Medical Physics*, 6 (1958) 431.

[54] B. ZIMM, R. STEIN AND P. DOTY, *Polymer Bull.*, 1 (1945) 90.
[55] H. BENOIT, *J. Polymer Sci.*, 11 (1953) 507.
[56] B. ZIMM, *J. Chem. Phys.*, 16 (1948) 1093, 1099.
[57] O. KRATKY AND G. POROD, *J. Colloid Sci.*, 4 (1949) 35.
[58] G. POROD, *J. Polymer Sci.*, 10 (1953) 157.
[59] L. TRELOAR, *Proc. Phys. Soc., (London)*, 55 (1943) 345.
[60] P. HORN, H. BENOIT AND G. OSTER, *J. Chim. Phys.*, 48 (1951) 530.
[61] J. FRESCO, *Trans. N.Y. Acad. Sci.*, 21 (1959) 653.
[62] C. LEVINTHAL AND C. THOMAS, *Biochim. et Biophys. Acta*, 23 (1957) 453.
[63] *Pabst Laboratory Circular*, OR–10, 1956.

Chapter 7

Physical Properties of Polynucleotides in Solution

In the following discussion we shall reserve the term *ordered system* for the case where a definite periodicity of secondary structure occurs, persisting over an appreciable fraction of the polynucleotide chain. In all such cases for which a detailed structural analysis has been made the most probable structure has been found to be helical in nature.

The dramatic success of the doubly stranded helical model, proposed by Watson and Crick[1] and subsequently refined by Wilkins *et al.*[2], in accounting for the observed physical properties of DNA has stimulated many investigators to search for similar structures in RNA and in the synthetic polynucleotides. The Watson–Crick structure will be discussed in detail in the next chapter. To anticipate its main features, the model consists of two anti-parallel chains wrapped in a double helix about a common axis. The bases are in the core of the helix and the sugar-phosphate backbones on the periphery. The helix is stabilized by hydrogen bonding between adenine and thymine and between guanine and cytosine. By pairing purines with pyrimidines, steric difficulties arising from the unequal sizes of the bases are avoided, as is the need for any chemical periodicity of nucleotide sequences along the individual strands, so long as complementarity exists between the two strands.

The structure is fairly open and a deep helical groove parallels the helically wound nucleotide layers (Fig. 37).

Further stimulus to the search for similar helical forms in other polynucleotide systems was furnished by the study of Donohue upon the sterically feasible hydrogen bonded base pairs[3]. It was found by Donohue that the Watson–Crick pairs by no means exhausted the list of possibilities.

Confining himself to steric factors concerning the bases only, Donohue approximated the purine and pyrimidine bases by regular pentagons and hexagons with sides equal to 1.36 Å and external $C-N$ and $C-O$ distances of 1.36 Å and 1.21 Å, respectively. The external nitrogens and oxygens were regarded as being in the amino and keto configurations, respectively. The cited dimensions are tolerably consistent with the available X-ray diffraction data of the bases.

The hydrogen bond distances $N-H...O$ and $N-H...N$ were taken as

2.85 Å and 3.00 Å, respectively. A maximum deviation from linearity of the N−H . . . X bond of 15° was allowed.

Subject to the above assumptions, a total of twenty-four hydrogen-bonded base pairings, which are cited in Table 13, were found to be sterically feasible. In each case the pair is stabilized by two hydrogen bonds joining the indicated pairs of

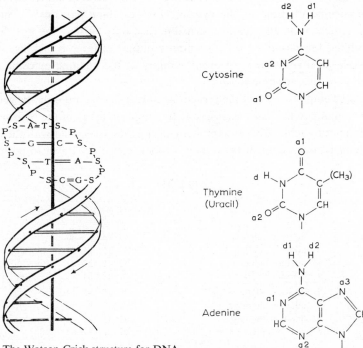

Fig. 37. The Watson-Crick structure for DNA.

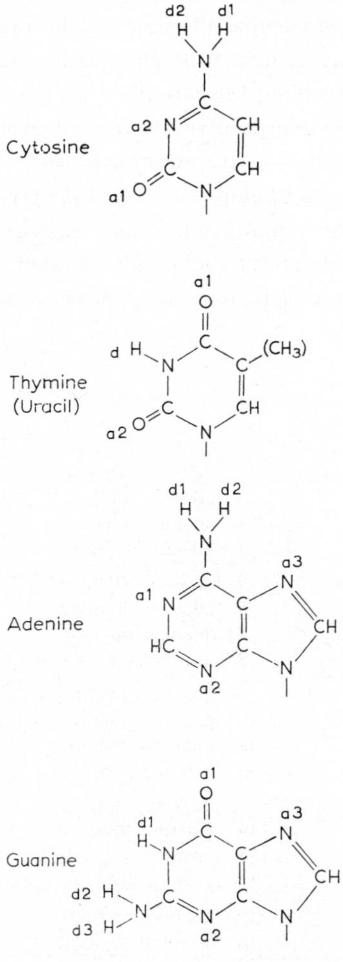

Fig. 38. Identification of groups[3] included in Table 13.

groups. The numbers designating the groups are identified in Fig. 38. Uracil may of course be substituted for thymine in any of the pairings of Table 13.

The hypoxanthine base of inosine is similar in structure to guanine, except for the presence of an external amino group at the C_2 position in the latter base. Thus for a number of pairings in which this group is not involved, hypoxanthine can replace guanine. This is the case for pairings 7, 9, 13, 14, and 15.

The original Watson–Crick pairings correspond to 5 and 15 in Table 13. While the adenine–thymine pair is still generally regarded as having the form of 5, there has been some modification proposed for the guanine–cytosine pairings[4, 5]. With only a slight distortion it is possible to combine pairings 15 and 16 in Table 13 to form the triply hydrogen bonded guanine–cytosine pair d1–a2; a1–d2; d2–a1. This possibility has been rendered somewhat attractive in view of recent evidence indicating that the guanine–cytosine linkage is considerably more stable than either the adenine–thymine or the cytosine–hypoxanthine pairings[6, 7]. Since the latter case differs from the guanine–cytosine case only in that the possibility of hydrogen bond formation via the C_2 amino group of guanine is lacking, it is not unreasonable to attribute the enhanced stability of the guanine–cytosine pair to the presence of this additional bond.

It should be emphasized that the preceding takes into account only the geometrical factors relating to the bases themselves. In actuality, many of the pairings listed may be difficult to achieve because of steric difficulties associated with the ribosed phosphate backbone. Most of them have, in fact, yet to be shown to occur.

TABLE 13

	base I	base II	hydrogen bonding (I-II)
1.	adenine	adenine	d2–a3; a3–d2
2.	adenine	adenine	d1–a1; a1–d1
3.	adenine	adenine	d2–a1; a3–d1
4.	adenine	thymine	d1–a2; a1–d
5.	adenine	thymine	d1–a1; a1–d
6.	adenine	cytosine	d1–a2; a1–d2
7.	adenine	guanine	d1–a1; a1–d1
8.	adenine	guanine	d1–a2; a1–d3
9.	guanine	guanine	d1–a1; a1–d1
10.	guanine	guanine	d1–a1; d2–a3
11.	guanine	guanine	d1–a3; d2–a1
12.	guanine	guanine	d3–a2; a2–d3
13.	guanine	thymine	d1–a1; a1–d
14.	guanine	thymine	d1–a2; a1–d
15.	guanine	cytosine	d1–a2; a1–d2
16.	guanine	cytosine	d1–a2; d2–a1
17.	guanine	cytosine	d1–a1; d2–a2
18.	thymine	thymine	d–a1; a1–d
19.	thymine	thymine	d–a2; a1–d
20.	thymine	thymine	d–a2; a2–d
21.	thymine	cytosine	d–a2; a2–d2
22.	thymine	cytosine	d–a2; a1–d2
23.	cytosine	cytosine	d2–a2; a2–d2
24.	cytosine	cytosine	d2–a1; a1–d2

In addition one cannot exclude the possibility that hydrogen bonding other than the interbase type may serve to stabilize some types of polynucleotide structure.

Among the possibilities are base-sugar bonds, base–phosphate bonds, and sugar-phosphate bonds.

There is as yet no quantitative information on the intrinsic free energy change upon formation of a single internucleotide hydrogen bond. In the case of bonding of the $-N-H\ldots O-$ type a reasonable guess as to the magnitude of the quantity in aqueous solution might be the –1.5 Kcal deduced by Schellman[8] from measurements upon the dimerization of urea. Schellman has concluded that the formation of such hydrogen bonds in water is energetically favored but only barely so. In the case of polypeptides the existence of *end effects* is sufficient to preclude the formation of the α-helix for degrees of polymerization less than about ten. In general it would be expected that the stability of helical structures in both the polypeptide and polynucleotide cases would be very sensitive to conditions, including temperature, electrostatic stress as controlled by charge and ionic strength, and solvent composition.

All of the proposed ordered polynucleotide structures which have gained wide acceptance have two features in common. They are helical but, unlike the polypeptide case, the stabilizing hydrogen bonding is *horizontal* rather than *vertical*; that is, a given base is bonded to another complementary base in another strand (or in another segment of the same strand) so that the helical regions are two or more strands thick. While not all of the Donohue pairings have been found to occur, all of the base pairings so far observed have been consistent with his scheme.

Hydrogen bonding is probably not the only source of the stability of the base pairs. It is quite probable that Van der Waals forces also make an appreciable contribution.

THE INCOMPLETELY ORGANIZED SYSTEMS: POLY A, POLY I, POLY U, AND POLY AU

Poly U appears to furnish us with what is at present the sole example of a polynucleotide for which there exists no evidence for any organized fine structure under normal conditions*. The following evidence leads almost inescapably to this conclusion, which holds for temperatures above $10°$ C:

(*a*) No X-ray diffraction evidence for an organized fine structure has been observed for fibres of poly U. The diffraction diagrams obtained so far have been of a completely amorphous character[9].

(*b*) Solutions of poly U display only a slight hypochromism ($< 10\%$), which furthermore is not temperature dependent[10, 11].

(*c*) Poly U displays no positive rotation. Its specific rotation is about –8° and is independent of temperature[10].

(*d*) The as yet cursory light scattering and birefringence measurements upon solutions of poly U are consistent with a molecular configuration which is highly

---

* Very recently, Lipsett (*Proc. Natl. Acad. Sci.*, 46 (1960) 445) has obtained evidence for the existence of an ordered state at very low temperatures ($< 8°$ C).

coiled, at least at ionic strengths of 0.1 or greater[12]. At an ionic strength of 0.1 there is no measurable birefringence of flow[11].

(e) The hydrogen ion titration curve of poly U appears to be of the normal polyelectrolyte type and displays none of the characteristics usually accompanying a helix-coil transition, such as hyper-sharpening[13]. Furthermore, the dissociation of a proton by the uracil group does not appear to be accompanied by any important change in molecular weight or configuration, at least at ionic strengths of 0.1 or greater[11].

The apparent failure of poly U to form any ordered structure is somewhat surprising in view of the fact that uracil-uracil hydrogen bonded base pairs are sterically feasible[3]. The probable absence of any structure is presumably a consequence of steric difficulties involving other aspects of the molecular organization.

The alkaline form of poly I, which prevails at pH's alkaline to the zone of titration of the hypoxanthine group ($>$pH 9), likewise appears to be essentially random in character. This follows from the highly coiled nature of the molecule at high ionic strengths, as well as from the flexibility indicated by its electrostatically induced extension at low ionic strengths[14]. Furthermore, only a slight hypochromism is observed[11], which is not temperature-dependent.

The random nature of the alkaline form of poly I is quite understandable, since the loss of a proton from the N_1 position leaves the hypoxanthine base without any potential hydrogen bond donor group. Moreover, the electrostatic stress involved in placing two negatively charged hypoxanthine groups in juxtaposition would probably be prohibitive.

Polyriboadenylic acid (poly A) was one of the first of the biosynthetic polynucleotides to be extensively studied and the first for which X-ray diffraction evidence for the occurrence of an ordered fine structure in the solid state was obtained. Fibers of poly A spun from aqueous solution give rise to a diffraction pattern indicative of an extensively organized structure, as will be discussed in the next chapter.

However, this high degree of organization does not appear to persist in solution at alkaline pH. Thus at pH's alkaline to the pK of the adenine group ($> \sim$pH 6) poly A has been found to possess many of the characteristics of a relatively unorganized system. The exact pH range corresponding to the limits of stability of the alkaline form of poly A is dependent upon ionic strength and temperature[15, 16].

Fig. 39 shows representative light scattering data, in the form of a Zimm grid, for a high molecular weight ($3 \cdot 10^6$) sample of poly A at neutral pH (6.5) and high ionic strength (0.5). The linear character of the limiting curve of c/R_θ as a function of $\sin^2 (\theta/2)$ is consistent with, and suggests, that the preparation consists of a polydisperse system of Gaussian coils, with a molecular weight distribution of the *random* type[14].

The computed radius of gyration, 690 Å, is far too small to be consistent with a rod-like configuration. The end-to-end separation computed therefrom on the coil model is 1700 Å. As the average degree of polymerization of this sample is about 9000 its length would be about 30,000 Å if it had the conformation of a completely extended helix. Thus the molecule is coiled to about 1/18th of its maximum extension. Even at an ionic strength as low as 0.01 it is still coiled to about 1/13th its contour length[14]. The degree of coiling displayed by the alkaline form of poly A is well within the rough limit of 1/3 the contour length which, from the work of Treloar[17], defines roughly the maximum extension at which deviations from Gaussian behavior begin to be significant. Thus, it can be stated that the light scattering data indicate that the gross over-all shape of the alkaline form of poly A is probably most closely represented by a random coil at ionic strengths of 0.01 or greater.

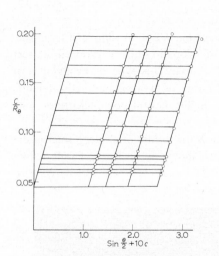 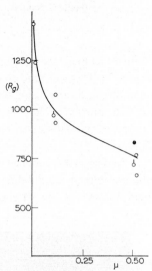

Fig. 39. A representative Zimm grid plot[14] for a sample of poly A of molecular weight 3 · 10⁶ in 0.5 M KCl at pH 6.5.

Fig. 40. Decrease in radius of gyration of a poly A preparation of molecular weight 3 · 10⁶ with increasing ionic strength[14]. O 0.01 M PO₄--- plus KCl, pH 6.5; ○̇ 0.01 M HCO₃- plus KCl, pH 8.5; • 0.01 M tris plus LiCl, pH 8.5.

The hydrodynamic properties of the alkaline form of poly A are likewise suggestive of a coiled configuration. Fresco and Doty[18] were able to prepare a homologous series of poly A samples whose molecular weight varied over a wide range. The relationship between molecular weight, as computed from the Flory-Mandelkern equation[19], and intrinsic viscosity was found to be of the form $[\eta] = KM^{0.65}$. The exponent 0.65 is typical of randomly coiled polymers. However, the argument is somewhat circular as the use of the Flory-Mandelkern equation implies the assumption of a randomly coiled configuration[19].

In agreement with the above picture, poly A at alkaline pH's has been found to display the contraction with increasing ionic strength characteristic of most flexible polyelectrolytes[14]. In the absence of any added electrolyte, poly A of molecular weight $3 \cdot 10^6$ shows a pronounced birefringence of flow[14]. At an ionic strength of 0.1 this disappears entirely[11]. Similarly, the intrinsic viscosity of alkaline poly A is pronouncedly ionic strength-dependent and decreases markedly with increasing ionic strength (Table 14).

TABLE 14

INTRINSIC VISCOSITY OF A POLY A PREPARATION AT TWO IONIC STRENGTHS[11]

Solvent	T (°C)	[η]
0.001 M NaOAc, pH 6.5	27.1	10.05
0.001 M NaOAc, pH 6.5, 0.1 M KCl	27.1	0.60

More direct evidence is furnished by light scattering. A poly A sample of molecular weight $3 \cdot 10^6$ was found to show a 40 per cent drop in radius of gyration between ionic strengths 0.01 and 0.50[14] as Fig. 40 shows. This type of behavior is in marked contrast to the relative invariance of radius of gyration and hydrodynamic properties with ionic strength for the rigid, highly helical polynucleotides, such as DNA.

A final piece of evidence in this connection is the failure of electron microscope observations of the alkaline form of poly A to show any evidence of well defined rigid fibres[20], as Fig. 41 shows.

Fig. 41. Electron microscopic picture[20] of poly A at alkaline pH.

From the preceding it is certainly possible to state, at least, what the structure of the alkaline form of poly A is not. It cannot consist of helices extending over a major fraction of the contour length. Such a high helical content would confer the unmistakable characteristics of a rigid, rod-like molecule. As we have seen, the available evidence is, without exception, in complete contradiction to this model.

Nevertheless there does exist some fairly compelling evidence for the occurrence of some degree of ordering. This is not necessarily inconsistent with an over-all coiled configuration, provided that the regions of ordering are intermittent and of limited extent. The molecule would derive its flexibility from the random sequences separating the regions of order. These would provide "hinge points" which could endow the molecule with the capacity to undergo extensive folding.

The evidence for a partially ordered state may be summarized briefly. Alkaline poly A has a remarkably high degree of hypochromism amounting to about 40% at 20° C and ionic strength 0.1[21]. Furthermore, the position of the absorption maximum is displaced appreciably from that for the monomer, from 260 mμ to 257 mμ[21]. The hypochromism alone is not very compelling evidence in view of the results of Michelson[22]. However, the degree of hypochromism has been found to be pronouncedly temperature-dependent[16, 21] as Fig. 42 shows. The decrease in

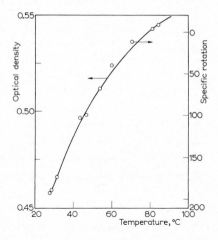

Fig. 42. Variation with temperature of absorbency[10] at 257 mμ and of specific rotation for poly A in 0.015 M citrate, 0.15 M NaCl, pH 7.

hypochromism with increasing temperature is not abrupt, as in the case of DNA, but occurs gradually. Moreover, the absorbency increases considerably in the presence of high concentrations of the hydrogen bond breaking agent urea[21]. In both cases the alteration in absorbency is completely reversible. If the observed hypochromism does reflect the extent of base stacking it is difficult to explain the effects of temperature and of urea on any basis other than the disruption of *some* structure.

Further evidence has been obtained from measurements of optical rotation. Poly A of molecular weight 10^5 or greater has a positive specific rotation of 155° at

22° C, in contrast to the monomer, AMP, which has a small negative specific rotation. The magnitude of $[a]_D$ for poly A is very temperature-dependent as Fig. 42 shows. Furthermore the decrease in dextrorotation with increasing temperature parallels the decrease in hypochromism. In the presence of 8 M urea $[a]_D$ falls[10] from 155° to 75° at 22° C. Formaldehyde pretreatment of poly A, which blocks the adenine C_6 amino group, also greatly reduces the dextrorotation[11]. The relevant data are summarized in Table 15.

TABLE 15

OPTICAL ROTATION OF POLYRIBONUCLEOTIDES

Polymer	Solvent*	$T(°C)$	$[a]_D$	Reference
poly U	0.15 M NaCl	22°	—8°	10
poly A	0.15 M NaCl	22°	155°	10
poly A	0.15 M NaCl	90°	—5°	10
poly A	0.15 M NaCl, 8 M urea	22°	75°	10
poly AU (1 : 1)	0.10 M KCl	28°	240°	11

* The pH is close to 7.0 in all cases.

The preceding strongly suggests that the alkaline form of poly A may consist of intermittent random and helical regions which are of limited extent. This is in fact our first encounter with what will become a familiar theme in this chapter.

As has been mentioned earlier, this kind of model is not in conflict with an over-all highly coiled shape for poly A or with the existence of considerable flexibility. There remains, of course, the problem of making the model structurally more explicit.

For the present it is probably best to differentiate between the structure of alkaline poly A in solution and in the fiber state, as there exist as yet no grounds for equating the two. The balance of the present discussion will be confined exclusively to the solution case.

It is unfortunately still uncertain whether the helical regions are parallel or antiparallel. If the former is the case they must involve the pairing of nucleotides from two *different* strands. The only evidence bearing on this question is the observation of Warner[13] that the number average molecular weight of alkaline poly A, as determined by end group analyses, is so close to the weight average molecular weight as to preclude the existence of molecular complexes to any important extent.

If correct, this observation would definitely eliminate the possibility of a parallel configuration for the helical regions. We are left with a model consisting of a single strand which is partially coiled back upon itself in places to form inter-mittent hairpin-like helical regions stabilized by hydrogen bonding of the "horizontal" type. The helical regions would necessarily be antiparallel in configuration. The two alternative possibilities are shown schematically in Fig. 43.

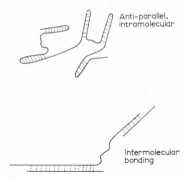

Anti–parallel,
intramolecular

Intermolecular
bonding

Fig. 43. Two alternative configurations for intermittently helical polynucleotides, such as RNA and the alkaline form of poly A.

It is not as yet possible to specify any details of the type of hydrogen bonding. Donohue has cited three possible adenine–adenine pairings[3]. In addition, there exists the possibility of bonding between adenine and the 2'-hydroxyl of ribose or the phosphoryl group.

A perhaps still more interesting example of an intermediate system is furnished by copolymers of adenylic and uridylic acids and by the copolymer of all four ribonucleotides.

Information on the macromolecular properties of the (1 : 1) AU copolymer is as yet scanty. However, the available data is indicative of a high degree of coiling as moderate ionic strengths, indicating that any helical content it may possess must be intermittent and cannot extend along the entire contour length[11]. The observed electrostatically induced expansion of the molecule at low ionic strengths, as reflected by a pronounced increase in intrinsic viscosity, also suggests too high a degree of flexibility to be consistent with a rigid, completely helical structure[11].

However, the X-ray diffraction pattern of fibres of the 1 : 1 AU copolymer are definitely consistent with some degree of ordering and have, in fact, considerable similarity to patterns obtained with natural RNA. There is evidence that some helical content persists in solution as well. Thus there is a high degree of hypochromism (about 40% for the 1 : 1 copolymer) which is, moreover, temperature-dependent[11]. The rise in absorbency at 260 mμ with temperature is not abrupt, as in the case of the highly ordered systems, but occurs gradually (Fig. 44).

Moreover, the absorbency of the 1 : 1 AU copolymer undergoes a sharp increase at a pH alkaline to the uracil pK[13] whereas poly U itself displays only a gradual decrease of absorbency in the zone of titration of the uracil group. This suggests that the loss of a proton from the uracil group is accompanied by the disruption of *some* ordered structure, with a consequent decrease in hypochromism.

Moreover, the 1 : 1 copolymer exhibits a high degree of dextrorotation (Table 15) whose decrease with temperature parallels the decrease in hypochromism. All in all, this copolymer in solution may probably be assigned tentatively to the class of intermediate systems.

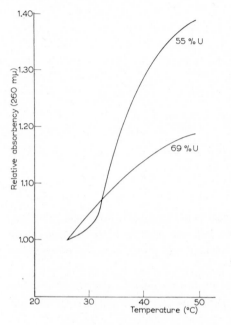

Fig. 44. Variation in absorbency at 260 mμ with temperature for several poly AU preparations of different uridylic content[11]. The solvent is 0.01 M NaOAc, 0.1 M KCl.

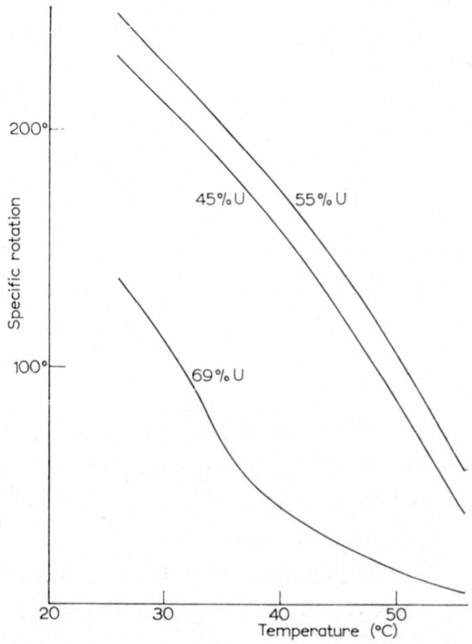

Fig. 45. Variation in specific rotation with temperature for the poly AU samples[11] of Fig. 44. The solvent is 0.01 M NaOAc, 0.1 M KCl, pH 6.5.

As the mole fraction of uridylic residues in the copolymer is increased beyond 0.5 a gradual loss of the properties suggestive of a partially ordered system occurs. Thus both the hypochromism and the dextrorotation, as well as their temperature dependence, decrease in magnitude with decreasing A : U mole ratio (Fig. 45).

Little is known about the nature of the helical sequences, which are presumably stabilized by adenine–uracil linkages and possibly by adenine–adenine linkages as well. As in the RNA case to be discussed subsequently, it is even uncertain whether the stabilizing hydrogen bonding occurs between bases in different strands or in the same strand bent back upon itself. In the latter case, the molecule would presumably consist of a number of hairpin-like ordered regions separated by random sequences (Fig. 43).

In any event, the random character of the base sequence in the copolymer virtually requires that the hydrogen bonded sequences be of limited extent, because of the inevitable occurrence of extensive mismatching.

THE INCOMPLETELY ORGANIZED SYSTEMS: RIBONUCLEIC ACID

The problems encountered in attempting to assign a structure to the AU copolymer reoccur in intensified form in the case of the copolymers which contain all four bases, into which category the natural RNA's fall. The biosynthetic AGUC copolymer may, in fact, profitably be discussed in conjunction with the natural RNA's, which it strongly resembles in behavior.

In recent years RNA of high molecular weight has become available from a number of sources. The RNA isolated from tobacco mosaic virus is of particular interest in view of its infectious properties, as demonstrated by Schramm and Gierer[23], by Fraenkel-Conrat[24], and by Commoner[25]. Tobacco mosaic virus (TMV) itself occurs as a thin rigid cylinder of length close to 3000 Å and molecular weight[26] close to $4 \cdot 10^7$. Only about 6% of its weight is RNA, the balance being protein[27]. Thus, if all of the RNA occurred as a single particle, its molecular weight would be in the neighborhood of $2 \cdot 10^6$.

X-ray work has shown fairly clearly that the structure of TMV has a screw axis and hence is based on a helix[28, 29]. The protein appears to occur as globular subunits of molecular weight about 20,000 which are helically arranged about an RNA core[30]. The implication is strong that the RNA itself has a helical configuration within the intact virus.

The molecular properties in solution of the RNA isolated from infectious tobacco mosaic virus (TMV) have been studied by a number of workers[31–34]. The more recent observations are consistent with a fairly homogeneous material of molecular weight[32, 34] close to $2.0 \cdot 10^6$.

At an ionic strength of 0.06 and pH 8.5, Boedtker[34] finds a radius of gyration of about 300 Å. A rod-like model for this molecule can certainly be discarded, as this radius of gyration corresponds to an end to end separation only about 1/25th that predicted for a completely extended rigid helix.

Furthermore, if the intrinsic viscosity and sedimentation constant are combined in the Flory–Mandelkern equation to compute a molecular weight upon the assumption of a randomly coiled configuration, a value[34] of $1.8 \cdot 10^6$ is obtained.

This figure is close enough to the light scattering value to indicate that the randomly coiled model provides a fairly self-consistent picture of the gross over-all configuration of the RNA from TMV, at least at high ionic strengths. Since the molecular weight observed is close to that predicted if all the RNA in the intact virus were one molecule, it appears likely that this is indeed the case and that this particle may be identified with the infectious unit.

The intrinsic viscosity was found by Boedtker to be ionic strength-dependent, a two-fold decrease occurring upon increasing the ionic strength from zero to 0.2 at neutral pH (Table 16). While this suggests some degree of molecular flexibility, the small magnitude of the viscosity decrease is puzzling, especially in view of the earlier report by Hopkins and Sinsheimer[32] that TMV RNA is a rod at zero ionic strength.

TABLE 16[34]

VISCOSITY OF TMV RNA AT 5°

Ionic strength	Solvent	pH	c (g/100 ml)	η_{sp}/c
0.20	phosphate	7.0	0.027	0.82
0.08	phosphate	7.5	0.0935	0.81
	plus versene		0.0537	0.77
0.06	phosphate	8.5	0.0745	0.82
			0.0435	0.705
			0.0396	0.725
0.06	versene	7.5	0.1235	0.82
			0.0740	0.775
			0.0247	0.70
0.04	phosphate	7.0	0.067	1.10
			0.032	1.19
0	water	6.0	0.023	1.60

It was also observed by Boedtker that the viscosity, but not the molecular weight, of this RNA was temperature dependent, a 50 per cent increase occurring reversibly between 6° and 25° C. In harmony with this observation, light scattering revealed a definite expansion of the molecule with temperature as Table 17 shows. This result was taken to indicate the reversible rupture of hydrogen bonds at the higher temperature which permitted some inflation of the coil.

TABLE 17

EXPANSION OF RNA MOLECULES FROM TMV WITH TEMPERATURE[34]

T (°C)	M_w ($\times$ 10^{-6})	Radius of gyration	η_{sp}/c
initial, 6°	2.0	306 Å	0.725
25°	1.9	375 Å	1.10
returned to 6°	1.9	326 Å	0.82

The solvent is phosphate buffer, 0.06 ionic strength, pH 8.5.

The macromolecular properties of the RNA isolated from the protoplasts of *E. coli* by Littauer and Eisenberg[35] appear to be similar in many respects to those of the RNA from TMV. However, this material was found to be definitely hetero-disperse. Crude preparations had three components, of sedimentation constants 3.2, 14–16, and 19–24 svedbergs. The two higher components were isolated and used for physical studies.

A much more pronounced dependence of intrinsic viscosity upon ionic strength was observed than for the TMV case. Thus a sixty-fold decrease in intrinsic viscosity occurred between ionic strengths of zero and 0.2 (Fig. 46). This was accompanied by a decrease in shear dependence; the viscosity being essentially Newtonian at ionic strengths greater than 0.001.

The flow birefringence properties of this material were also indicative of a flexible molecule displaying the usual polyelectrolyte expansion at low ionic strengths (Fig. 47). The positive birefringence observed at zero ionic strength disappeared entirely at an ionic strength of 0.2.

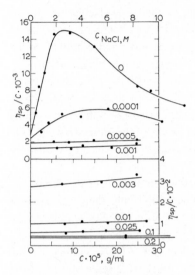

Fig. 46. Reduced specific viscosity[35] of the RNA from *E.coli* as a function of concentration and ionic strength at neutral pH.

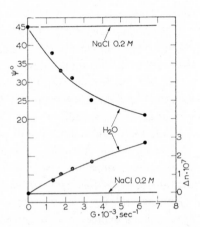

Fig. 47. Extinction angle and degree of birefringence of the RNA from *E.coli* as a function of gradient at two ionic strengths[35].

Doty and co-workers[7, 36] have studied the RNA from calf liver microsomes. For samples prepared by the phenol method, two distinct boundaries are seen in the ultracentrifuge, with sedimentation coefficients of $28 \cdot 10^{-13}$ and $18 \cdot 10^{-13}$ in $0.02\ M$ phosphate. The intrinsic viscosity was only 0.41.

After a heating cycle to 85° C and back to room temperature, the viscosity dropped to 0.22 and only a single boundary, of sedimentation coefficient equal to $8.2 \cdot 10^{-13}$, appeared upon ultracentrifugal examination. A similar treatment of the RNA from TMV was without effect.

A combination of sedimentation and viscosity data led to a molecular weight of 120,000 for the thermally treated material. It was concluded by Doty and co-workers that the initial material, as prepared by the phenol method, consisted largely of molecular aggregates, which were broken up by the thermal treatment. An examination of a series of degraded samples revealed the following relationship between sedimentation coefficient and molecular weight, in $0.01\ M$ phosphate, pH 7:

$$S_0^{20°} = K\,M^{0.5}$$

This exponential dependence is typical of randomly coiled polymers, to which class this material was accordingly assigned.

Timasheff and co-workers[37] have prepared and studied a highly polymerized RNA from ascites-tumor cells. Ultracentrifugal analysis indicated the presence of two components, of sedimentation coefficients $32 \cdot 10^{-13}$ and $15 \cdot 10^{-13}$. Light scattering data, averaged over the entire system, yielded a molecular weight of $1.1 \cdot 10^6$ and a radius of gyration of 320 Å, in 0.02 M Na phosphate and 0.08 M NaCl. The low radius of gyration of these molecules indicated a highly coiled shape. This view was confirmed by direct electron microscopic examination.

In summary, all of the RNA's so far examined appear to have a compact, highly coiled configuration at moderate ionic strengths. In the case of the RNA from TMV, the intramolecular hydrogen bonding appears to be sufficiently strong to prevent much inflation of the molecule, even at very low ionic strengths. On the other hand the RNA from *E. coli* does undergo the usual polyelectrolyte expansion under these conditions.

While there can be little doubt that the over-all configuration of the RNA's so far studied is not that of a rigid, completely helical molecule, there nevertheless exists rather compelling evidence for some degree of ordering. The evidence is of the same type as that discussed earlier for the AU copolymers.

The natural RNA's so far examined, as well as the AGUC copolymer, all have a high degree of hypochromism, which is, moreover, quite temperature-dependent. The increase in absorbency with temperature is relatively gradual, as in the case of the AU copolymer. The zone of the thermal transition depends upon

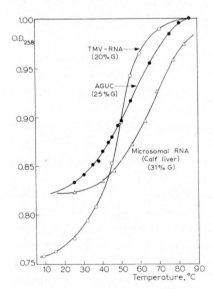

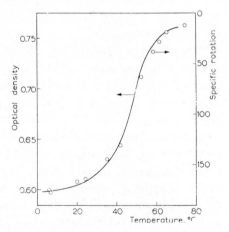

Fig. 48. Temperature dependence of ultraviolet absorbency for several RNA preparations of varying guanine content[7]. 0.1 M phosphate buffer, pH 7.

Fig. 49. Parallel variation with temperature (°C) of absorbency at 258 mμ and specific rotation for the RNA from TMV[7]. 0.1 M phosphate buffer, pH 7.

the chemical composition and is displaced to higher temperatures with increasing guanine content as Fig. 48 shows[7]. Unlike the DNA case, the decrease in hypochromism at elevated temperatures is completely reversible.

The increase in effective *melting point* with increasing guanine content finds its parallel in the case of DNA and serves to reinforce the conclusion that the cytosine–guanine linkage possesses exceptional stability.

The natural RNA's also display at low temperatures a high degree of dextrorotation. In the case of the RNA from TMV the specific rotation $[\alpha]_D$ at 20° C is about[7] $+190°$. At 80° C this falls to a value close to zero. The latter figure is close to that predicted for a mixture of the constituent nucleotides. The decrease in magnitude of $[\alpha]_D$ with temperature parallels the decrease in hypochromism[7] as Fig. 49 shows. Further evidence for a fractional helical content of RNA is obtained from a consideration of the rates of phosphorolysis. At 25° C the rates of phosphorolysis of the RNA's from TMV and calf liver microsomal particles, as well as the AGUC copolymer, are low in comparison with the rate of phosphorolysis[7] of the unorganized polynucleotide poly U. Moreover, the temperature dependence of the rate is very much greater than in the former case. It has been found that the ratio of the change in absorbency between 40° C and 25° C to the change between 90° C and 25° C varies linearly with the ratio of phosphorolysis rates[7, 38] at 40° C and 25° C. Thus the temperature-dependence of phosphorolysis rate parallels that of hypochromism[7].

The above phenomena have been attributed by Doty and co-workers to the existence of numerous helical regions of limited extent in the RNA molecule. The fact that the biosynthetic AGUC copolymer behaves in an entirely similar manner indicates that the occurrence of fractional ordering is not dependent upon the presence of any specific nucleotide sequence. The gradual nature of the thermal transitions is probably attributable to the shortness and heterogeneity of the helical regions.

Haschemeyer *et al.*,[39] have reported some preliminary observations upon the varying degree of ordering in the RNA of tobacco mosaic virus. They observed that the hypochromism and dextrorotation of this material were quite sensitive to ionic strength and the presence of bivalent metallic cations and attributed this to different degrees of helical content.

As in the case of the AU copolymers, the details of the helical fine structure are still uncertain. In particular it is uncertain whether the helical regions arise through an intermolecular association or through an intramolecular process involving the bending back upon itself of a single strand to form a series of hairpin-like helical regions separated by random sequences. It is at present even difficult to exclude the possibility of singly stranded helical regions stabilized by hydrogen bonding of the *vertical* type parallel to the fiber axis.

In any event the helical regions are probably stabilized by more than one type of Donohue pairing. If this picture of the structure of RNA is correct, it may be concluded that the matching requirements for helical structures are much less stringent than has been generally believed. It is possible that Van der Waals forces help to confer stability upon a helical region in the absence of complete complementarity.

THE ORDERED SYSTEMS: DNA

The basic key to an understanding of the solution properties of DNA has been provided by the Watson–Crick structure[1]. The available evidence, while overwhelmingly in favor of this fundamental picture of the DNA molecule, still does not exclude the possibility that localized deviations from this structure may occur. Thus there is some evidence that the $A-T$ and $G-C$ equivalence observed for many preparations of DNA may reflect the over-all average composition rather than that of individual fractions[40]. If this view is substantiated, it follows that disordered regions of limited extent may occur in the native DNA molecule as a consequence of the resultant mismatching.

Studies of the solution properties of DNA are inevitably complicated by the high degree of polydispersity shown by most of the samples examined so far. This molecular weight heterogeneity was concealed for a long time by the inaccessibility to schlieren optics of the very dilute ($<0.01\%$) concentration range where DNA molecules sediment as independent entities. Thus sedimentation diagrams in the usual concentration range of $0.1\%-1\%$ showed only a single narrow peak, as a consequence of the hypersharpening effect brought about by the extreme dependence of sedimentation constant upon concentration. However, the introduction of ultraviolet absorption optics permitted the extension of measurements to concentrations an order of magnitude lower, revealing a wide distribution of sedimentation constants[41-43] in the case of DNA from calf thymus and other sources.

Efforts to accomplish molecular weight fractionations are still at an early stage of development and virtually no physical data upon DNA fractions are available. Thus the conclusions which have been reached about the physical state of DNA in solution must be viewed with the reservations appropriate to studies upon systems which are certainly heterogeneous in molecular weight and possibly so in configuration and chemical composition.

Light scattering has proved to be by far the most applicable of the various available physical techniques for studying the size and shape of naturally occurring DNA. The most obvious feature of the very extensive data is the wide variability of the average molecule weights and radii of gyration obtained. This is the case even if attention is centered upon DNA isolated from a single source, the thymus gland of the calf[44]. The distribution of reported molecular weights is roughly trimodal, with peaks at about $3 \cdot 10^6$, $6 \cdot 10^6$ and $15 \cdot 10^6$ as Table 18 shows. The more recent measurements, using material isolated by the best preparative techniques, appear to indicate average values in the range 6–10 million for DNA from this source. The possibility has been advanced that the observed variation

TABLE 18

MOLECULAR PARAMETERS OF CALF THYMUS DNA SAMPLES

Molecular weight ($\times 10^{-6}$)	Contour length (Å)	Radius of gyration (Å)	Reference
3.5	18,000	1160	a
3.5	18,000	1630	a
3.9	20,000	1460	b
5.9	30,000	2120	c
5.8	30,000	2170	d
5.1	25,000	2490	e
6.0	31,000	2040	b
6.0	31,000	2660	b
5.0	26,000	1880	f
6.9	35,000	2050	g
16.5	85,000	2100	b
15.0	77,000	2550	b
11.6	60,000	2240	b

[a] P. DOTY AND B. BUNCE, *J. Am. Chem. Soc.*, 74 (1954) 5029.
[b] C. SADRON, *Proc. Third Int. Congr. Biochem., Brussels*, (1955) 125.
[c] S. KATZ, *J. Am. Chem. Soc.*, 74 (1952) 2238.
[d] F. HELDERS AND J. FERRY, *J. Phys. Chem.*, 60 (1956) 1536.
[e] R. STEINER, *Trans. Faraday Soc.*, 48 (1952) 1185.
[f] J. ROWEN, *Biochim. et Biophys. Acta*, 10 (1953) 391.
[g] M. REICHMANN, S. RICE, C. THOMAS AND P. DOTY, *J. Am. Chem. Soc.*, 76 (1954) 3047.

may result from the presence of traces of denatured protein, which serve as cross-linking agents[43].

If the intact DNA molecule had the form of an essentially perfect Watson–Crick double helix, it can be confidently predicted that its configuration would be that of a thin, rigid rod. Any appreciable bending or torsional motion of the intact helix would require an intolerable distortion of valence bonds, or else an energetically unfavored formation of non-linear hydrogen bonds[44]. As the separation of bases is known to be close to 3.4 Å, a length can be computed for this model equal to $0.5 \times 3.4 \times$ degree of polymerization.

For a thin rod the radius of gyration is equal to $L\sqrt{12}$. Even a superficial examination of the light scattering data of Table 18 reveals that the observed lengths are much too small, by a factor of three to five, to be consistent with this model. To reconcile this degree of coiling with the known structure it is necessary to postulate that DNA consists of ordered doubly stranded helical sections separated by regions of disorder which are sufficiently numerous to endow the molecule with some degree of flexibility.

If the rigid rod model can be rejected, it is plausible to examine next the true random coil with a high ratio of fully extended length to persistence length. Qualitatively, the high degree of flexibility required for this model is rendered unlikely by the relative insensitivity of the shape of DNA to electrostatic stress. Thus, in contrast to synthetic polyelectrolytes such as methacrylic acid, the intrinsic viscosity[45, 46] at zero shear gradient of thymus DNA is independent of ionic strength for ionic strengths greater than 10^{-4}.

Thus the apparently limited flexibility of DNA is not encouraging with regard to the true random coil model. Further evidence in this connection has been obtained by Doty, McGill and Rice[47], who examined the sedimentation, viscosity, and light scattering behavior of thymus DNA which had been subjected to controlled ultrasonic scission. The evidence is strong that ultrasonic treatment of DNA produces simultaneous cleavage of both chains with little concomitant single chain scission or denaturation. This follows from the failure of any change in ultraviolet absorbency to accompany even extensive degradation and from the absence of any appreciable signs of collapse upon electron microscopic examination of the sonicates[47]. Thus sonic degradation would appear to provide a means of preparing intact DNA fragments of varying length.

Employing this approach, the above workers found that the sedimentation constants and intrinsic viscosities of these fragments obeyed the relationships:

$$S_0^{20°} = 0.063 \ M_w^{0.37}$$

$$[\eta] = 1.45 \cdot 10^{-6} M_w^{1.12}$$

The coefficient of M_w in the expression for $[\eta]$ is 1.12, which is above the limiting value for randomly coiled, solvent-immobilizing polymers, 1.0, although barely so. The coefficient of M_w in the $S_0^{20°}$ equation, 0.37, approaches the lower limit for coils, 0.33.

Further information on configuration was obtained from the variation of radius of gyration with molecular weight. This was found to be of the form:

$$R_G = 8.3 \cdot 10^{-9} \ M_w^{0.5}$$

This relationship is clearly inconsistent with the rod model, which would, of course, predict a linear variation of R_G with M_w. The coefficient 0.5 is, in fact, that predicted for the random coil model.

Qualitatively, the model best able to bring all these observations into harmony would appear to be that of a stiff coil with a large persistence length, whose behavior would thus be intermediate to the rod and coil extremes.

Geiduschek and Holtzer[44] and Peterlin[48] have re-examined the light scattering behavior of native DNA in terms of this model, which has been formalized as the worm-like chain of Porod[49]. The form of P_θ will of course depend upon both the molecular configuration and the distribution of molecular weights. As the exact form of the latter is not known, a rigorous correlation of P_θ with the model is not possible. By treating the system as if it were monodisperse, Geiduschek and Holtzer have effectively attributed all of the deviation from monodisperse random coil behavior to the effects of chain stiffness.

The method of the above authors was essentially to match the experimental curve of $K \cdot c/R_\theta$ plotted *versus* $\log \sin^2 (\theta/2)$ with theoretical curves of P_θ^{-1} *versus* $\log h^2 R_G^2$ for varying values of L/a, where a is the persistence length and L the contour length. The best value of L/a was obtained by inspection. The results, for two different samples of thymus DNA, are shown in Table 19 (from reference 44).

TABLE 19[44]

M_w	R_G	L/a	L	a
$6.6 \cdot 10^6$	2200 Å	300	66,000 Å	220 Å
$5.5 \cdot 10^6$	2300 Å	90	38,700 Å	430 Å

While the differences between the above two samples appear unduly large in view of their similar molecular weights, the calculation probably suffices to give at least the order of magnitude of the persistence lengths. The values of this parameter are remarkably large and are quite consistent with the stiff coil model for DNA in solution.

We are left, of course, with the problem of deciding just what kind of imperfections in the helical duplex could provide sufficient flexibility to result in the observed degree of folding. One possibility is that the Watson–Crick base pairings are not quite perfect and that occasionally an *incorrect* nucleotide occurs in one of the strands, resulting in an amorphous hinge point. Another possibility is that a few breaks in the primary strands are present, which endow the duplex with some degree of flexibility at these points.

There is little evidence either for or against the first explanation. The results of Thomas[51] are definitely against the second.

Before leaving this topic it is desirable to mention a piece of evidence which does not appear to be in accord with this model. Electron microscopic observation of DNA has generally revealed extensions which are much too great to be consistent with this model and which, in fact, approach those of rigid rods rather closely. In all probability, however, the apparent inconsistency is not real and many well reflect some degree of straightening of the DNA molecule upon drying[20, 50].

The currently accepted duplex structure for DNA was advanced originally on largely stereochemical grounds. However it has been possible to obtain direct evidence for its persistence in solution thru studies of the kinetics of degradation of DNA by pancreatic deoxyribonuclease.

Thomas has correlated the extent of scission of phosphodiester linkages with the fall in molecular weight produced by deoxyribonuclease attack at neutral pH[51]. Under these conditions, for each diester linkage which is hydrolyzed, there is produced a secondary phosphate whose ionization at this pH results in the consumption of hydroxyl ion. Thus the number of bonds hydrolyzed could be obtained directly by a pH-stat type of measurement. The molecular weight was obtained by light scattering.

Qualitatively, it is easy to see that, if the DNA were single stranded, each bond scission would result in a drop in molecular weight. For a doubly stranded molecule, a fall in molecular weight could occur only when breaks in the two strands coincided. Thus altogether different kinetics would be predicted for the two cases.

Introducing the plausible assumption that the enzymatic attack was essentially random in nature, Thomas was able to demonstrate that the decline in molecular weight with the fraction of bonds hydrolyzed was very much too gradual to be consistent with a single stranded structure. Thus the rupture of 100 bonds per molecule resulted in only about a 20 per cent fall in molecular weight. If the molecule were single stranded, over a hundred-fold drop would be expected.

The difficulties involved in assessing such factors as the number of pre-existing breaks in the strands and the proximity required for breaks in both strands to permit molecular dissociation precluded any exclusive interpretation of the results. However, Thomas was able to show that the data were consistent with a duplex structure with a low frequency of occurrence of primary chain breaks.

It is of interest that Thomas found no evidence for any shrinkage of the DNA molecule apart from that resulting directly from degradation. Thus R_G^2/M was constant for quite a wide range of extents of degradation. This would appear to indicate that breaks in the primary strands do not endow the DNA with enhanced flexibility to an important extent. This result therefore tends to rule out such breaks as a contributing factor to the finite flexibility of the intact molecule.

One of the most extensively studied features of DNA is its capacity to undergo a process which, by analogy with globular proteins, has been referred to as denaturation. This process, which occurs at extremes[52-61] of pH, at elevated temperatures[53, 55], or at very low ionic strengths[62, 63], is always reflected by a decrease in hypochromism and, if the ionic strength is not too low, by a contraction to a

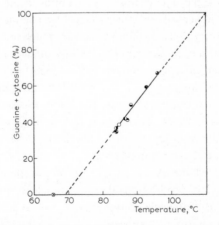

Fig. 50. Thermal denaturation of DNA from several sources, as reflected by changes in ultraviolet absorbency[6].

more compact form. However, if care is taken to avoid chemical degradation, most workers * have failed to find any drop in molecular weight, although occasional claims to the contrary have appeared[52].

The destruction of the secondary structure of DNA by heat or pH represents the earliest studied example of a helix-coil transition for polynucleotides. Let us consider first the thermal denaturation.

If followed by changes in hypochromism, the transition is remarkably sharp, usually going to completion over a range[6,7] of 5°. The midpoint of the thermal transition depends upon the base composition, which varies from source to source. For the samples so far studied the midpoint ranges from 84° C to 96° C at an ionic strength of 0.2 and neutral pH, as Fig. 50 shows.

While the sharpness of the thermal transition persists, whatever the criterion of denaturation, the precise nature of the temperature dependence may vary somewhat with the property observed. Thus for the thermal denaturation of transforming principle from *Hemophilus influenzae*, the fraction of biological activity retained after one hour at a particular temperature does not correspond to the ratio of specific viscosity to its initial value[44]. This, however, is not too surprising in view of the heterogeneity of the DNA and the complicated nature of the process.

When DNA is heated for a finite time at a temperature well above the transition zone and then cooled to room temperature, the properties of the denatured DNA thereby produced contrast vividly with those of the intact molecule, as Table 20

TABLE 20

EFFECT OF THERMAL DENATURATION UPON PROPERTIES OF CALF THYMUS DNA[44]

Sample	M_w	$[\eta]$	R_G (Å)	$s_0^{20°}$ ($\cdot 10^{13}$)
native	7.7	72	3000	21
denatured	7.7	4	1000	21

* Denaturation was brought about by heating at 100° C, 0.15 ionic strength, and neutral pH.

shows. The intrinsic viscosity is smaller by a factor of twenty and is almost independent of shear. Furthermore, the intrinsic viscosity is now markedly dependent upon ionic strength. At ionic strengths of the order of 0.1 the radius of gyration has decreased threefold. In fact the properties of thermally denatured DNA are consistent with a molecule which approaches the properties of a true random coil more closely than does native DNA.

It is of particular interest that exposure to a temperature within the transition zone serves only to lower the specific viscosity of DNA (as measured at 25° C after cooling) to a value characteristic of the temperature[7]. This final value is

---

* Very recently Doty, Marmur, Eigner and Schildkraut reported a drop in molecular weight upon the thermal denaturation of several bacterial DNA's (*Proc. Natl. Acad. Sci.*, 46 (1960) 461).

reached within about twenty minutes and further heating fails to produce any further fall in viscosity, unless heating is continued for so long a time that chemical degradation becomes appreciable.

Unquestionably, it is necessary to disentangle several factors before this observation can be attributed unequivocally to the attainment of some type of quasi-equilibrium. Indeed, it is entirely possible that this behavior may reflect simply either the heterogeneity of the samples, which may contain DNA molecules of different base composition and hence different denaturation temperatures, or else the internal heterogeneity of the DNA itself, as it is known that the $C-G$ linkages are thermodynamically more stable than the $A-T$ linkages[7].

In the latter connection it has been observed that the midpoint of the thermal transition of DNA varies for DNA's from different sources and appears to be correlated with the guanine content, increasing with increasing mole fraction of guanine[6]. We have already noted a similar effect in the case of RNA.

Current theories of the helix-coil transition, which will be discussed in a later chapter, are consistent with the occurrence of a partially denatured state. In view of the stringent matching requirements of the Watson–Crick structure, it is obvious that any extensive rupture of bonding will be almost impossible to reverse completely. However, it is difficult to predict how long a given sequence of thermally broken linkages must be before reformation of the initial structure upon cooling becomes impossible. The conclusion that some degree of reformation of hydrogen bonding occurs is rendered almost inescapable by the partial recovery of hypochromism upon cooling as Figs. 51 and 52 show[7].

In general it may be said that, as we shall see later, the concept of a continuous mechanism for the denaturation of DNA is better grounded theoretically than that of an *all or none* process. However, the evidence to date cannot be said to favor conclusively the existence of intermediate states, in view of the uncertain contribution of heterogeneity.

Indeed, one piece of evidence must be cited which is somewhat contrary to the

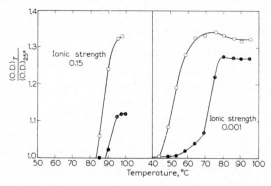

Fig. 51. A comparison of the ultraviolet absorbency of DNA when measured directly at an elevated temperature and when measured after cooling to room temperature[7]. o Elevated temperature, • Room temperature.

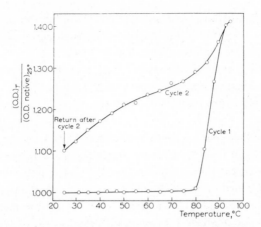

Fig. 52.   Temperature dependence of ultraviolet absorbency of DNA before and after exposure to elevated temperatures[7]. Calf thymus DNA, 0.15 M NaCl+0.015 M Na-citrate, pH 7.

occurrence of intermediate denatured states. Electron microscopic examination of DNA after exposure to temperatures within its transition zone has failed to reveal the presence of any structures intermediate to the completely collapsed and the intact rigid state[64]. However, it is by no means certain that a molecule consisting of intermittent helical and random regions would be distinguishable from a completely denatured molecule by this criterion.

The midpoint of the thermal transition is quite dependent upon ionic strength and is shifted to lower temperatures with decreasing ionic strength. Indeed, Thomas[62, 63] has found that, in the absence of added electrolyte, denaturation, as judged by a decrease in hypochromism, proceeds spontaneously at 25° C. This serves to underline the marginal character of the stability of the base pairings, which cannot tolerate the intense electrostatic stress occurring under these conditions.

The addition of 8 M urea has only a minor effect upon the thermal denaturation of DNA, lowering the melting point by about 20° at an ionic strength[65] of 0.1 at neutral pH.

The denaturation of DNA at extremes of pH appears to be an even less clear-cut process than thermal denaturation. We shall consider first the denaturation occurring at acid pH's, which is by far the most extensively studied case.

The guanine, adenine, and cytosine bases[55] are all titrated at pH's acid to pH 5. At least three factors will influence the character of the structural transition accompanying their binding of protons:

(a) The actual rupture of hydrogen bonds. If the locus of proton binding is at the N_1 position for the adenine and cytosine bases, the latter will no longer be able to serve as an acceptor for hydrogen bonding of the type described earlier. If the proton is bound by the amino groups, the latter could serve as donors only at the cost of a considerable and probably prohibitive distortion of valence bond angles. In either event, however, only one of the two bonds uniting each base pair could be ruptured in this manner.

(*b*) Localized electrostatic repulsion. The mutual repulsion of similarly charged bases packed into the core of the double helix must certainly be an important factor in promoting disruption of the helical form.

(*c*) Over-all charge neutralization. The titration of the bases serves to neutralize partially the net negative charge of the DNA polyion. This would be expected to favor a collapse of the molecule, once the rigidity conferred by its helical structure is lost.

The earliest evidence that a structural change of DNA occurred at extremes of pH was deduced from the shape of the titration curves themselves. When fairly intact DNA became available it was soon observed that the forward and back titration curves obtained upon titrating a sample from neutral pH to pH 2 at room temperature did not coincide[55]. The change corresponded to increased binding at intermediate pH's for the back titration and formally reflected an increase in pK of the bases involved (Fig. 53). Subsequent titration curves in either direction were always close to the curve obtained for the back titration of the initial cycle[55].

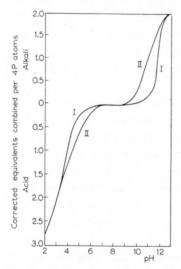

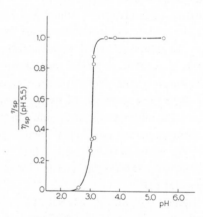

Fig. 53. Hydrogen ion titration curves of DNA at 25° C[55]. Curve I is that for native DNA which is brought to acid or alkaline pH's for the first time. Curve II is that obtained for DNA upon back titration from extremes of pH and for subsequent forward titration[55].

Fig. 54. Drop in viscosity of thymus DNA at acid pH's and room temperature[65]. The solvent is 0.2 M NaCl. The concentration of DNA is 0.1%.

The behavior obtained upon carrying out an analogous alkaline cycle between neutral pH and pH 12 was entirely similar.

It was also soon recognized that exposure of DNA to the zones of pH at which the titration anomalies became apparent brought about a drastic change in physical properties, including a pronounced and abrupt drop in viscosity, as Fig. 54 shows[55, 56], a decrease in hypochromism[53, 55] and a fall in radius of gyration[55, 65-67].

However, it was soon observed that the alteration in physical properties did not parallel the titration curve exactly and that a considerable fraction of the available bases could be titrated at acid pH without altering the physical properties appreciably. According to Cox and Peacocke[56, 57] this fraction varies from 5 to 75%, depending upon the temperature and ionic strength. The fraction of reversibly titratable sites increases with increasing ionic strength and decreasing temperature. The criterion of irreversible denaturation used by these workers is the appearance of irreversibility in the titration curve.

There is still some uncertainty in both the magnitude and sign of the temperature dependence of the reversible region of the titration curve. In any event, the enthalpies of ionization of the bases involved are certainly quite small (< 5 Kcal)[68, 69].

At 5° C and ionic strength 0.1, Sturtevant, Rice, and Geiduschek report that about 65% of all possible protons may be bound without important enthalpy or viscosity change[68]. Beyond this point, which occurs at about pH 2.6, a pronounced absorption of heat amounting to 1250 calories per mole phosphorus occurs over a very narrow pH range. This is accompanied by a marked drop in viscosity and parallels the appearance of irreversibility in the titration curve. At 40° the transition occurs at about pH 3.5 (Fig. 55).

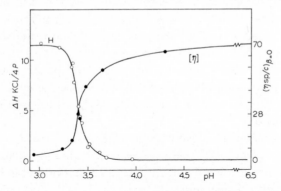

Fig. 55.   Heat evolution and viscosity change[68] for thymus DNA at acid pH's (40° C).

We are here confronted with a real dilemma. The failure of *irreversible* changes to accompany the titration of a large fraction of the available groups is understandable if the disordered sequences thereby produced are of limited extent and hence capable of rematching. However, if the endothermic effect can be attributed solely to the rupture of hydrogen bonds (assuming zero enthalpies of ionization of the bases), the Sturtevant-Rice-Geiduschek result would appear to indicate either that most of the bases can be titrated without rupturing *any* hydrogen bonds or that there exists a class of hydrogen bonds with effectively zero enthalpy of formation.

The former is in fact the interpretation favored by these authors. Taken literally, it is clearly inconsistent with the currently prevailing concepts of the source of stability of the DNA helix and if correct would require a major revision of these concepts. However, as Peacocke has pointed out[69], the values of the heats of ionization of the bases are still rather uncertain. It is possible that correction of the data of Sturtevant, Rice, and Geiduscheck for the heats of ionization might remove the anomaly.

The careful hydrogen ion titration data of Cox and Peacocke[56,57] and of Cavalieri and Rosenberg[73] have shown that the extent of reversibility of the titration curve depends markedly upon the temperature. Thus, if herring sperm DNA is titrated to pH 2.7 and back to neutrality at 25° C, the forward and back titration curves do not coincide, the backward curve corresponding to definitely higher values of the base pK's. Subsequent titration cycles are identical and reversible, coinciding with the initial back titration curve. Cox and Peacocke consider that the initial forward titration has been accompanied by a transition to a completely denatured state. Any re-formation of hydrogen bonding accompanying the back titration to neutrality must be of an irregular and hence readily reversible nature. Sturtevant, Rice, and Geiduschek[68] have in fact obtained direct calorimetric evidence for the re-formation of some hydrogen bonds.

When the initial titration cycle is carried out at 0.4° C the divergence of the forward and backward branches [53,56,57] is much less than at 25° C. If an initial cycle at 0.4° C is followed by a forward titration at 25° C, the resultant curve is intermediate to those for intact and completely denatured DNA at this temperature. Cox and Peacocke conclude that the initial forward titration at 0.4° C, in contrast to that at 25° C, has *irreversibly* disrupted the hydrogen bonding only to a partial extent. From a quantitative comparison of the titration curves at 25° C of intact DNA and DNA which has undergone the cycle at 0.4° C, they deduce that only 40% of the DNA hydrogen bonds have been irreversibly ruptured by the latter process.

If the initial cycle to pH 2.7 and back is carried out at –0.4° C, the forward and back branches are identical and no irreversible denaturation appears to occur by this criterion, despite the fact that the maximum extent of proton binding is close to that for the higher temperatures.

TABLE 21 [53]

REVERSIBLE AND IRREVERSIBLE DENATURATION OF DNA*

T (°C)	pH	η_{sp}/C
22.3	6.1	0.172
	2.6	0.01
	6.1**	0.029
1.8	6.1	0.170
	2.6	0.124
	6.1**	0.165

  * DNA 0.063 g/l in 0.2 M NaCl.
 ** Reneutralized after exposure to pH 2.6.

TABLE 22[53]

pH LIMITS FOR THE ONSET OF IRREVERSIBLE DENATURATION OF DNA

(T °C)	Ionic strength	pH range (titration)	pH range (spectral)
1	0.007	3.1–2.8	
23	0.007	4.0–3.7	4.3–3.6
1	0.20	2.6	
23	0.20	2.6	2.9–2.6
63	0.20		4.2–3.7

Further supporting evidence for these conclusions comes from the work of Cavalieri and Rosenberg[53] upon calf thymus DNA. These authors find that the drop in viscosity in 0.2 M NaCl at 1.8° C is very much less than at 22° C. The drop in viscosity at the lower temperature, but not at the higher, is largely recovered upon back titration to neutrality, as Table 21 shows. Table 22 cites the pH limits at which irreversible denaturation occurs[58]. A similar result has been obtained by Geiduschek and Holtzer as Fig. 56 shows.

These latter data, which were obtained at 5° C, indicate that some degree of recovery of the initial gross shape is possible even if a profound structural collapse has occurred. The result is all the more remarkable in that some recovery occurs even after exposure to pH 2.4 at which 60% of the native structure has been destroyed, as judged by the calorimetric technique.

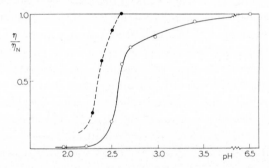

Fig. 56. Partial recovery of the viscosity drop of thymus DNA at acid pH's. The open circles represent the viscosity after altering the pH from neutrality. The closed circles show the viscosity after exposure to the given pH and back titration to neutrality[44].

If DNA is kept at pH 2.6 for prolonged periods a slow drop in molecular weight with time occurs, which reflects the hydrolysis of phosphodiester bonds. Thomas and Doty[70] have followed this degradation process by means of light scattering. It may be shown that, in the case of random bond scission, the drop with time of weight average molecular weight for a doubly stranded molecule is given by (assuming an initially random distribution of molecular weights):

$$\frac{M_w^0}{M_w} = 1 + 1/2\, p^2\, fu_w$$

where M_w, M_w^o are the weight average molecular weight at a given time and at zero time, respectively; p is the fraction of all bonds which have been broken; f is the average number of bonds on each strand between residual cross linkages; and u_w is the initial weight average degree of polymerization of each strand.

The experimental results at pH 2.6 and 25° C were consistent with very large (> 1000) values of f. It was concluded that only a few residual hydrogen bonds remained under these conditions and that the process observed corresponded to the random scission of very large rings of denatured DNA.

The apparent failure so far of efforts to demonstrate an actual separation of the two strands at acid pH's remains somewhat surprising. It is possible that a few bases per strand may remain untitrated at pH's above 2 and serve to hold the two strands together. Below pH 2 the issue is confused by the onset of relatively rapid acidic degradation.

In all probability the irreversible production of a denatured sequence in DNA, as a consequence of the binding of protons, is a two-step process. The first step involves the reversible rupture of one of the $A-T$ or $C-G$ hydrogen bonds as a result of the proton binding. At sufficiently low temperatures ($-0.4°$ C) the remaining bond, together with secondary Van der Waals forces, are sufficient to maintain base pairing. Under these conditions the two complementary strands remain in register, so that back titration to neutrality brings about an exact re-formation of the original structure, as judged by titration behavior and physical properties. At sufficiently high temperatures ($> 25°$ C) the relatively weak forces holding the base pairs together are unable to withstand the thermal motion. The base pairs separate and large rings of random sequences form. This is accompanied by the appearance of the characteristics of the denatured state. At intermediate temperatures the separation of base pairs is incomplete, as is the extent of denaturation. The relatively gradual approach with increasing temperature to the 100% irreversibly denatured state probably reflects the microheterogeneity of the DNA rather than the attainment of quasi-equilibrium, as the $A-T$ and $C-G$ pairings differ in stability.

There remains to be considered the very interesting recent observation of Geiduschek[44] that methanol is a solvent for DNA, provided that the concentration of electrolyte (NaCl) is less than about 10^{-3} M. As the fraction of methanol is increased there occurs at 80% (v/v) methanol a very sharp structural transition corresponding to a dramatic collapse of the molecule, as observed by viscosity and light scattering. Surprisingly enough, the transition appears to be completely reversible if carried out at $6°$ C.

The capacity of methanol to break hydrogen bonds is not remarkable and clearly some other explanation must be sought for this effect. One possibility is that the reduction in effective dielectric constant accompanying the addition of methanol sufficiently enhances the mutual electrostatic repulsion of the similarly charged phosphates to force the nucleotide pairs apart. Why the process should be completely reversible with regard to macromolecular properties remains a mystery. It would be desirable to examine the reversibility by other criteria as well.

Still another anomalous denaturation process has been reported by Katz, who found that a pronounced drop in viscosity and a decrease in radius of gyration, together with some increase in molecular weight, accompanied the binding of $HgCl_2$ by thymus DNA[71]. The mechanism of this process remains obscure.

An atypical DNA

Our account of the properties of natural DNA would be incomplete without mention of one example which appears to violate most of the generalizations of the preceding section. The Φ X 174 virus was early recognized to have several anomalous properties. In particular, the efficiency of inactivation of the virus as a result of ^{32}P decay was found to approach 1.0. This is in marked contrast to the behavior of other organisms, such as T2 coliphage, for which the efficiency of killing is lower by a factor of 10 or more.

Sinsheimer successfully isolated the DNA of the infectious particle and found it to have a molecular weight[72] close to $1.7 \cdot 10^6$. From the known size and DNA content of the intact virus, this would allow only one DNA molecule per virus particle.

The base composition of the DNA was found to show a definite deviation from the Watson–Crick pattern. Thus, the relative base contents were:

adenine	1.0
thymine	1.3
guanine	1.0
cytosine	0.8

The degree of hypochromism was much less than is usually observed for DNA. The increase in absorbency upon exhaustive digestion with pancreatic deoxyribonuclease was only 11 per cent, as compared with a usual increase of the order of 30 per cent.

The absorbency of the intact molecule was dependent upon the ionic strength and the temperature. A decrease in ionic strength, or an increase in temperature, resulted in a drop in absorbency. In both cases the variation was gradual, and there was no sign of the fairly sharp thermal transition characteristic of DNA from other sources. Indeed the observed behavior was quite reminiscent of that displayed by RNA, or by thermally denatured DNA.

Another departure in properties from other DNA's was observed upon formaldehyde treatment of this material. The characteristic spectral changes which accompany the attack of this reagent upon the primary amino groups of adenine, guanine, and cytosine proceeded readily under mild conditions (room temperature and neutral pH). While this test is not very conclusive, there was a definite implication that many of the primary amino groups were accessible for reaction.

Moreover, the dimensions of the molecule, as determined by light scattering, indicated a high degree of coiling at moderate ionic strengths. The radius of gyration in 0.02 M NaCl was 1140 Å. This decreased to 440 Å in 0.2 M NaCl and to 325 Å in 0.02 M NaCl, plus $4 \cdot 10^{-3}$ M Mg^{++}.

Thus, at ionic strengths greater than 10^{-2}, this molecule is coiled to 1/15th, or less, of its contour length. It furthermore displays a considerable degree of flexibility, as is evidenced by the expansion under electrostatic stress at low ionic strengths. Clearly this molecule does not have the rigidity characteristic of the intact helical duplex.

Finally, the nature of the decrease in molecular weight with time upon degradation by pancreatic deoxyribonuclease was very different from that observed in the case of thymus DNA. There was no lag period and the shape of the curve resembled that predicted for the random scission of a single strand.

It was concluded by Sinsheimer that the properties of this material were best accounted for by a system consisting of randomly coiled single strands. In fact, the over-all solution properties strongly resemble those of RNA. The question of the existence of any partial helical content was left open, although there is no reason to doubt that the analogy to RNA extends to this as well.

THE ORDERED POLYNUCLEOTIDE SYSTEMS: POLY A PLUS POLY U

Not long after the initial discovery and isolation of the polynucleotide phosphoryl ase of *Azotobacter vinelandii*, the important observation was made by Warner[73, 74] that poly A and poly U could, in the presence of a sufficient concentration of electrolyte, interact at neutral pH to form molecular complexes. The evidence obtained by Warner for complexing was as follows.

It was observed that the absorbency at 259 mμ of poly A–poly U mixtures did not correspond to the expected sum for a non-associating mixture. The deviations were in the direction of decreased absorbency, a lowering of 25 per cent being observed for a 1 : 1 adenine : uracil (A : U) mole ratio. An increase in hypochromism of this magnitude suggested strongly that the interaction was not confined to a few contacts per molecule, but probably involved an extensive degree of nucleotide pairing.

It was also observed that the equimolar mixture, when examined electrophoretically at a pH (9.6) in the vicinity of the uracil pK, migrated as a single component, with a mobility intermediate to that of its constituents. Since the mobilities of poly A and poly U were $10.6 \cdot 10^{-5}$ cm^2 volt^{-1} sec^{-1} and $13.2 \cdot 15^{-5}$ cm^2 volt^{-1} sec^{-1} under these conditions (ionic strength 0.1, 0° C), resolution of the two components would be expected in the absence of any interaction.

More direct evidence was obtained by sedimentation. Upon mixing a poly A sample with $S_0^{20°}$ equal to $5.3 \cdot 10^{-13}$ with a poly U sample with $S_0^{20°}$ equal to $2.2 \cdot 10^{-13}$ in an A : U mole ratio of 1 : 1, only a single peak was observed in the ultracentrifuge with $S_0^{20°}$ equal to $9.9 \cdot 10^{-13}$.

Miles has recently obtained supplementary evidence for the existence of a poly A–poly U complex by means of infra-red spectroscopy in D$_2$O solution[75]. Using the integrated band intensity method, he was able to show that a mixture of AMP and UMP had an infrared spectrum which was quantitatively identical, within experimental error, with the sum of the spectra of the two components measured separately. However, a mixture of poly A and poly U displayed a wide departure from additivity. Thus the 6.02 μ carbonyl band of poly U showed a marked decrease in intensity for the mixture. A decrease in intensity also occurred in the 6.15 μ region.

The initial discovery of Warner was soon followed by the still more dramatic observation by Rich and Davies that X-ray diffraction patterns of dried oriented fibers of the equimolar complex were consistent with the existence of a high degree of ordered fine structure and that the pattern was in fact very reminiscent of that produced by natural DNA[76]. Because of the close chemical analogy of uracil to thymine this at once raised the possibility that the equimolar complex might have a doubly stranded helical structure stabilized by adenine-uracil hydrogen bonding which was similar to the adenine-thymine bonding postulated for native DNA. This is illustrated by Fig. 57.

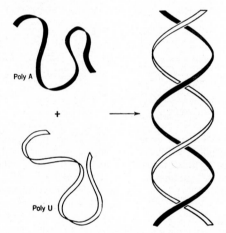

Fig. 57. Schematic version of the combination of poly A and poly U to form a double helix.

Subsequent observations have, indeed, provided a consistent confirmation of this view. It was soon observed that the equimolar complex displayed the thermal and alkaline denaturation phenomena characteristic of native DNA[12,13]. Furthermore, the observation that formaldehyde pretreatment of the poly A prevented the interaction is consistent with a direct involvement of the adenine 6-amino group as a hydrogen-bond donor[12].

In addition, detailed analysis of the X-ray diffraction pattern proved to be consistent with this type of structure[5,9], as will be discussed in the next chapter.

Grunberg-Manago has examined the effect of complex formation between poly A and poly U upon the rate of phosphorolysis by the *Azotobacter* enzyme[38]. The rates of phosphorolysis of the individual polynucleotides were of the same order of magnitude. However, the initial rate fell by a factor of three for a 1 : 1 mixture, and a 1 : 3 mixture was barely attacked at all. Thus the involvement of the poly A and poly U in an ordered complex appears to inhibit the phosphorolysis reaction.

The first detailed ultraviolet spectral mixing curves were obtained by Felsenfeld and Rich[77-79]. In the complete absence of added electrolyte no spectral change was observed upon mixing, the mixing curve being simply a straight line corresponding to the expected sum of the optical densities of the two components in the given proportions. At an ionic strength of 0.01 a downward bulge in the curve developed slowly with time (Fig. 58).

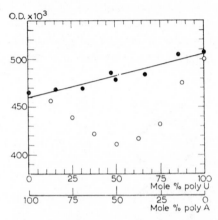

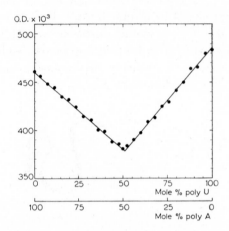

Fig. 58. Slow formation of the A + U complex at low ionic strength[78] (0.01 Na cacodylate, pH 6.5). The ordinate is the optical density at 259 mμ. • zero time; ○ 24 hours.

Fig. 59. Rapid mixing curve[78] for poly A plus U in 0.1 M NaCl, 0.01 M glycyl-glycine, pH 7.4, $T = 25°$ C. The ordinate is the optical density at 259 mμ. $S_o^{20°}$ for poly A = 8.0 · 10^{-13}; $S_o^{20°}$ for poly U = 3.2 · 10^{-13}. Under these conditions only the (A + U) complex species is present.

However, at an ionic strength of 0.1 in uni-univalent electrolyte and neutral pH, the mixing curve obtained at short intervals after combination (using a rapid mixing device) was found to be V-shaped, consisting of two straight lines intersecting at a mole fraction of uridylic residues equal to 0.50, as Fig. 59 shows. This experiment and those to be described subsequently were carried out with a poly A and poly U with sedimentation constants equal to 8.0 · 10^{-13} and 3.2 · 10^{-13}, respectively.

However, after prolonged standing (48 hours) under the above conditions, there was revealed the slower development of a definite downward bulge at mole fractions of uridylic residues greater than 0.50. This suggested the formation of a complex of different composition at high U : A mole ratios.

Both the kinetics and equilibria of the interaction processes were found to be profoundly dependent upon the nature and concentration of the added electrolyte. Divalent cations, including Mg^{++} and Mn^{++}, had roughly the same effect as a

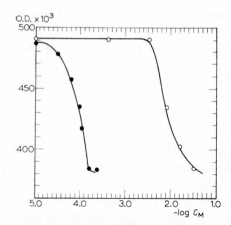

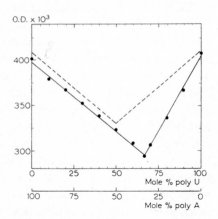

Fig. 60. Spectral alteration at equilibrium resulting from the addition of metal ions to a 1 : 1 A : U mixture in distilled water[78]. The abscissa is the logarithm of total metal concentration. The ordinate is the optical density at 259 mμ. • MnCl$_2$; ○ NaCl.

Fig. 61. The equilibrium absorbency[78] of mixtures of poly A and poly U in 0.1 M NaCl, 0.01 M glycyl-glycine, and 1.2 · 10^{-3} M MgCl$_2$, pH 7.4. The dashed line corresponds to the mixing curve at very short reaction times and represents the formation of the 1 : 1 complex only. The ordinate is the optical density at 259 mμ.

hundred-fold higher concentration of univalent cation (Fig. 60). In the presence of 10^{-2} M Mg^{++} or 0.7 M Na$^+$ the equilibrium mixing curves regained their V-shaped appearance, but the position of the sharp minimum was now at a mole fraction of uridylic residues equal to 0.67 (Fig. 61). Under these conditions equilibrium was attained relatively rapidly.

TABLE 23

TIMES REQUIRED FOR THE REACTION $(A + U) + U \rightarrow A + 2U$ TO GO
HALF WAY TO EQUILIBRIUM[78], *

Electrolyte	Molar concentration	$t^{\frac{1}{2}}$ (minutes)
MgCl	7.3 · 10^{-4}	8
	1.2 · 10^{-3}	6
	2.4 · 10^{-3}	4
	6.1 · 10^{-3}	1.3
	1.2 · 10^{-2}	0.5
	0.12	0.2
	0.24	0.1
NaCl	0.35	6
	0.60	1.2
	1.1	0.4

* $S_o^{20°}$ of poly A = 8.0 · 10^{-13}; $S_o^{20°}$ of poly U = 3.2 · 10^{-13}.

The fact that V-shaped mixing curves could be obtained with sharp minima at U : A mole ratios of either 1 : 1 or 2 : 1, depending upon conditions, led these workers to postulate the stoichiometric formation of two successive complexes corresponding to these U : A ratios. These will be referred to as the A + U and the A + 2U complex species. Table 23 shows the dependence of the rate of formation of the A + 2U species (in terms of the time required for the reaction to go half way to equilibrium) upon the nature and concentration of added electrolyte for the particular poly A and poly U preparations cited above[78].

Both the rate and extent of formation of the A + 2U complex were subsequently found to be very dependent upon the molecular weight of the interacting constituents. Beers and Steiner, working with poly A and poly U samples of considerably higher molecular weights, found that the formation of the (A + 2U) complex was much more rapid and complete than for the preceding preparations, under comparable conditions[12]. Thus the minimum in the equilibrium mixing curve was displaced to a mole fraction of U equal to 0.67 at an ionic strength as low as 0.1 for this system[12].

It was now clear that at sufficiently high ionic strengths or in the presence of sufficient divalent cation, formation of the (A + 2U) complex could go to completion and that the stepwise reaction could be written schematically:

$$A + U \ ---\rightarrow AU$$

$$AU + U \ ---\rightarrow AU_2 \ (\text{U in excess})$$

Remarkably enough, the decrease in absorbency per mole nucleotide appears to be exactly the same for the second step as for the first.

Felsenfeld and Rich were also able to follow the stepwise formation of the (A + 2U) complex in the ultracentrifuge. Working with the same poly A and poly U preparations described earlier, they found that the sedimentation constant for the complex species was 50 per cent greater at a U : A mole ratio of 2 : 1 than at a ratio of 1 : 1, under conditions favoring complete formation of the (A + 2U) complex[78].

It is not possible to make a *quantitative* general statement on the relative stability of the (A + U) and (A + 2U) species, in view of the pronounced dependence upon the molecular weight of the constituents. Qualitatively, however, it is clear that the (A + 2U) complex is energetically less favored, and that its formation occurs at a slower rate.

As will be discussed in the following chapter, the X-ray diffraction pattern of fibers of the (A + U) complex is suggestive of a doubly stranded helical structure stabilized by adenine-uracil hydrogen bonding similar to that postulated for adenine and thymine in the Watson–Crick model for DNA[76]. The hydrogen bonds in this case are formed between the C_6 amino group of adenine and the C_6 carbonyl of uracil and between the N_1 of uracil and the N_1 of adenine. It has been plausibly suggested that the second poly U strand of the (A + 2U) complex is inserted in the wide helical groove of the (A + U) complex and is stabilized by hydrogen bonds between the C_6 amino group of adenine and the C_6 carbonyl of uracil and between the N_7 of adenine and the N_1 of uracil[77]. According to this model addition of the second poly U strand could occur without disturbing either the bonding or the configuration of the $(A+U)$ complex.

Corroborative evidence for this mode of bonding was soon forthcoming from the observation that formaldehyde pretreatment of the poly A, which eliminates the capacity of the C_6 amino group to serve as a hydrogen bond donor, completely blocks the interaction process[12]. Furthermore, the disruption of the $(A+U)$ complex at pH's alkaline to the uracil pK is consistent with this model, since the enolization and subsequent dissociation of the uracil N_1 hydrogen would eliminate this group as a hydrogen bond donor[12].

Felsenfeld has made an intensive quantitative study of the extent of binding of Mg^{++} or Mn^{++} required to allow formation of the $(A+U)$ complex to proceed to completion in the absence of any other electrolyte[80, 81]. In this study spectrophotometric measurements of the decrease in absorbency at 259 mμ were combined with conductiometric titration data.

In water the binding properties of poly A and poly U were found to be identical. In both cases the *end point* occurred sharply when one equivalent of Mg^{++} or Mn^{++} was bound per phosphate group. In view of the similar behavior of poly A and poly U it is quite likely that the site of binding is the phosphate group.

For a 1 : 1 mixture at a total nucleotide concentration of $7.4 \cdot 10^{-4}$, the reaction proceeds to completion when one equivalent of divalent cation is bound per phosphate. At lower nucleotide concentrations a slight excess of divalent cation is required, which increases with decreasing nucleotide concentration. This may reflect some dissociation of the Mg^{++} or Mn^{++} complex at low nucleotide concentrations.

Felsenfeld has also studied the effect of the addition of various amino acids upon the interaction. While glycine, which possesses no net charge at neutral pH, is inactive, the cationic forms of lysine and histidine do promote the interaction, being roughly equivalent to NaCl.

Qualitatively it appears to be clear that the factor dominating the rate of poly A–poly U combination is the degree of masking of the electrostatic repulsion resulting from the similarly charged phosphates. The enhanced effect of the divalent cations almost certainly reflects the extensive binding of these cations by the phosphates. As a consequence of the charge neutralization accompanying binding, the electrostatic repulsion arising from the similarly charged phosphates is greatly reduced, permitting the reaction to occur. Binding of the univalent cations is much less pronounced. In this case the reduction in electrostatic repulsion probably proceeds primarily via a screening of the negative charges by counterions.

The poly A–poly U interaction has been found to proceed to completion at nucleotide concentrations as low as 10^{-5} molar, indicating that the mutual affinity of the two polynucleotides is very high. This raises a question of the intrinsic reversibility of the process, with particular regard to the rate of dissociation of an adenine-uracil pair. This latter rate will, of course, govern the capacity of the

(A + U) complex to eliminate imperfections in its helical ordering by lateral slippage of the poly A and poly U strands. As a result of this *annealing* process an energetically favored, highly helical final state, in which the maximum number of adenine–uracil linkages are formed, should be attainable. If the interaction were effectively irreversible such an elimination of "faults" and regions of mismatching would be impossible.

The problem has been resolved by the elegant analysis by Felsenfeld of the poly A–poly U mixing curves [79]. Starting with the experimental fact that, depending upon the conditions, the mixing curves can have the form of two straight lines intersecting at $X_u = 0.50$, or at $X_u = 0.67$, he was able to show, by the analysis discussed in the preceding chapter, that such behavior was only consistent with an interaction which was reversible and which proceeded to completion.

Further, more direct, evidence for the reversibility of the process, resulted from the observation that the addition of an excess of poly A to a complex preformed at a high U : A mole ratio resulted in a drop in molecular weight, as would be expected if the equilibrium were displaced [12] in the direction $AU_2 + A \rightarrow AU$.

If the kinetics of the interaction process are followed by means of light scattering at a neutral pH and a high ionic strength (0.5), it is found that the molecular weight attains a value close to its final one very quickly [12]. However, a slow increase in radius of gyration, which proceeds over several hours at room temperature, is, as Figs. 62 and 63 show, observed. This almost certainly reflects the relatively slow

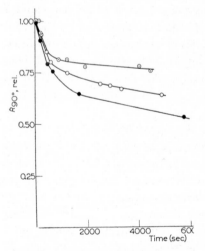

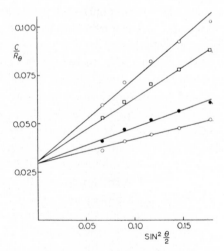

Fig. 62. Change with time of relative reduced intensity at 90° for poly A-poly U mixtures of varying A : U mole ratio[12]. The solvent is 0.5 M KCl, 0.01 M NaOAc, pH 6.5; $T = 26°$ C. The molecular weights of the poly A and poly U are $2.2 \cdot 10^6$ and $7.0 \cdot 10^5$, respectively. The total concentration is 0.05 g/l. ⊙ A:U = 3.95; ○ A:U = 1.52; • A:U = 0.99.

Fig. 63. Angular variation of reciprocal reduced intensity for the system of Fig. 62 as a function of time[12]. The concentrations of poly A and poly U are 0.0282 g/l and 0.0286 g/l respectively. ○ 200 sec after mixing; • 1000 sec; □ 13,400 sec; ○ 24 h.

elimination of residual defects and areas of mismatching by mutual slippage of the chains. The removal of such defects presumably results in the formation of a more perfect helical structure and thus corresponds to a directly observable molecular annealing process. This serves to enhance the rigidity of the molecule by eliminating the *hinge points* occurring at regions of mismatching. This increase in rigidity is reflected by an apparent extension of the molecule.

At pH's acid to the zone of titration of the adenine group, the rate of interaction of poly A and poly U falls off rapidly, becoming immeasurably slow[12] at pH 5.3. This indicates that only the alkaline form of poly A interacts with poly U.

Hydrogen ion titration data indicate that the alkaline branch of the titration curve of the equimolar AU complex displays a very rapid rise at about pH 10, depending upon the temperature and ionic strength[13]. Thus the titration curve of the uracil groups is both displaced and sharpened as a result of their involvement in the helical complex with poly A. Ultraviolet spectral data, in agreement with the above, show that the absorbency at 259 mμ of the equimolar complex is constant until a critical alkaline pH is attained and then displays an almost discontinuous increase to a value corresponding to that for the non-associated mixture as Fig. 64 shows[12].

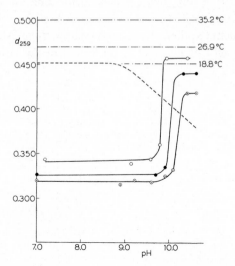

Fig. 64. Variation in absorbency[12] at alkaline pH for an equimolar poly A-poly U mixture in 0.10 *M* KCl. The dashed line (---) shows the variation for poly U alone at the same total concentrations (4.6 · 10⁻⁵ molar). The dots and dashes (-.-.-.) show the variation for poly A alone (4.6 · 10⁻⁵ molar) at the indicated temperatures. ⊙ 18.8° C; • 26.9° C; ○ 35.2° C.

Analogously, the absorbency of the complex is almost independent of temperature at neutral pH until a critical temperature range is attained, at which point the absorbency increases very sharply to that predicted for the non-associated mixture[7, 13]. The *melting point*, or midpoint of the thermal transition, increases with increasing ionic strength[11].

References p. 235/236

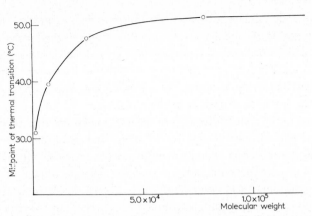

Fig. 65. Dependence of the midpoint of the thermal transition of the poly A plus poly U equimolar complex upon the molecular weight of the poly A component[11]. The solvent is 0.1 M KCl, 0.01 M NaOAc, pH 6.5. The poly A preparations were obtained by controlled alkaline degradation of a single sample. Molecular weights were computed from the sedimentation coefficient, using the relation of Fresco and Doty[18].

The position of the melting point is dependent upon the degree of polymerization[11] of the poly A and poly U. For a single poly U preparation with $S_0{}^{20°}$ equal to $8.5 \cdot 10^{-13}$, the melting point of the equimolar complex is almost independent of the molecular weight of the poly A for values of the latter greater than 10^5

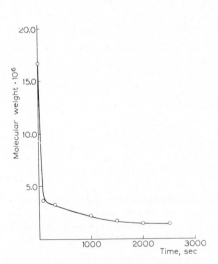

Fig. 66. Fall in molecular weight with time[12] for a poly A plus poly U mixture at pH 10.4. The solvent is 0.5 M KCl. The concentrations of poly A and of poly U are 0.025 g/l and 0.085 g/l, respectively. The preparations are the same as those of Fig. 62.

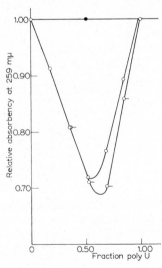

Fig. 67. Relative absorbency at 259 mμ as a function of composition for mixtures[82] of poly U ($S_0{}^{20°}=8.5 \cdot 10^{-13}$) with several AU copolymers in 0.1 M KCl and 0.01 M NaOAc, pH 6.5. The temperature is 26° C. o poly AU, 18% U, $S_0{}^{20°}=$ $8.3 \cdot 10^{-13}$; o poly AU, 38% U, $S_0{}^{20°}=4.6 \cdot 10^{-13}$; • poly AU, 50% U, $S_0{}^{20°}=2.7 \cdot 10^{-13}$.

(Fig. 65). At lower molecular weights the melting point falls off rapidly and the transition becomes less abrupt (Fig. 65).

The type of behavior described above for the alkaline and thermal "denaturation" processes is characteristic of the cooperative quasiphase transitions which will be discussed in a later chapter.

TABLE 24

THE EFFECT OF ALKALINE pH UPON THE STATE OF ASSOCIATION OF THE POLY A — POLY U COMPLEX

Composition of solution	pH	Treatment	Time at cited pH	$M_w \cdot 10^{-6}$
poly A*, 0.025 g/l; poly U**, 0.085 g/l; 0.5 M KCl	6.7		24 hours	16.7
same	10.4	pH altered by addition of $CO_3^=$ buffer to molarity of 0.01	2500 sec	1.6
same	9.0	pH readjusted by dropwise addition of 0.1 M HCl	500 sec	4.1

* $M_w = 2.2 \cdot 10^6$.   ** $M_w = 7.0 \cdot 10^5$.

Thus the (A+U) complex can undergo a denaturation very similar in many ways to that of natural DNA. However, unlike the natural DNA case, alkaline denaturation of the (A+U) complex appears to result in some actual separation of the strands, manifested by a pronounced drop in molecular weight as Fig. 66 and Table 24 show[12]. Upon reneutralization of the solution an increase in molecular weight occurs, but not to the original value. This may possibly be the result of some alkaline degradation.

It has also been found that copolymers of adenylic and uridylic acids can interact with poly U provided that the fraction of uridylic residues[82] in the poly AU is less than about 0.40. Dilution of the poly A chain to this extent leaves almost unchanged the branch of the mixing curve corresponding to mole fractions of uridylic residues (in poly U) less than 0.50, at temperatures below the melting point (Fig. 67).

However, the temperature zone at which thermal denaturation occurs is displaced progressively to lower temperatures with increasing substitution of the poly A, and the transition becomes less abrupt, as Fig. 68 shows.

THE ORDERED SYSTEMS: POLY A+POLY I AND POLY I+POLY C

The hypoxanthine base of inosinic acid has the potentiality of hydrogen bonding with adenine[3]. It has been shown by Rich that a complexing reaction between poly A and poly I does occur in solution[83]. Like the poly A + poly U interaction the process is reflected by a pronounced alteration in the ultraviolet absorption spectrum and the drop in absorbency at 254 mμ may be used as a convenient index of the extent of reaction.

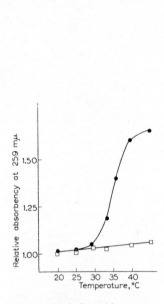

Fig. 68. Variation with temperature of relative absorbency[82] at 259 mμ of equimolar mixtures of poly U with poly A and with poly AU (38% U). The solvent is 0.1 M KCl, 0.01 M NaOAc, pH 6.5. • poly AU; □ poly A.

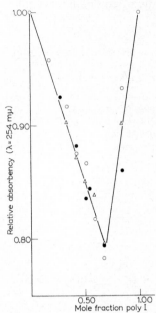

Fig. 69. Equilibrium mixing curves[11] for poly A plus poly I at 26° C. The solvent is 0.001 M NaOAc, plus NaCl to indicated molarity. The different points correspond to different ionic strengths. The molecular weights of the poly A and poly I are 5.6 · 10⁵ and 2.5 · 10⁵, respectively. ○ 0.1 M NaCl; • 0.2 M NaCl; △ 0.33 M NaCl.

In both its kinetics and stoichiometry this process is very reminiscent of the poly A + poly U interaction. Thus the equilibrium mixing curves at ionic strengths of 0.1 or greater are V-shaped and linear, with a sharp minimum at a mole fraction (X_I) of poly I equal to 0.67 (Fig. 69). At short reaction times there is some indication of a transient minimum at $X_I = 0.50$ (34). Thus, although there has been made no analysis as rigorous as for the (A + U) reaction, the existing data are entirely consistent with, and suggest, a basically similar molecular mechanism consisting of the combination of linear poly A and poly I strands to form a doubly stranded complex and the addition, at high I : A mole ratios, of a second poly I strand. In view of the linearity of the mixing curves, it is reasonable to make a similar conclusion about the reversibility of the process.

The rate of interaction of poly A and poly I is strongly dependent upon ionic strength. The rate increases markedly with increasing ionic strength and, as in the poly A+poly U case, divalent cations exert a disproportionate affect in enhancing the rate.

Formaldehyde pretreatment of the poly A results in the abolition of the (A+I) interaction[11]. This strongly suggests that the 6-amino group of adenine is, as in the poly A+poly U case, essential for the interaction, in all probability as a hydrogen bond donor.

Rich has concluded, upon the basis of analysis of the X-ray diffraction pattern of oriented fibers, that the (A+I) equimolar complex has the configuration of a doubly stranded helix stabilized by hydrogen bonding corresponding to pair 7

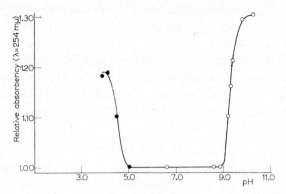

Fig. 70. Variation with pH of the relative absorbency[11] at 254 mμ of equimolar poly A plus poly I mixtures in 0.1 M NaCl. The temperature is 26° C. The preparations are those of Fig. 69.

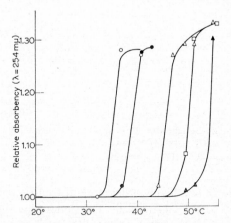

Fig. 71. Variation with temperature of the relative absorbency at 254 mμ of equimolar poly A plus poly I mixtures at pH 6.5 and varying ionic strengths[11]. The total concentration is 2.1 · 10⁻⁵ moles nucleotide/l. The buffer is 0.001 M NaOAc; o 0.068 M NaCl; • 0.095 M NaCl; △ 0.205 M NaCl; □ 0.308 M NaCl; ▲ 0.545 M NaCl.

cited by Donohue[3], with hypoxanthine replacing guanine. According to this model the stabilizing hydrogen bonding is between the C_6 amino group of adenine and the C_6 carbonyl of hypoxanthine and between the N_1 nitrogen of adenine and the N_1 nitrogen of hypoxanthine.

The (A + I) equimolar complex has been found to undergo denaturation at extremes of pH and at elevated temperatures (Figs. 70 and 71). As in the (A + U) case, the process may be conveniently followed by observing the absorbency at 254 mμ. For poly A and poly I of reasonably high molecular weight (10^5), the alkaline and thermal transitions are remarkably sharp and have the characteristics of cooperative processes.

In the case of the thermal transition the position of the "melting point" or midpoint of the transition is very dependent upon ionic strength and is displaced to higher temperatures with increasing ionic strength (Fig. 71). The addition of Mg^{++} also serves to raise the melting point. The presence of urea lowers the melting point[11]. However, the transition retains its sharpness over the complete range of ionic strengths studied.

As in the poly A plus poly U case, denaturation is accompanied by a pronounced drop in molecular weight, suggesting that the process involves an actual separation of the poly A and poly I strands (Table 25). Both the thermal and alkaline denaturations are quantitatively reversible, as judged by spectral and light scattering data.

TABLE 25

VARIATION OF THE MOLECULAR WEIGHT OF A POLY A — POLY I

MIXTURE WITH TEMPERATURE

Concn. Poly A XXI (g/l)	Concn. Poly I IV (g/l)	Temperature (°C)	M_W^*
0.021	0.024	21.0	$2.5 \cdot 10^6$
		30.5	$2.5 \cdot 10^6$
		35.0	$2.5 \cdot 10^6$
		38.0	$2.5 \cdot 10^6$
		41.6	$0.885 \cdot 10^6$
		44.6	$0.80 \cdot 10^6$

* Weight-average molecular weight after 30 minutes at indicated temperature.
The solvent is 0.1 M NaCl, 0.001 M NaOAc, pH 6.6. The molecular weights of the poly A and poly I are $5.6 \cdot 10^5$ and $2.5 \cdot 10^5$, respectively.

Still another example of a highly ordered multistranded complex is furnished by the interaction[84] of poly I and poly C. This interesting interaction, which was discovered by Davies and Rich[84] is, like the processes described earlier, reflected by a profound alteration in the ultraviolet absorption spectrum, corresponding at most wavelengths to an increase in hypochromism, as Fig. 72 shows.

If the absorbency at 235 mμ is taken as a direct measure of the extent of reaction, the mixing curve at an ionic strength of 0.1 and neutral pH was found to consist of two straight lines intersecting sharply at a 1 : 1 mole ratio[84]. The same kind of argument as was applied earlier to the (A + U) and (A + I) cases indicates that the reaction is reversible and stoichiometric and that the complex is two stranded (or conceivably four stranded). No evidence for the formation of an (I+2C) species has as yet been reported.

The formation of the equimolar complex could also be followed in the ultra-centrifuge. At neutral pH and ionic strength 0.1, the sedimentation constant of the 1 : 1 complex ($S_0^{20°}=13.9 \cdot 10^{-13}$) was found to be considerably greater than that of the separate poly I ($S_0^{20°}=7.4 \cdot 10^{-13}$) and poly C ($S_0^{20°}=5.5 \cdot 10^{-13}$) components.

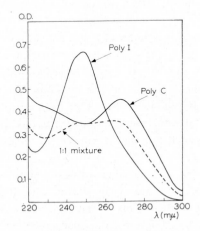

Fig. 72. The ultraviolet absorption spectra of poly I, poly C, and a 1 : 1 mixture of the two[84]. The solvent is 0.1 M NaCl, 0.01 M NaOAc, pH 7.4. The temperature is 23° C.

As in the case of the other systems both the extent and the rate of reaction are controlled by the concentration of electrolyte present. For the above preparations no reaction at all occurred in 10^{-4} M NaCl. In 0.01 M NaCl the reaction required two hours to reach equilibrium and in 0.10 M NaCl only a few minutes.

The detailed fine structure of the (I+C) complex is still uncertain. The X-ray diffraction pattern of fibers of this material does not seem to resemble that obtained in the (A+U) and (A+I) cases but, rather surprisingly, is quite similar to that of natural RNA[84].

THE ORDERED SYSTEMS: POLY I

It has already been mentioned that the available evidence appears to indicate that poly I has an essentially unorganized structure at pH's alkaline to the zone of titration of its hypoxanthine groups. However, at more acid pH's there is strong evidence for the existence of some degree of molecular organization.

Thus it was found by Rich[85] that the optical density at 250 mμ of a poly I solution at pH 7 decreased by 18 per cent as the molarity of NaCl increased from 0.01 to 1.0. This ionic strength-dependent enhancement of hypochromism suggested that a corresponding alteration in secondary structure was occurring.

Furthermore, the sedimentation coefficient of the same poly I sample showed a parallel ionic strength dependence, increasing from 5.9 svedbergs in 0.2 M NaCl to 8.9 svedbergs in 0.65 M NaCl. In 1.0 M NaCl molecular aggregation proceeded to a quite high level; a very diffuse and rapidly sedimenting boundary being observed.

The observed alteration in properties which accompanied ionization of the hypoxanthine group was also suggestive of a change in the extent of molecular organization. Thus the sedimentation coefficient of the same poly I preparation dropped to 2.4 svedbergs at pH 10 (in 0.1 M NaCl). This was accompanied by a marked loss in hypochromism, which was completely reversed upon readjustment of the pH to neutrality.

Similarly, the ultraviolet absorbency of poly I has been found to be temperature dependent[7]. However, the increase with increasing temperature occurs at somewhat lower temperatures than in the case of the other ordered systems discussed earlier and moreover appears to be relatively gradual.

Thus the available data on the solution properties of poly I are consistent with the existence of an ordered, multi-stranded structure, the extent of formation of which depends upon such external parameters as ionic strength, temperature, and pH.

Rich has also found that oriented fibers of poly I show a pronounced negative birefringence[85]. An analysis of the X-ray diffraction pattern produced by such fibers has led Rich to propose a triply stranded helical structure for poly I. This structure is of a type quite different from that suggested for the (A+2U) and (A+2I) molecular complexes. The scheme of inter-base bonding proposed corresponds to cyclic triads which are stabilized by hydrogen bonds between C_6 carbonyls and the N_1 positions of the hypoxanthine groups. A total of three hydrogen bonds is formed. However, the available data were not sufficiently conclusive to exclude the possibility of a four-stranded structure.

To what extent the structure prevailing in solution can be equated to that observed for the solid state remains uncertain. It is clear that molecular aggregates persist in solution and that their formation appears to be correlated with an increase in hypochromism. Certainly the most plausible working hypothesis is to identify these aggregates provisionally with the helical triplet believed to occur in the solid state.

The explanation for the relatively gradual thermal transition is also unclear. It may be that the helical content in solution is only fractional. As will be discussed in Chapter 8, an intermittently helical system would be expected to behave in this manner.

THE ORDERED SYSTEMS: THE ACID FORM OF POLY A

It was early observed by Beers and Steiner[15] that the hydrogen ion titration curve of poly A was distinctly anomalous. The onset of hydrogen ion binding occurred at about pH 6, depending upon the ionic strength and temperature, whereas the pK of the adenine group itself is at about 3.8. As approximately one equivalent of hydrogen ions per nucleotide unit was bound by the group titrating at pH 6, this binding could not possibly be attributed to secondary phosphate groups, especially in the absence of any evidence for branching. Moreover, the titration curve was abnormally steepened, the initial rise being almost vertical until about 0.5 equivalents of hydrogen ion were bound per nucleotide unit, with a gradual levelling off subsequently. This type of behavior was strongly suggestive of a cooperative structural transition.

The exact form of the titration curve was very dependent upon the ionic strength and temperature, although the general appearance remained the same. An increase in ionic strength or temperature resulted in a displacement of the initial sharp region of the titration curve to lower pH's, as Figs. 73 and 74 show.

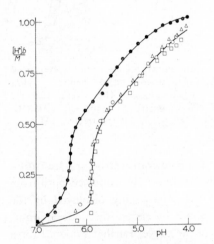 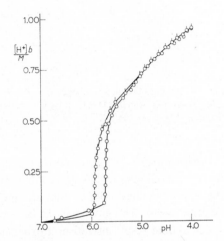

Fig. 73. Hydrogen ion titration curves[14] of poly A at two ionic strengths at 26° C. The molecular weight is $2.5 \cdot 10^6$. ● 0.01 M KCl, $0.53 \cdot 10^{-3}$ moles nucleotide/l; ○ 0.1 M KCl, $0.10 \cdot 10^{-3}$ moles nucleotide/l; △ 0.1 M KCl, $0.27 \cdot 10^{-3}$ moles nucleotide/l; □ 0.1 M KCl, $0.46 \cdot 10^{-3}$ moles nucleotide/l.

Fig. 74. Hydrogen ion titration curve[14] of poly A at two temperatures in 0.1 M KCl. The molecular weight is $3.0 \cdot 10^6$. The concentration of poly A is $0.52 \cdot 10^{-3}$ moles nucleotide/l. ◊ $T = 26°$ C; ○ $T = 40°$ C.

Formaldehyde pretreatment of the poly A was found largely to eliminate the binding of protons at pH's alkaline to 5.0[15, 86]. This, and the stoichiometry of the process, indicated fairly conclusively that the adenine group itself was being titrated in this region.

It was also found that a discontinuous change in the ultraviolet absorption spectrum occurred in the pH region corresponding to the sharpest portion of the titration curve, as Figs. 75 and 76 show. The hypochromism is increased and the position of the maximum is shifted from about 257 mμ to 252 mμ. The influence of temperature and ionic strength upon the spectral transition paralled entirely their effect upon the titration curve. Formaldehyde pretreatment of the poly A abolished the spectral shift entirely.

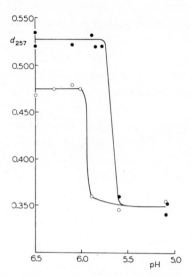

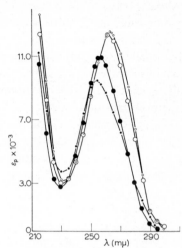

Fig. 75. The decrease in absorbency at acid pH for poly A in 0.1 M KCl at two temperatures[14]. o 28° C; • 49° C.

Fig. 76. The ultraviolet absorption spectrum of poly A at neutral and acid pH, before and after formaldehyde treatment[14]. The solvent is 0.01 M KCl; T=26° C. ● pH 7.0; • pH 5.0; o HCHO-treated, pH 7.0; o HCHO-treated, pH 5.0.

It was clear from these results that some form of cooperative structural transition was accompanying the binding of a proton by adenine. This followed both from the abnormal elevation of the pK and the hypersharpening displayed by the titration curve. The latter cannot be accounted for by electrostatic effects alone, which should result instead in a broadening of the curve. Further evidence for a structural transition was furnished by the large increase in dextrorotation accompanying the titration of the adenine group[10].

The abolition of the spectral transition and the elimination of proton binding in the region of pH 5–6 by formaldehyde pretreatment indicated that the C$_6$ amino group of adenine was probably directly involved in the acid-stable form. The effect of Ca^{++} in displacing the zone of hydrogen ion binding to lower pH's suggested that the phosphate group likewise was important[86].

Other evidence, including the effect of increased ionic strength in displacing the transition to lower pH's and the failure of urea to inhibit the transition[16], suggested that electrostatic forces were important in stabilizing the acid form or forms of poly A and that the transition involved the juxtaposition of a positively charged adenine with a negatively charged phosphate.

Unfortunately, the alteration in physical properties accompanying the titration of adenine presents a far from clear-cut picture. Thus the size and shape of the acid-stable form are very dependent upon the exact manner in which the transition is carried out, as Table 26 shows.

Some increase in molecular weight is always observed. Its magnitude increases sharply with increasing ionic strength and with increasing concentration of poly A.

TABLE 26

MOLECULAR WEIGHTS AND DIMENSIONS OF POLYRIBOADENYLIC ACID AT ACID AND ALKALINE pH'S

Preparation	pH	Solvent	Max. concn.*	M_w** $\cdot$ 10^{-6}	$R_g(\text{Å})$***
Poly A XIV	6.5	0.01 M NaOAc, 0.1 M KCl		2.2	840
	4.1	0.01 M NaOAc, 0.1 M KCl	0.044	13.3	1410
	4.1	0.01 M NaOAc, 0.1 M KCl, 7.7 M urea	0.046	6.6	
Poly A XV	6.5	0.01 M NaOAc		2.50	1090
	4.7	0.01 M NaOAc	0.028	3.7	690
	4.7	0.01 M NaOAc	0.47	4.2	760
Poly AU III****	6.5	0.01 M NaOAc, 0.1 M KCl		0.48	450
	3.3	0.01 M NaOAc, 0.1 M KCl	0.083	0.52	240
Poly A XVII	6.5	0.01 M NaOAc, 0.1 M KCl		2.4	770
	5.6	0.1 M NaOAc	0.115	2.7	830
	5.6	0.1 M NaOAc	0.69	5.5	1620
Poly A XX	6.5	0.01 M NaOAc, 0.1 M KCl		0.44	400
	4.0	0.01 M NaOAc, 0.1 M KCl	0.065	1.54	680
	4.0	pH altered in H₂O, then electrolyte added to 0.01 M NaOAc, 0.1 M KCl	0.065	1.02	570

* When cited refers to the concentration at which the pH was altered to an acid value.
** Weight-average molecular weight.
*** Weight-average radius of gyration, computed assuming a *random* distribution of particle sizes.
****Adenylic-uridylic copolymer (25 per cent U).

Under the appropriate conditions, increases in molecular weight of tenfold or more are observed.

For a given ionic strength and poly A concentration, the size and shape depend upon the order of addition of electrolyte. If the pH of a salt-free solution is altered to an acid value and then electrolyte added to a given ionic strength, the increase in molecular weight is less and the relative extension greater than if the pH is altered in the presence of salt, as Table 26 shows.

If the acidification is made at very low ionic strength (0.01) and polymer concentration (<0.1 g/l) an actual drop in radius of gyration occurs, despite the simultaneous occurrence of an increase in molecular weight.

Centering attention upon the properties of the aggregates, Fresco and Doty were able to prepare a homologous series of these by varying the concentration of poly A at which acidification occurred[18]. The pH was altered to an acid value in water and then electrolyte added to an ionic strength of 0.15. Under these conditions the aggregates appeared to be homologous, yielding a linear logarithmic relationship between intrinsic viscosity and molecular weight. From the exponen-

References p. 235/236

tial dependence of viscosity upon molecular weight ($[\eta] = K M^{0.91}$) it was concluded that the aggregates formed under these conditions were more rigid than the alkaline form of poly A.

Fresco also found X-ray evidence that the acid-stable aggregates had an ordered helical structure and postulated that this could be identified with the doubly stranded helical structure proposed by Rich and co-workers[10]. This proposal was particularly attractive in view of the fact that the latter structure predicted a close approach of the adenine and phosphate groups and invoked the presence of a hydrogen bond between the C_6 amino group of adenine and the phosphate. Such a structure would thus acquire great stability from favorable electrostatic factors.

However, the relatively limited extent of aggregation observed when the transition is carried out at very low concentration and low ionic strength suggests that an alternative intramolecular process may also occur under these conditions. This might involve the formation of hairpin-like helical regions, possibly of the same type as those occurring in the alkaline form of poly A. The molecular shrinkage occurring under these conditions is probably explicable by the occurrence of numerous faults or gaps in the ordered structure, which endow it with sufficient flexibility to shrink upon the relief of electrostatic stress following the titration of the adenine group.

REFERENCES

[1] J. Watson and F. Crick, *Nature*, 171 (1953) 737.
[2] M. Feughelman, R. Langridge, W. Seeds, A. Stokes, H. Wilson, C. Hooper, M. Wilkins, R. Barclay and L. Hamilton, *Nature*, 175 (1955) 834.
[3] J. Donohue, *Proc. Natl. Acad. Sci.*, 42 (1956) 60.
[4] L. Pauling and R. Corey, *Arch. Biochem. Biophys.*, 65 (1956) 164.
[5] A. Rich, *Rev. Mod. Phys.*, 31 (1959) 191.
[6] J. Marmur and P. Doty, *Nature*, 183 (1959) 1426.
[7] P. Doty, H. Boedtker, J. Fresco, R. Haselkorn and M. Litt, *Proc. Natl. Acad. Sci.*, 45 (1959) 482.
[8] J. Schellman, *Compt. rend. trav. lab. Carlsberg, Ser. Chim.*, 29 (1955) 223, 230.
[9] A. Rich, in W. McElroy and B. Glass, *The Chemical Basis of Heredity*, Baltimore, 1957, p. 557.
[10] J. Fresco, *Trans. New York Acad. Sci.*, 21 (1959) 653.
[11] R. Steiner, unpublished data.
[12] R. Steiner and R. Beers, *Biochim. et Biophys. Acta*, 33 (1959) 470.
[13] R. Warner, *Proc. Fourth Int. Congress of Biochemistry*, Vienna, 1958, vol. IX.
[14] R. Steiner and R. Beers, *Biochim. et Biophys. Acta*, 26 (1957) 336.
[15] R. Beers and R. Steiner, *Nature*, 179 (1957) 1076.
[16] R. Steiner and R. Beers, *Biochim. et Biophys. Acta*, 32 (1959) 166.
[17] L. Treloar, *Proc. Phys. Soc. (London)*, 55 (1943) 345.
[18] J. Fresco and P. Doty, *J. Am. Chem. Soc.*, 79 (1957) 3928.
[19] P. Flory, *Principles of Polymer Chemistry*, Ithaca, 1953.
[20] C. Hall, *Proc. Fourth Int. Congress of Biochem.*, 1958, vol. IX.
[21] R. Warner, *J. Biol. Chem.*, 229 (1957) 711.
[22] A. Michelson, *J. Chem. Soc.*, (1959) 1371.
[23] A. Gierer and G. Schramm, *Nature*, 177 (1956) 702.
[24] H. Fraenkel-Conrat, *J. Am. Chem. Soc.*, 78 (1956) 882.
[25] B. Commoner, *Cellular Biology, Nucleic Acids, and Viruses*, N.Y. Acad. Sci., (1957) 237.
[26] H. Boedtker and N. Simmons, *J. Am. Chem. Soc.*, 80 (1958) 2550.
[27] C. Knight, *Advances in Virus Research*, New York, 2 (1954) 153.
[28] J. Watson, *Biochim. et Biophys. Acta*, 13 (1954) 10.
[29] R. Franklin, *Nature*, 175 (1955) 379.
[30] F. Crick and J. Watson, *Nature*, 177 (1956) 473.
[31] H. Schuster, G. Schramm and W. Zillig, *Z. Naturforsch.*, 11b (1956) 339.
[32] G. Hopkins and R. Sinsheimer, *Biochim. et Biophys. Acta*, 17 (1955) 476.
[33] A. Gierer, *Nature*, 179 (1957) 1297.
[34] H. Boedtker, *Biochim. et Biophys. Acta*, 32 (1959) 519.
[35] U. Littauer and H. Eisenberg, *Biochim. et Biophys, Acta*, 32 (1959) 320.
[36] B. Hall and P. Doty, *Microsomal Particles and Protein Synthesis*, Washington Academy of Sciences, 1958.
[37] S. Timasheff, R. Brown, J. Colter and M. Davies, *Biochim. et Biophys. Acta*, 27 (1958) 662.
[38] M. Grunberg-Manago, *Biokhimiia*, 23 (1958) 287.
[39] R. Haschemeyer, B. Singer and H. Fraenkel-Conrat, *Proc. Natl. Acad. Sci*, 45 (1959) 313.
[40] A. Bendich, H. Pahl, G. Korngold, H. Rosenkrantz and J. Fresco, *J. Am. Chem. Soc.*, 80 (1955) 3949.
[41] K. Shooter and J. Butler, *Nature*, 177 (1956) 1033.
[42] K. Shooter and J. Butler, *Trans. Faraday Soc.*, 52 (1956) 734.
[43] J. Butler, *Proc. Fourth Int. Congress of Biochemistry, Vienna*, 1958, vol. IX.
[44] E. Geiduschek and A. Holtzer, *Advances in Biological and Medical Physics, New York*, 6 (1958) 431.
[45] B. Conway and J. Butler, *J. Polymer Sci.*, 12 (1954) 199.
[46] J. Pouyet, *Compt. rend.*, 234 (1952) 152.
[47] P. Doty, B. McGill and S. Rice, *Proc. Natl. Acad. Sci.*, 44 (1958) 432.
[48] A. Peterlin, *J. Polymer Sci.*, 10 (1953) 425.
[49] G. Porod, *Monatsh. Chem.*, 80 (1949) 251.
[50] C. Hall, *Ann. N.Y. Acad. Sci.*, 81 (1959) 723.
[51] C. Thomas, *J. Am. Chem. Soc.*, 78 (1956) 1861.

[52] P. ALEXANDER AND K. STACEY, *Biochem. J.*, 60 (1955) 194.

[53] L. CAVALIERI AND B. ROSENBERG, *J. Am. Chem. Soc.*, 79 (1957) 5352.

[54] L. CAVALIERI AND A. STONE, *J. Am. Chem. Soc.*, 77 (1955) 6499.

[55] D. JORDAN, in E. CHARGAFF AND J. DAVIDSON, *The Nucleic Acids*, New York, 1955, p. 447.

[56] R. COX AND A. PEACOCKE, *J. Chem. Soc.*, (1956) 2499.

[57] R. COX AND A. PEACOCKE, *J. Chem. Soc.*, (1957) 4724.

[58] J. GULLAND, D. JORDAN AND H. TAYLOR, *J. Chem. Soc.*, (1947) 1131.

[59] D. JORDAN, A. MATHIESON AND S. MATTY, *J. Chem. Soc.*, (1956) 154.

[60] C. SADRON, *Proc. Third. Int. Cong. Biochem., Brussels*, 1955, p. 125.

[61] J. CREETH, J. GULLAND AND D. JORDAN, *J. Chem. Soc.*, (1947) 1141.

[62] R. THOMAS, *Bull. soc. chim. Biol.*, 35 (1953) 609.

[63] R. THOMAS, *Biochim. et Biophys. Acta*, 14 (1954) 231.

[64] C. HALL AND M. LITT, *J. Biophys. and Biochem. Cytol.*, 4 (1958) 1.

[65] P. DOTY, *J. Cell. and Comp. Phys.*, 49, Suppl. 1 (1957) 27.

[66] M. REICHMANN, B. BUNCE AND P. DOTY, *J. Polymer Sci.*, 10 (1953) 109.

[67] P. HORN, J. LERAY, J. POUYET AND C. SADRON, *J. Polymer Sci.*, 9 (1952) 531.

[68] J. STURTEVANT, S. RICE AND E. GEIDUSCHEK, *Disc. Faraday Soc.*, 25 (1958) 138.

[69] A. PEACOCKE, *Disc. Faraday Soc.*, 25 (1958) 213.

[70] C. THOMAS AND P. DOTY, *J. Am. Chem. Soc.*, 78 (1956) 1854.

[71] S. KATZ, *J. Am. Chem. Soc.*, 74 (1952) 2238.

[72] R. SINSHEIMER, *J. Molec. Biol.*, 1 (1959) 43.

[73] R. WARNER, *Fed. Proc.*, 15 (1956) 379.

[74] R. WARNER, *Ann., N.Y. Acad. Sci.*, 69 (1957) 314.

[75] H. MILES, *Biochim. et Biophys. Acta*, 30 (1958) 324.

[76] A. RICH AND D. DAVIES, *J. Am. Chem. Soc.*, 78 (1956) 3548.

[77] G. FELSENFELD, D. DAVIES AND A. RICH, *J. Am. Chem. Soc.*, 79 (1957) 2023.

[78] G. FELSENFELD AND A. RICH, *Biochim. et Biophys. Acta*, 26 (1957) 457.

[79] G. FELSENFELD, *Biochim. et Biophys. Acta*, 29 (1958) 133.

[80] G. FELSENFELD AND S. HUANG, *Biochim. et Biophys. Acta*, 34 (1959) 234.

[81] G. FELSENFELD AND S. HUANG, *Biochim. et Biophys. Acta*, 37 (1960) 425.

[82] R. STEINER, *Ann. N.Y. Acad. Sci.*, 81 (1959) 742.

[83] A. RICH, *Nature*, 181 (1958) 521.

[84] D. DAVIES AND A. RICH, *J. Am. Chem. Soc.*, 80 (1958) 1003.

[85] A. RICH, *Biochim. et Biophys. Acta*, 29 (1958) 502.

[86] R. STEINER AND R. BEERS, *J. Polymer Sci.*, 31 (1958) 53.

Chapter 8

The Secondary Structure of the Ordered Polynucleotides

FUNDAMENTALS OF X-RAY DIFFRACTION

A detailed discussion of the theory and technique of X-ray diffraction is clearly beyond the scope of this book. In the section to follow it is not intended to attempt to do more than clarify the meaning of the commonly occurring concepts and terminology and discuss briefly the kinds of information obtainable. In no sense is this necessarily cursory exposition meant as a substitute for the complete treatments found in the standard texts[1-9].

X-rays are a form of electromagnetic radiation produced by the collision with a stationary target of a beam of electrons moving with high velocity. Although X-rays span the wavelength region from 0.01–1000 Å, only wavelengths between 0.7 and 2 Å are of importance for crystallographic purposes.

For diffraction work the K α line produced by X-ray tubes with a copper target is particularly popular. Its wavelength is 1.54 Å. This line is normally isolated from the K β line by the use of an appropriate filter, usually nickel. By this means a practically monochromatic beam may be obtained.

In this chapter we shall be concerned with the diffraction of X-rays by crystalline materials. An idealized perfect crystal is a highly regular arrangement of atoms with complete periodicity in all three dimensions, except of course for the inevitable discontinuity at the edges. Because of this property of periodicity any crystal may be regarded as made up of a number of repeating units. The crystal thus consists of a repetition of a three-dimensional pattern composed of a relatively small number of atoms.

The repeating group of atoms occupies a small parallelepiped, called the unit cell. This is characterized by the lengths of its edges, or axes, represented by the letters a, b, c, and by the included angles α, β, γ. The unit cell is normally defined by the smallest and least oblique parallelepiped possessing the full symmetry of the structure, although other parallelepipeds may be chosen in special circumstances.

As an aid to developing the basic theory of the diffraction of X-rays by real crystals it is convenient to introduce a simplified model which contains only a single type of point scatterer. The set of all atoms, each of which occupies the same position in the basic repeating unit, forms such a point lattice. A real crystal having S atoms in its unit cell consists of S interpenetrating point lattices, which are identical in geometrical form. Thus a description of the form and symmetry of the point lattice suffices to describe the scheme of repetition of the real crystal, but not the mutual arrangement of the different atoms in the unit cells.

There are 14 possible lattice types, all of which occur in actual crystals. In seven of these the unit cell is of the primitive type and may be formed by joining any lattice point with its three nearest non-coplanar neighbors and completing the parallelepiped. In these cases the simple cell formed in this way possesses the full symmetry of the lattice. In the remaining types the simple cell formed in this manner shows less than the full lattice symmetry. However, a multiple cell can be defined which does exhibit the full symmetry, which is the same as that of one of the seven simple lattices. The unit cell characteristics of the seven simple lattices are given in Table 27.

The various lattice types are subject to a number of symmetry operations which leave the lattice form unchanged.

Of these, rotation and rotation–inversion do not involve translation. Rotation as a symmetry operation refers to rotation thru $2\pi/n$ about an axis, where $n = 1, 2, 3, 4, 6*$. Rotation–inversion means rotation thru $2\pi/n$ about an axis, followed by inversion thru a point on the axis.

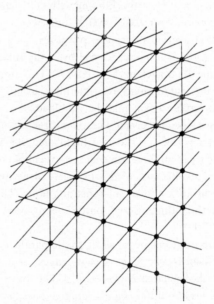

Fig. 77. Parallel planes drawn thru atoms in a cross-section of a crystal[3].

The symmetry elements which do involve translation are the screw axes and the glide planes. An n_p screw axis corresponds to an n-fold rotation with a translation of p/n of the unit length in the direction of the axis of rotation. The trans-

---

* Note that a five-fold rotation axis cannot occur.

lations accompanying a glide plane are always parallel to the plane and are a simple fraction of some cell dimension.

TABLE 27

LATTICE SYSTEMS

System	Elements
triclinic	$a, b, c; \alpha, \beta, \gamma$
monoclinic	$a, b, c; \beta, \gamma = \alpha = 90°$
orthorhombic	$a, b, c; \alpha = \beta = \gamma = 90°$
tetragonal	$c, a = b; \alpha = \beta = \gamma = 90°$
hexagonal	$c, a = b; \gamma = 120°; \alpha = \beta = 90°$
rhombohedral	$a = b = c; \alpha = \beta = \gamma$
cubic	$a = b = c; \alpha = \beta = \gamma = 90°$

Each point lattice contains many sets of parallel planes with constant spacing, as is illustrated by Figs. 77 and 78. Each set of planes may be conveniently characterized by three integral indices h, k, l, which are called Miller indices.

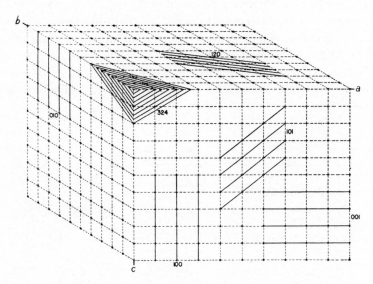

Fig. 78. Sets of parallel planes in a cubic crystal.

These are defined with respect to the crystal axes and are proportional to the reciprocals of the smallest integral intercepts of the planes at the three axes, being equal to the number of parts into which the set of planes subdivides the axial periods of the space lattice. Thus:

intercepts	indices
1 ∞ ∞	(100)
∞ 1 ∞	(010)
11 ∞	(110)
32 ∞	(230)
236	(321)
111	(111)

At a quite early stage in the development of X-ray diffraction, the scattering of X-rays by sets of parallel planes of constant separation d was considered by Bragg, who showed that, for an intense scattering or *reflection* of X-rays by such a system to occur, the following condition must hold[1-9]:

$$n\lambda = 2d \sin \theta \qquad (1)$$

Here λ is the wavelength of the (monochromatic) X-ray beam, θ is the angle between the beam and the reflecting planes, and n, an integer, is the order of the diffraction.

The Bragg equation is simply a statement of the requirement that, for constructive interference or reinforcement to occur, the path difference between X-rays reflected by successive planes of the set must be an integral multiple of λ, so that they are in phase. Each set of parallel planes, characterized by a particular set of Miller indices, will have its characteristic Bragg angle. Each set of planes in the space lattice will occur for each of the atoms in the repeating unit of the real lattice (Fig. 79).

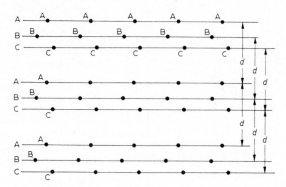

Fig. 79. Reflecting planes in a material with several atoms per repeating unit[3].

While the Bragg equation is basic to the theory of X-ray diffraction by crystals, it is obviously inadequate to the problem of describing diffraction by most real crystals, which contain more than one kind of atom. An adequate treatment of real systems requires a more complicated analysis, making use of the new concept of the reciprocal lattice.

The concept of reciprocity is really implicit in the Bragg relationship. At constant wavelength, θ varies inversely as d; so that the larger the spacings, the closer are the reflections to the direction of the incident beam.

The reciprocal lattice may be visualized as follows. Corresponding to the intersecting sets of parallel planes in the real space lattice there is a three dimensional network of points in the reciprocal lattice. Each infinite set of planes in real space may be represented by an infinite set of points along a direction parallel to that of the normal to the planes. The first point of the set, at distance λ/d from the origin, has coordinates h, k, l, corresponding to the indices of the set of planes which it represents. The other points will have coordinates $2h, 2k, 2l$; $3h, 3k, 3l$; etc., and distances from the origin equal to $2\lambda/d$, $3\lambda/d$, etc.

The lattice reciprocal to a given space lattice may formally be constructed as follows. An arbitrary origin is chosen, from which normals are erected to the different sets of planes of indices h, k, l. Point hkl in reciprocal space, corresponding to planes hkl, lies on this normal at a distance λ/d_{hkl} from the origin.

The unit cell of a space lattice may be defined by the three pairs of planes which form its sides. Their Miller indices are 100, 010, and 001. The three points reciprocal to these planes in reciprocal space will have coordinates 100, 010 and 001.

These three points, plus the origin, define a lattice of reciprocal points.

Like the real lattice, the reciprocal lattice is built up from unit cells. If the axes of the real unit cell are represented by the three vectors $\vec{a}$, $\vec{b}$, and $\vec{c}$, then the corresponding primitive translations for the reciprocal unit cell, $\vec{A}$, $\vec{B}$, and $\vec{C}$, observe the following relationships:

$$\vec{A} \cdot \vec{b} = \vec{A} \cdot \vec{c} = \vec{B} \cdot \vec{a} = \vec{C} \cdot \vec{a} = \vec{C} \cdot \vec{b} = \vec{B} \cdot \vec{c} = 0 \tag{2}$$

$$\vec{A} \cdot \vec{a} = \vec{B} \cdot \vec{b} = \vec{C} \cdot \vec{c} = \lambda \tag{3}$$

Equation (2) expresses the fact that the tranlation $\vec{A}$ of the reciprocal unit cell is perpendicular to the bc plane of the real unit cell, etc. This follows obviously from the manner in which the reciprocal lattice has been defined above. From equations (2) and (3) the lengths of the axes of the reciprocal cell may be written down as:

$$|\vec{A}| = \lambda \sin \alpha / |\vec{a}| \Delta$$

$$|\vec{B}| = \lambda \sin \beta / |\vec{b}| \Delta$$

$$|\vec{C}| = \lambda \sin \gamma / |\vec{c}| \Delta$$

where

$$\Delta^2 = \begin{vmatrix} 1 & \cos\gamma & \cos\beta \\ \cos\gamma & 1 & \cos\alpha \\ \cos\beta & \cos\alpha & 1 \end{vmatrix}$$

and α, β, γ are the angles of the axes of the real lattice. If the real lattice is orthogonal the reciprocal lattice is orthogonal also and $\Delta = 1$. Thus, in this case, the lengths of the reciprocal axes are equal to $\lambda/|\vec{a}|$, $\lambda/|\vec{b}|$, and $\lambda/|\vec{c}|$, respectively.

From the manner in which the reciprocal lattice was generated, it has been shown that for each set of planes in the real lattice characterized by the three indices h, k, and l, there exists a point in the reciprocal lattice at a distance from the origin equal to λ/d_{hkl}, where d_{hkl} is the spacing of the hkl planes. Furthermore, the vector uniting each reciprocal lattice point with the origin is perpendicular to the corresponding plane in the real lattice. The latter vector has components $h\vec{A}$, $k\vec{B}$, and $l\vec{C}$ and the reciprocal lattice point itself may be characterized by the three numbers h, k, and l. The distance from the origin of each such point is equal to

$$(h^2|\vec{A}|^2 + k^2|\vec{B}|^2 + l^2|\vec{C}|^2)^{1/2}$$

and, for a cubic lattice, is given by

$$\frac{\lambda}{|\vec{a}|}(h^2 + k^2 + l^2)^{1/2}$$

From the manner in which the reciprocal lattice has been defined it is easy to see that for each Bragg reflection there is a reciprocal lattice point which may in fact be thought of as corresponding to this Bragg reflection. It might therefore be expected that the relationship of the reciprocal lattice to the observed diffraction pattern would be very close.

The introduction of a new concept, that of the *sphere of reflection*, helps to make the potentialities of the reciprocal lattice somewhat more evident. This is of unit radius, with the crystal at its center. The incident X-ray beam travels along a diameter of the sphere. Its point of exit from the sphere is taken as the origin of the reciprocal lattice. It may be shown that a strong diffraction is possible only if some point of the reciprocal lattice lies on the sphere of reflection, the direction of the diffracted beam being given by the vector uniting the center with the point of intersection. For a perfect lattice points of intersection are unlikely. However, if the lattice is slightly imperfect the points of the reciprocal lattice may be thought of as somewhat smeared out areas in space rather than infinitesimal points. Thus, in an actual case, it is quite likely that one or more of these may intersect the sphere of reflection and give rise to strong diffractions. This probability may be enhanced by rotating the crystal slightly about an axis. The reciprocal lattice rotates with the real lattice and many of its points may therefore be swept across the sphere of reflection. A photograph obtained in this way is called a rotation photograph. These points are illustrated by Fig. 80.

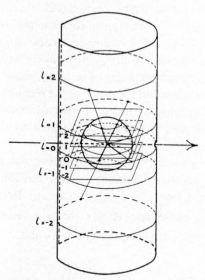

Fig. 80. The sphere of reflection and the formation of layer lines on a moving crystal photograph[5].

Let us consider a diffraction spectrum obtained in this way for an orthogonal lattice which is rotated about its c axis. The reciprocal lattice will likewise rotate about an axis passing thru its origin parallel to the c axis. The reciprocal lattice points lie in horizontal layers parallel to the AB plane and perpendicular to c. During the rotation process the points in each layer remain at a constant vertical distance from the AB plane. Hence the points of intersection of the layer points with the unit sphere will lie on the surfaces of a family of cones whose apex is at the center of the sphere. The semi-vertical angles of these cones are given by:

$$l \lambda = c \cos \Phi_l, (l \text{ is an integer}) \tag{4}$$

Thus a cylindrical photographic plate placed normal to the incident beam will record these as parallel curves.

It is instructive to compare this system with a hypothetical linear lattice consisting of a vertical row of points of constant separation d. Instead of a reciprocal lattice of discrete points we have here effectively a family of planes normal to the row lattice and of spacing λ/d. These will intersect the sphere of reflection in a series of circles forming the bases of a family of cones with the line of points as axis, and semi-angles given by:

$$l \lambda = d(\cos \Phi_l - \cos \Phi_0) \tag{5}$$

where Φ_0 is the angle made by the incident beam with the line of points. Since the direction of the diffracted beams will follow the surfaces of these cones the diffraction pattern will be recorded by a cylindrical film as a series of parallel lines.

From the coordinates of a spot on a rotation photograph two coordinates describing the position of the corresponding reciprocal lattice point may be obtained directly. These are the distance of the point from the axis of rotation (ξ) and its distance from the equatorial plane (σ). The latter plane is the horizontal plane containing the incident beam and the origin of the reciprocal lattice. The computation is greatly facilitated by the use of a "Bernal chart" which gives ξ and σ values for all positions on a cylindrical film (for a fixed camera radius) in the form of contours of equal ξ and σ.

Many points in reciprocal space will, of course, not be lattice points. These nevertheless have a definite significance. If the directions of the incident and diffracted beams in real space for a Bragg reflection from the hkl planes of the lattice are given by $\vec{S}_0$ and $\vec{S}$ respectively, then the vector uniting the reciprocal attice point hkl with the origin is equal to $\vec{S} - \vec{S}_0$ and

$$\vec{S} - \vec{S}_0 = h\vec{A} + k\vec{B} + l\vec{C} \tag{6}$$

The vector $\vec{S} - \vec{S}_0$ is normal to the hkl planes and bisects the angle between the incident and reflected beams.

If the incident and diffracted beams do not obey the Bragg relationship then the vector $\vec{S} - \vec{S}_0$ must be written in the more general form

$$\vec{S} - \vec{S}_0 = \xi'\vec{A} + \eta'\vec{B} + \sigma'\vec{C} \tag{7}$$

where ξ', η', σ' are generalized coordinates of a point in reciprocal space. Thus every point in reciprocal space represents some combination of incident and diffracted beams. The lattice points correspond to combinations consistent with the Bragg relationship.

The discussion so far has been confined to idealized point lattices. A real crystal with S atoms in the unit cell will consist of S interpenetrating point lattices all similar in orientation. This group of lattices will produce reflections in the same directions as a single point lattice. However, since the different lattices are mutually displaced and are composed of different kinds of atoms, the intensities and phases of their reflections will be different. Thus, the reflections from the crystal will occur in the same directions as for one of its lattices, but the intensities and phases will be different.

In general two kinds of information are sought from X-ray diffraction patterns. These are the distribution of atoms in the unit cell and the geometry of the repeating scheme. The second problem can be solved unambiguously, as it requires only a knowledge of the position of the diffraction maxima. The first problem is both more important and much more difficult as it requires in addition a knowledge of both the intensities and the phases. The phases are not, in general, obtainable directly.

With the aid of the concept of the reciprocal lattice the determination of the geometry of the space lattice is relatively simple. If a diffraction pattern is obtained by means of a crystal rotation photograph, the first step is to determine the coordinates ξ and σ of each spot, preferably by means of a Bernal diagram. From the ξ and σ values for the point h, k, l in the reciprocal lattice its distance from the origin, d^*_{hkl}, which is equal to $(\xi^2 + \sigma^2)^{1/2}$, may be computed.

From d^*_{hkl} the spacing d_{hkl} of the corresponding hkl planes of the real lattice is obtainable as $d^*_{hkl} = \lambda/d_{hkl}$.

The dimensions of the unit cell are computable from the layer line spacings observed upon rotating the lattice about its three axes successively. If σ_n is the distance from the equator of the nth layer line, then $\sigma_n = n\lambda/a$. Thus the lengths of the three edges of the unit cell may be obtained. It should be noted that no interplanar spacings are necessarily determined by this method, but only a periodicity along a crystallographic axis. This is because the measurement is not of the position of a single reflection, but of the locus of many, namely, of a layer line separation.

Thus the determination of the space geometry of a highly crystalline material is relatively straightforward. Let us now turn to the much more involved problem of the determination of the configuration of the contents of the unit cell itself.

An interference function has been defined for the space lattice whose magnitude for particular directions of incidence and diffraction yields a measure of the intensity of the diffracted beam in terms of the intensity scattered by a single structural unit. The interference function exhibits a periodic variation in reciprocal space with very sharp maxima at the reciprocal lattice points. The observed intensity for the entire crystal will depend upon the intensity scattered by the contents of a unit cell in the given direction and upon the interference function.

The amplitude of the beam scattered in a given direction by the atoms in a unit cell is given by the amplitude of the vectorial sum of the waves scattered in that direction by the individual atoms[2,4,6]. The result is a complex function including a phase angle and is called the structure factor F. Its modulus $|F|$ is the structure amplitude. The amplitude of a wave scattered in a given direction by atom j, divided by that of the wave scattered by a single electron, is called the scattering factor f_j of the atom. For high frequency radiation f_j is approximately equal to the number of electrons in the atom for small scattering angles.

For diffraction by crystals f_j will depend upon the Bragg angle. If x_j, y_j, z_j are the coordinates of atom j in terms of the a, b, c axes and u_j, v_j, w_j are defined as x_j/a, y_j/b, and z_j/c, respectively, then for scattering in the direction of the hkl reflection:

$$F(hkl) = \Sigma_j f_j \exp\{-2\pi i(hu_j + kv_j + lw_j)\} \tag{8}$$

The summation is carried out over all the atoms in the unit cell[2,4]. The structure amplitude $|F(hkl)|$ and the phase angle α (hkl) are given by[4]:

$$|F\,(hkl)|^{2} = \{\Sigma_{j}\,f_{j}\cos\,2\,\pi\,(hu_{j}+kv_{j}+lw_{j})\}^{2}$$
$$+\,\{\Sigma_{j}\,f_{j}\sin\,2\,\pi\,(hu_{j}+kv_{j}+lw_{j})\}^{2} \tag{9}$$
$$\tan\,\alpha\,(hkl) = \frac{\Sigma_{j}\,f_{j}\sin\,2\,\pi\,(hu_{j}+kv_{j}+lw_{j})}{\Sigma_{j}\,f_{j}\cos\,2\,\pi\,(hu_{j}+kv_{j}+lw_{j})}$$

The square of the structure factor is proportional to the scattering intensity and may be thought of as being somewhat analogous to the function P_{θ} for light scattering. Both functions are obtained by summing the contributions of all components of the system.

F may also be expressed in terms of the coordinates of reciprocal space. Thus[4]:

$$F\,(\xi',\,\eta',\,\sigma') = \Sigma_{j}\,f_{j}\,\exp\,[-2\,\pi\,i\,(\xi'u_{j}+\eta'v_{j}+\sigma'w_{j})] \tag{10}$$

The right hand side of equation (10) is equal to the Fourier transform of the function which represents the spatial distribution of electron density in the unit cell. Equation (10) shows the form of the transform for a group of discrete scattering points. If it is legitimate to consider the electron density as a continuous function in real space then the transform may be alternatively defined as follows[4]:

$$T\,(\xi',\,\eta',\,\sigma') = \int\int\int_{-\infty}^{\infty}\varrho\,(u,v,w)\,\exp\,[-2\,\pi\,i\,(\xi'u+\eta'v+\sigma'w)]\,du\,dv\,dw \tag{11}$$

Equations (10) and (11) are of central importance in the analysis of X-ray diffraction data. A very close relationship exists between the observed diffraction pattern and the Fourier transform in reciprocal space. Thus it is possible to postulate a structure, compute the Fourier transform, and compare it with the observed pattern.

Equation (11) may, in principle, be inverted to obtain the electron density function:

$$\varrho\,(u,v,w) = \frac{1}{V}\,\Sigma_{h,k,l}|F\,(h,k,l)|\,\cos\,[2\,\pi\,(hu+kv+lw)-\alpha\,(h,k,l)] \tag{12}$$

α unfortunately cannot be determined directly. However, if the origin is a center of symmetry, $\alpha = \pm\pi$ and equation (12) reduces to:

$$\varrho\,(u,v,w) = \frac{1}{V}\,\Sigma_{h,k,l}\pm|F\,(h,k,l)|\,\cos\,2\,\pi\,(hu+kv+lw) \tag{13}$$

Although in some simple cases the correct signs may be chosen without doubt, in general the use of equation (13) involves considerable ambiguity, as we have only half the necessary information.

Each term in equation (12) corresponds to a sinusoidal distribution of electron density, whose wavelength is equal to the corresponding hkl spacing. Without a knowledge of the phase, there are, of course, an infinite number of solutions.

In many applications it is useful to compute the distribution for a projection of scattering material upon a plane or a line. Thus the projection $\varrho\ (uv)$ on the ab plane is defined for orthogonal axes by[4]:

$$\varrho\ (uv) = \int_0^1 \varrho\ (u,v,w)\ dw \qquad (14)$$

It may be shown that:

$$\varrho\ (uv) = \frac{1}{A} \sum_{h,k} |F\ (h,k,0)| \cos\ [2\ \pi\ (hu+kv) - \alpha\ (h,k,0)] \qquad (15)$$

where A is the area of the projection of the unit cell. The projection $\varrho\ (u)$ upon the a axis is defined by:

$$\varrho\ (u) = \int_0^1 \int_0^1 \varrho\ (u,v,w)\ dv\ dw \qquad (16)$$

Also, it may be shown that:

$$\varrho\ (u) = \frac{1}{a} \sum_{h} |F\ (h00)| \cos\ \{2\ \pi\ hu - \alpha\ (h00)\} \qquad (17)$$

Fibrous materials such as polypeptides and polynucleotides cannot be obtained as single crystals. When such molecules occur in ordered states a high degree of orientation normally occurs only in the direction of the fiber axis. The lateral orientation of the crystallites is usually imperfect.

An X-ray diffraction pattern of such a fiber has many characteristics of a rotation photograph of a true crystal. In the fiber case there is no need for rotation about the fiber axis, as a wide range of lateral orientations are present. In taking an X-ray diffraction photograph of a fiber it is usual to have the fiber axis vertical. Thus the direction vertical to the origin and parallel to the fiber axis is called the meridian. That horizontal to the origin and normal to the fiber axis is called the equator.

The fiber repeat distance is readily obtainable directly, if strong layer line spacings are present, from the relationship $\sigma_n = n\lambda/r_0$, where r_0 is the fiber repeat distance. From the spacing of equatorial reflections the distance of reflecting planes parallel to the fiber axis may often be obtained.

In the case of protein crystals the use of isomorphous replacement has permitted direct phase determination in some cases and hence a direct application of Fourier analysis. In the case of polynucleotides the application of Fourier analysis has usually been indirect. That is, a structure has been postulated and a Fourier transform has been computed for it and compared with the positions and intensities of the observed reflections.

In a perfectly oriented fiber, meridional reflections must be absent if the fiber is perpendicular to the beam. This is because the meridional reflections arise from reflecting planes perpendicular to the fiber axis and hence the Bragg condition, which requires equality of the angles of incidence and reflection, cannot be realized. In practice, however, there is usually a sufficient dispersion of the orientations of the fiber axes so that the Bragg condition is realizable for a fraction of the fibrils and a meridional reflection occurs. In this case the meridional reflection may deviate slightly from the corresponding layer lines.

The helical type structure so important in the polynucleotide and polypeptide cases has several distinctive features in its predicted X-ray diffraction. Among these is the characteristic absence of reflections on the meridian corresponding to the layer line repeat. This has been shown to be a consequence of the mutual cancellation of reflected waves from adjacent points on the helix and results in zero amplitude for all orders on the meridian until the mth order is reached, where m is the number of points on one turn of the helix. In practice the absence of spots on the meridian of a fiber diagram is often regarded as suggestive of a helical structure.

Cochran, Crick, and Vand[10] have made a detailed treatment of the expected diffraction properties of a thin, continuous helical wire. The (infinitely long) helix may be defined by the equations:

$$X = r \cos \frac{2 \pi Z}{P}$$

$$Y = r \sin \frac{2 \pi Z}{P} \tag{18}$$

$$Z = Z$$

where r = radius; P = axial spacing.

The Fourier transform at a point (ξ', η', σ') in reciprocal space is given by:

$$T(\xi', \eta', \sigma') = \int \exp[2 \pi i (X \xi' + Y \eta' + Z \sigma')] \, dV \tag{19}$$

where dV is a volume element of the helix and is directly proportional to dZ.

Thus

$$T = \int_0^P \exp[2 \pi i (r \xi' \cos 2 \pi \frac{Z}{P} + r \eta' \sin 2 \pi \frac{Z}{P} + Z \sigma')] \, dZ \tag{20}$$

or

$$T = \int_0^P \exp[2 \pi i \left(Rr \cos (2 \pi \frac{Z}{P} - \varphi) + Z \sigma' \right)] \, dZ \tag{21}$$

where

$$R^2 = \xi'^2 + \eta'^2$$

and

$$\tan \varphi = \eta'/\xi'$$

The right-hand side of equation (21) is equal to zero except when $\sigma' = n/P$, where n is an integer. This is in accord with the fact that the diffraction pattern of a helix with an exact vertical repeat distance P is confined to layer lines at heights $\sigma' = n/P$ in reciprocal space.

Hence $\qquad T\left(R,\ \varphi,\ \dfrac{n}{P}\right)=\displaystyle\int_0^P \exp\left[2\ \pi\ i\left\{Rr\ \cos\ (2\ \pi\ \dfrac{Z}{P}-\varphi)+\dfrac{nZ}{P}\right\}\right]\ dZ$ \qquad (22)

The above integral may be evaluated by means of the identity:

$$\int_0^{2\pi} \exp\ (iX\ \cos\ \Phi)\ \exp\ (i\ n\ \Phi)\ d\ \Phi=2\ \pi i^n\ J_n\ (X')$$ \qquad (23)

where

$$X'=2\ \pi\ Rr,\ \Phi=2\ \pi\ Z/P$$

and J_n is an nth order Bessel function. From equations (22) and (23) we have:

$$T\left(R,\ \varphi,\ \dfrac{n}{P}\right)=J_n\ (2\ \pi\ Rr)\ \exp\left[i\ n\left(\varphi+\dfrac{\pi}{2}\right)\right]$$ \qquad (24)

This equation gives directly the amplitude and phase of the X-ray scattering on the nth layer line. Several statements can be made as to the form of T from what is known of the properties of Bessel functions. The modulus

$$|T|=|J_n\ (2\pi Rr)|$$

is independent of φ and hence has cylindrical symmetry. For small values of $2\pi Rr$, $|T|$ decreases rapidly with increasing n. The function predicts a series of sharp maxima on a given layer line which correspond to spots in the diffraction pattern. The intensity is, of course, proportional to the square of the modulus.

The continuous wire model is, of course, somewhat unrealistic. If the helix is broken up into a series of points the central part of the pattern is unchanged but further patterns are superimposed upon it[10]. These are identical with the first but have their origins on the meridian on the mth, $2m$th, $3m$th, etc., layer lines. The resultant pattern has empty diamond-shaped regions above and below the center.

In principle, therefore, many features of the helix can be obtained directly from the photograph. The layer line spacing yields the pitch of the helix. The number of the layer line on which the first meridional reflection occurs gives the number of residues per turn. It may also be shown that the angle between the sides of the above-mentioned diamond and the meridian is equal to the pitch angle[3]. The diameter of the helix is computable from the pitch and the pitch angle[3].

The above description applies only to a single helix. A double helix has a generally similar pattern, except that its symmetry properties are such that the odd order layer lines are absent. The remaining even order layer lines have intensity distributions varying as the squares of even ordered Bessel functions. The layer lines thus have twice the separation of those for the single helix case. Analogously a triple helix would yield only every third layer line.

The preceding is, of course, explicitly for an idealized point lattice. However, each atom of a group of a real helical structure will lie on a simple helix with corresponding atoms of other groups. The actual observed pattern will correspond to the summation of the contributions of the various helical sets of atoms, due account being taken of phase.

References p. 264

DETAILED FINE STRUCTURE OF THE ORDERED POLYNUCLEOTIDE SYSTEMS: DNA

The first example of the elucidation of the secondary structure of an ordered poly-nucleotide is of course furnished by the doubly stranded helical model for natural DNA. While the basic features of this structure were clarified by Watson and Crick[11], much of our knowledge about the detailed configuration comes from the work of Wilkins and his collaborators[12-16].

In obtaining the precise structure of DNA it is unfortunately impractical to use the diffraction data to refine an initial rough model, as DNA gives a fiber diagram in which considerable overlapping of spots occurs and in which large angle diffraction is weak. The original doubly stranded structure was proposed on largely stereochemical grounds and its subsequent correction and refinement has proceeded from a combination of stereochemistry and X-ray diffraction. The method adopted has involved the building of a molecular model in which the positions of the subunits are fixed to within narrow limits. A Fourier transform is computed from this model and compared with the actual X-ray diffraction pattern. Deviations from the observed pattern are progressively reduced by modifying the configuration of the model and studying the configurational changes in the Fourier transform thereby produced[12-16].

To recapitulate, the basic Watson–Crick structure consists of two polynucleotide chains helically wrapped around each other with the sugar-phosphate chains on the periphery and the purine and pyrimidine bases in the core. The two strands are oriented in an antiparallel manner so that rotation by 180° does not alter the appearance of the molecule. The backbone sugar-phosphate chains are

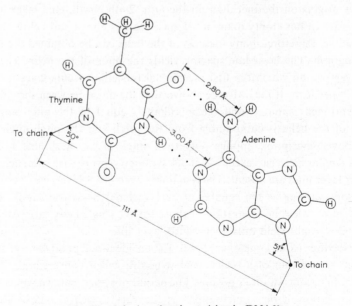

Fig. 81. Adenine–thymine pairing in DNA[26].

organized about a diad axis normal to the fiber axis and passing through the center of each base pair. The planar purine and pyrimidine bases are roughly perpendicular to the fiber axis.

The structure is stabilized by hydrogen bonding between purine and pyrimidine bases in the core of the helix. Each adenine is paired with a thymine and each guanine with a cytosine. The nature of the bonding and the distances involved are as shown in Figs. 81 and 82. The adenine–thymine base pairing corresponds to example 5 in Donohue's system (see Chapter 7). The most probable guanine–cytosine pairing corresponds to a combination of examples 15 and 16.

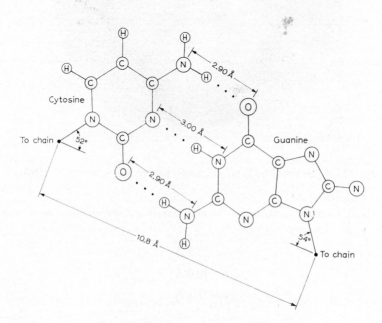

Fig. 82. Guanine–cytosine pairing in DNA[26].

The X-ray diffraction pattern of DNA, illustrated by Fig. 83, was early recognized to have many features consistent with a helical structure[12, 13]. Among these are the absence of meridional reflections and the nearly periodic rise and fall of intensity along each layer line.

It has been found by Wilkins and co-workers[14–16] that DNA can exist in three forms which give different diffraction patterns and which have been postulated to differ structurally to a minor extent. All are, of course, of the basic Watson–Crick type. All were early shown by Wilkins and co-workers, and by Franklin and Gosling[17] to have ten residues per turn.

At lower relative humidities (less than about 70%) the sodium salt of DNA crystallizes in the A form. This is very highly regular and crystalline and shows up to 100 independent reflections. This truly crystalline form corresponds to a

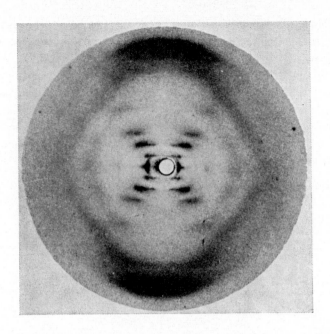

Fig. 83. A representative X-ray diffraction pattern for the B form of DNA[3].

face-centered monoclinic lattice, the characteristic   parameters of whose unit cell are:

$$a = 22.2 \text{ Å}$$
$$b = 40.0 \text{ Å}$$
$$c = 28.1 \text{ Å}$$

A repeat unit of two DNA molecules is contained in the unit cell, with the helical axis in the c direction.

In the A form the bases are not strictly perpendicular to the helical axis, being tilted about 25° to that axis. The lattice contains about 40% water. A detailed Fourier analysis has shown that this proposed structure is consistent with the X-ray data[16].

At higher relative humidities a transition occurs to the slightly more extended B form. The degree of crystallinity is less than for the A form and this configuration must be regarded as paracrystalline. There is a quite strong reflection on the meridian at 3.4 Å. The fiber axis repeat is 34.6 Å with ten residues per turn. The phosphates on the periphery of the molecule are at a radius of 9 Å and are separated by 7 Å along a given chain.

In the model of Wilkins and co-workers, the nucleotide pairs are normal to the fiber and are closer to the helical axis than in the case of the A form. The sugar ring in each nucleotide is placed so that its plane is inclined as much as possible to the helix axis. This has the effect of making the electron density distribution decrease gradually toward the outside of the molecule.

The model of Wilkins also introduces a modification in the usually accepted configuration of the ribose rings. The available information upon furanose rings occurring elsewhere indicates that they are nonplanar, a slight puckering occurring[18-20]. Spencer has attributed this pucker to unacceptably short distances between the hydrogen atoms attached to adjacent ring atoms[21]. Puckering would relieve these short contacts. The most probable atom to be displaced is C'_2 or C'_3.

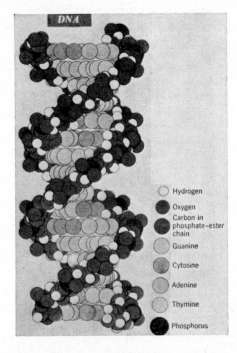

Fig. 84. A model of the proposed structure for the B form of DNA[26].

However, Wilkins and co-workers have utilized a planar ribose ring in their model, thereby avoiding several anomalously short interatomic distances. This is attributed to a distortion of bond angles as a result of electrostatic compression of the polynucleotide chain by attractive forces between the phosphates and the hydrated sodium counter ions[14]. The general appearance of the postulated structure for the B form is shown in Fig. 84.

In order to compute a transform for the proposed B structure it was necessary to make some assumptions about the position of the sodium counter ions and the water in the structure. The assumption was made that all the available space around the molecules was filled with water. The sodium ions were placed at 5 Å from the negatively charged oxygen atoms of the phosphate groups.

The lattice structure of the B form is never very perfect in the case of the sodium salt of DNA, but as many as sixteen reflections have been indexed. In many cases continuous streaks occur along the layer lines superimposed upon the crystalline reflections. This is an indication of imperfect crystallinity; that is, some of the repeat units are arranged at random in the direction of the fiber axis.

Fourier transforms were computed for the above model. Fig. 85 compares the observed and computed intensities along the layer lines. The agreement is quite reasonable.

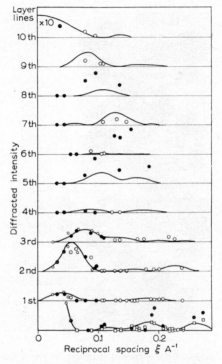

Fig. 85. A comparison of the Fourier transform with the observed diffraction pattern for the proposed model for the B form of DNA[14].

The lithium salt of DNA behaves in a somewhat different manner. As in the case of the sodium salt, a crystallization occurs at low relative humidities[16]. However, this crystallization is not accompanied by a transition to the A form. Thus in this case it is possible to study the B modification in highly crystalline form. The dimensions of the unit cell can thus be obtained and are as follows, at 66 per cent relative humidity[16]:

$$a = 22.72 \text{ Å}$$
$$b = 31.28 \text{ Å}$$
$$c = 33.60 \text{ Å}$$

Still another modification of the DNA structure has recently been discovered by Wilkins and co-workers[22]. The lithium salt of the B form has been found to undergo a transition to a new configuration, called the C form, upon lowering the relative humidity from 66 to 44 per cent. The model proposed by these workers for the C form involves only a minor modification of the B model. Thus the base pairs are moved about 2 Å away from the fiber axis and tilted by about 5°. The pitch of the helix was altered so that there were about 9.3 instead of 10 base pairs per turn.

In general X-ray diffraction patterns of DNA from different sources are quite similar, indicating that the basic structure is probably similar in all cases and thus is invariant to altering base composition. Among the sources examined are calf thymus, mouse sarcoma, human leukemic leukocytes, human spleen, human lymphocytes, fowl lymphocytes, pneumoccus, *E. coli*, paracentrotos sperm, avian tubercle, bacteriophage T_7, and bacteriophage T_2. The DNA from T_2 phage has not yet been observed to form an A structure.

In the case of DNA there is, of course, excellent reason to believe that the structure discussed above persists in solution. The evidence supporting this conclusion has been cited in the preceding chapter. While the physico-chemical data on solutions of DNA cannot, of course, permit a direct determination of the molecular fine structure it is virtually certain that *some* multistranded helical structure persists in dilute solution and it is very highly likely that this structure is the same as that prevailing in dry fibers.

Wilkins and co-workers have extended X-ray diffraction observations upon DNA fibers to very high relative humidities and have found that the basic structure, as manifested by the 3.4 Å meridional reflection and the layer lines, is still faintly visible even at separations of neighboring molecules as high as 44 Å.

Riley and Oster[23] have examined dilute gels of DNA by X-ray diffraction and have concluded that regular micelles of DNA molecules exist in concentrated solution and that these disperse as the solutions become more dilute. It is difficult to understand what kind of forces could stabilize such micelles, especially as formation of the latter would require the juxtaposition of similarly charged phosphates. A re-examination of this question would probably be desirable.

There remains the question of whether the structure observed for protein-free DNA is characteristic of its state in the intact cell, where it occurs as a complex with basic protein. The general appearances of the X-ray patterns of DNA and nucleoprotamine are very similar but some difference in molecular structure is indicated by the fact that the first layer line of the latter is definitely stronger than that for DNA[14]. Also, deoxyribose nucleoprotamine occurs in a hexagonal crystalline form, in contrast to DNA. This difference in lattice form reflects a different packing together of the molecules, which in turn indicates a difference in shape of the two.

Wilkins and co-workers have suggested that the protamine polypeptide chain is wrapped helically around the DNA helix. As about two-thirds of the protamine

References p. 264

molecule consists of positively charged arginine residues it is possible to pair each arginine with a phosphate if the non-basic amino acid residues are introduced as loops between two arginines. A structure of this type would give the observed increase of intensity of the first layer line and would retain unchanged the basic structure of its DNA component.

Wilkins has also made direct observations upon the nucleoprotein of *Loligo* sperm in the intact spermatophore[15]. Low dosage and long exposure times were used so that the sperm retained its viability. The X-ray diffraction patterns still showed the characteristic features of the B form of DNA. Thus the available evidence suggests that the same basic structure prevails for all gradations of environment extending from the intact cell to the protein-free system in aqueous solution.

POLYRIBOADENYLIC ACID PLUS POLYRIBOURIDYLIC ACID

The X-ray diffraction pattern of fibers of the 1 : 1 poly A + poly U complex has many points of analogy to that of DNA[23-25]. Both have the large empty area on the meridian characteristic of helical structures of this type. The poly A + poly U pattern has a layer line spacing of 34 Å and a strong meridional reflection in the region 3 to 4 Å. This indicates that there are 10 residues per turn of the helix in both cases. The diameter of the (A + U) complex is slightly larger than that of DNA. This may arise from the presence of an additional hydroxyl group in the ribose moiety of the former.

Poly A plus poly U can crystallize in a hexagonal array with a lateral distance between molecules of 28.8 Å. Both the helical pitch and the separation of the molecules increase with relative humidity. The fibers are negatively birefringent.

The structure proposed by Rich and Davies is of the doubly stranded helical type, stabilized by adenine-uracil hydrogen bonding between the C_6-amino group of adenine and the C_6-carbonyl of uracil and between the N_1 ring nitrogen of adenine and the N_1 of uracil[24]. The bases are in the core of the helix and are roughly perpendicular to the fiber axis. This latter feature accounts for the strong negative birefringence of poly A + poly U fibers. The nature of the bonding is similar to that shown by Fig. 81.

One difference between the (A + U) and DNA diffraction patterns is the enhanced intensity of the first layer line for the former system[25]. This could be accounted for if the chain arrangement were parallel rather than anti-parallel or if the diameter were slightly larger than for DNA[25]. The latter explanation appears to be the more probable.

Unfortunately a detailed Fourier analysis has yet to be published for this system. Until this is done some question must remain on the details of the structure. However, there is little doubt that the over-all model as presented above is basically correct.

In this case the evidence is excellent that the above structure persists in solution and may be identified with the kinetic unit. The relevant data have been summarized in the preceding chapter.

THE 1 : 2 POLYRIBOADENYLIC ACID PLUS POLYRIBOURIDYLIC ACID COMPLEX

The structure of the (A+2U) complex has yet to be examined in detail by X-ray diffraction. On stereochemical grounds it has been proposed that the (A+U) structure remains intact and that the second poly U strand lies in the deep helical groove of the doubly stranded complex and is stabilized by hydrogen bonds between the C_6-carbonyl of uracil and the C_6-amino group of adenine and between the N_1-nitrogen of uracil and the N_7-nitrogen of adenine[27]. Such a structure would have only a slightly greater diameter than the (A+U) complex and could be formed with a minimal distortion of the bond angles and distances of the latter.

Zubay[28] has recently proposed an alternative model for this complex. The kind of interbase bonding invoked for his model has the form of a cyclic triad, rather similar to the structure currently favored for poly I. The hydrogen bonds are between the adenine C_6 amino group and the C_6 carbonyl of the first uracil; between the N_1 of the first uracil and the C_6 carbonyl of the second uracil; and between the N_1 of the second uracil and the N_1 of adenine. The adenine group is tilted about 40° from the perpendicular to the fiber axis.

The structure of Zubay suffers from the disadvantage of allowing a total of only three hydrogen bonds as compared with the four which stabilize the structure suggested by Rich and co-workers. Furthermore, the unbonded character of one of the amino hydrogens would tend to introduce an instability into the structure.

This structure was originally advanced primarily on the grounds that it reconciled the observation that the formation of the (A+2U) complex was favored by the presence of Mg^{++} with the belief that the binding of Mg^{++} by poly A involved a chelation of Mg^{++} between the amino group and the N_7 of adenine. Such a chelation would be permitted by Zubay's structure but not by that of Rich. However, more recent work has indicated that the phosphate group is the more likely point of attachment of Mg^{++} and that the adenine group is probably not directly involved (see Chapter 10). Thus Zubay's structure is left without any advantage to compensate for the disadvantages cited earlier and must be regarded as less likely than the structure advanced by Rich.

However, any conclusion on the conformation of the A+2U complex must certainly remain tentative until a detailed X-ray analysis is published. It has been stated that the available X-ray information is consistent with the model of Rich[29].

Here again there is excellent reason to believe that the triple helix persists in solution and, indeed, much of the evidence for its existence has been obtained from physico-chemical data upon solutions.

References p. 264

POLYRIBOINOSINIC ACID

Rich has examined the X-ray diffraction pattern produced by oriented fibers of poly I at 66 per cent relative humidity[30]. The dried fibers display a strong negative birefringence, with $\Delta n = -0.08$.

The poly I pattern is quite different from that produced by any other of the natural or synthetic polynucleotides (Fig. 86). Of the three layer lines seen on the diffraction pattern, two are nonmeridional and occur at spacings of 9.8 Å and 5.2 Å, while the third very strong reflection is meridional and occurs at 3.4 Å. No larger layer-line

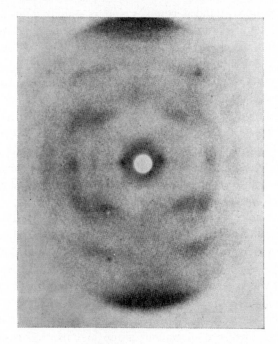

Fig. 86. X-ray diffraction pattern[30] obtained for poly I.

spacings are present. The first layer line has two closely spaced independent maxima, of which the inner is the more intense. The other two layer lines have but a single maximum.

The equator has a series of reflections, the first and most intense of which is at a spacing of 23.8 Å. The next three reflections correspond to successive orders of this spacing.

A number of conclusions can be drawn from the above data. The intense meridional reflection at 3.4 Å is similar to those occurring with natural DNA, with poly A plus poly U, and with poly A plus poly I. It is logical to attribute it to a stacking of the planar purine rings at right angles to the fiber axis, as this spacing corresponds to the expected separation of the rings[30].

The spacing of the three layer lines is non-integral, that is, they are not successive orders of a fundamental repeat distance. However, the reciprocal lattice spacing between the equator and the first layer line equals that between the 3.4 Å and 5.2 Å layer lines. This is characteristic of helical structures with a non-integral number of residues per turn.

Rich has considered several helical models, containing one, two, or three strands. Single stranded models were found to be implausible because the required screw rotation of $125° \left(= 360° \div \dfrac{9.8}{3.4} \right)$ would not permit any overlap of the hypoxanthine residues. Any stabilizing hydrogen bonding would be sterically unfeasible for such a molecule. Furthermore, such a model would be too narrow to account for the equatorial reflections.

A two-stranded model would have a screw rotation of $125°/2$ or $62.5°$. An attempt to build such a structure with molecular models revealed that it was sterically inconsistent with any base hydrogen bonding in the core. However, a three-stranded model with a screw rotation of $125°/3$ or $41.6°$, which is stabilized by interbase hydrogen bonding, can be built.

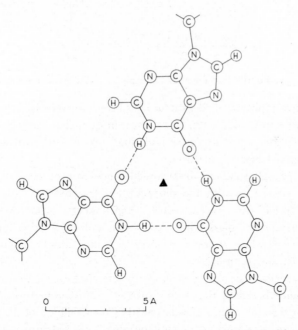

Fig. 87. Proposed scheme of base pairing for the poly I helical form[30].

Such a triply stranded structure has been postulated by Rich to have the hydrogen bonding shown in Fig. 87. There are three hydrogen bonds per set of three bases. These are between the 1-nitrogen and the 6-carbonyl of the hypoxanthine group in each case. The helices must be right-handed, as left-handed helices are sterically infeasible.

A Fourier transform has been computed for this model and has indeed been found to predict the observed layer line spacings (Fig. 88). In addition such a structure would have a diameter close to 24 Å, which is consistent with the observed equatorial reflection at 23.8 Å.

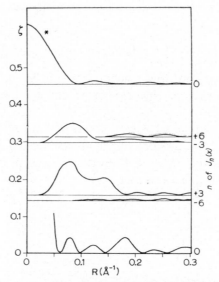

Fig. 88.   The Fourier transform for the triply stranded helical form of poly I[30].

Thus the above triply stranded structure has been shown by Rich to be consistent with the available diffraction data. However, it must again be emphasized that this kind of information is not *exclusive* and much more work will be required to establish this model beyond question.

In particular an alternative four-stranded model can be constructed which is likewise fairly consistent with the diffraction data. However, such a structure would have a hole in the center about 2.3 Å in diameter, which would introduce considerable instability unless filled with water molecules. Also the diameter of this model is 28 Å which is less consistent with the 23.8 Å equatorial spacing than the triply stranded model.

The above structure has yet to be shown positively to persist in solution. However, the evidence is strong that some form of multistranded, ordered structure does prevail for the kinetic unit of poly I at pH's below the pK of the hypoxanthine group and, *a priori*, the most reasonable hypothesis is to identify it with the structure observed in the solid state.

There still remains considerable question over the fraction of helical content which prevails for poly I in solution. The degree of hypochromism appears to increase gradually with ionic strength[30]. Hall has found electron microscopic evidence for rods only for the quite high ionic strength[31] of 1.0. The fragmentary existing evidence thus suggests that the helical content may be fractional, increasing with increasing ionic strength.

POLY A PLUS POLY I

Rich[32] has obtained X-ray diffraction patterns for oriented fibers of the 1 : 1 complex of poly A plus poly I. The dried salt-free fibers were brittle and displayed a high negative birefringence ($\Delta n = -0.09$).

The over-all features of the patterns, which were obtained at 66 per cent relative humidity, were similar to those of the B form of DNA. Several layer lines appear near the meridian in the region 3–4 Å, including a meridional reflection at about 3.4 Å. There is also a large empty area on the meridian.

The innermost maxima on the first, second, and third layer lines are non-meridional and lie on straight lines proceeding radially from the origin. This and the absence of reflections from the meridian are strongly suggestive of a helical structure.

The occurrence of the familiar meridional reflection at 3.4 Å points to a stacking of the planar purine bases at right angles to the fiber axis, which is compatible with the negative birefringence of the fibers. This in turn suggests the presence of a doubly stranded helical structure stabilized by inter-base hydrogen bonding. The layer line spacing indicated that such a helix must have a pitch of 38.8 Å. Hence the basic screw rotation is $31.5° \left(= 360° \div \dfrac{38.8}{3.4} \right)$.

Two fairly strong equatorial reflections occur as well as several weak ones. The spacing of the equatorial reflections appears to indicate a hexagonal lattice with $a = 24.4$ Å.

Rich has carried out a very rough Fourier analysis by considering the contribution of the phosphate groups alone to the X-ray scattering. Such an analysis has indicated an average diameter of the molecule which is close to 19 Å. This suggests strongly that the phosphates lie on the periphery of the double helix.

The final structure postulated by Rich for the equimolar complex is quite similar to that indicated for the analogous poly A plus poly U complex. The purine bases

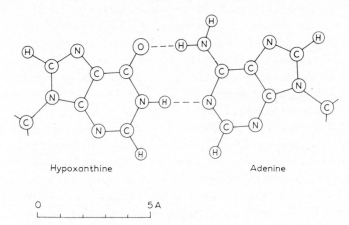

Hypoxanthine   Adenine

0 _____ 5 A

Fig. 89. Proposed base pairing arrangement for the poly A + poly I equimolar complex.

are in the core of the double helix with the sugar phosphate backbones on the periphery. The type of hydrogen bonding specified, which corresponds to pairing number 7 of Donohue, is shown in Fig. 89. The bonding is between the 1-nitrogen of the hypoxanthine base and the 1-nitrogen of adenine and between the 6-amino group of adenine and the 6-carbonyl of hypoxanthine.

A detailed Fourier transform has yet to be published for this model. For the present it must be regarded as tentative although certainly highly plausible. The available evidence is also strongly consistent with its persistence in solution.

THE 1 : 2 POLYRIBOADENYLIC ACID PLUS POLYRIBOINOSINIC ACID COMPLEX

No direct evidence is as yet available on the detailed fine structure of this complex. It has been surmised, on stereochemical grounds, that its structure is analogous to that of the A plus 2U complex[32]. In this model the A plus I double helix would remain intact, with the second poly I strand lying in the deep helical groove and forming hydrogen bonds between the C_6-amino group of adenine and the C_6-carbonyl of hypoxanthine and between the N_1-nitrogen of hypoxanthine and the N_7-nitrogen of adenine.

POLYRIBOADENYLIC ACID

Fibers of poly A drawn from solutions of neutral pH show generally a well defined X-ray pattern with many characteristically helical features[33, 34]. Prominent among these is the relative absence of meridional reflections. Only one truly meridional reflection appears to occur. This is at 3.8 Å rather than the usual 3.4 Å. The fiber axis repeat is at about 15 Å. From the meridional spacing the fiber axis translation between nucleotide residues is 3.8 Å. The innermost equatorial reflection is at 15.6 Å, which suggests a unit cell with roughly that diameter.

A doubly stranded helical model has been proposed for poly A which is in good agreement with the available X-ray evidence. This model consists of two helically wound strands with the sugar-phosphate backbones on the periphery and the bases in the core of the molecule. The helical backbones are parallel rather than antiparallel. The chains are related by a parallel diad and two hydrogen bonds unite pairs of adenine residues at the same level. The hydrogen bonding is between the C_6-amino group and the N_7-nitrogen.

As only one of the amino hydrogens is involved in this base pairing, it is sterically feasible for the second hydrogen to form an additional hydrogen bond to one of the non-esterified oxygen atoms in the phosphate group of the other strand. If this additional bond is present the phosphate group is brought closer to the central axis, giving the molecule an effective radius of 8 Å. Optimal Van der Waal's contact between vertically adjacent bases is attained by slightly tilting them in the direction of the pitch of the helix.

Unfortunately no detailed Fourier analysis has as yet been published for this model, which must thus remain tentative although quite promising.

To what extent this structure may persist in solution is still very unclear. The X-ray patterns have normally been obtained for fibers spun from presumably neutral or alkaline solutions whose pH was not controlled. However, it is not likely that the model proposed above could correspond to the helical regions of the alkaline form of poly A, as the available evidence indicates that the latter is single stranded and thus could not form a parallel structure.

There is a strong possibility that this kind of model may prevail for the aggregates of poly A formed at acid pH's, particularly as it would permit the juxtaposition of a positively charged adenine and a negatively charged phosphate. Fresco has indeed obtained some X-ray evidence for gels of acid poly A which is consistent with this model[35].

In any event the evidence is strong that poly A can form more than one type of helical structure in solution. At present it is clearly premature to make any exclusive structural assignment.

RIBONUCLEIC ACID

In the case of natural RNA it can be said that scarcely a start has been made toward a detailed picture of the helical fine structure. Rich and Watson have carried out a parallel study of DNA and RNA[36]. Diffuse, poorly defined reflections were observed for the latter system with a definite resemblance to the DNA pattern. In particular the by now familiar absence of meridional reflections occurred, with the likewise familiar exception of a strong reflection at 3–4 Å.

About all that can be said at present on the fine structure of RNA is that the available data do not conflict with the postulated partially helical model which has been proposed or with the postulated doubly stranded character of the hairpin-like helical regions.

The statements made for RNA hold as well for poly AU and poly AUGC, whose diffraction patterns show a definite resemblance to those of RNA.

Even less is known of the detailed fine structure of polyribocytidylic acid and of that of the equimolar complex of poly C and poly I. All that can be said is that some helical structure is present.

REFERENCES

[1] I. FANKUCHEN, in A. WEISSBERGER, *Technique of Organic Chemistry*, Vol. I, New York, 1945, p. 585.

[2] M. BUERGER, *X-ray Crystallography*, New York, 1942.

[3] A. STOKES, in J. BUTLER AND J. RANDALL, *Progress in Biophysics*, Vol. 5, London, 1955, p. 140

[4] C. BAMFORD, A. ELLIOTT AND W. HANBY, *Synthetic Polypeptides*, New York, 1956, p. 215.

[5] A. WILSON, *X-ray Optics*, London, 1949.

[6] C. BUNN, *Chemical Crystallography*, Oxford, 1945.

[7] R. JAMES, *Optical Principles of the Diffraction of X-rays*, London, 1948.

[8] K. LONSDALE, *Crystals and X-rays*, New York, 1948.

[9] H. LIPSON AND W. COCHRAN, *The Determination of Crystal Structure*, London, 1953.

[10] W. COCHRAN, F. CRICK AND V. VAND, *Acta Cryst.*, 5 (1952) 581.

[11] J. WATSON AND F. CRICK, *Nature*, 171 (1953) 737.

[12] M. WILKINS, A. STOKES AND H. WILSON, *Nature*, 171 (1953) 738.

[13] M. WILKINS, W. SEEDS, A. STOKES AND H. WILSON, *Nature*, 172 (1953) 759.

[14] M. FEUGHELMAN, R. LANGRIDGE, W. SEEDS, A. STOKES, H. WILSON, C. HOOPER, M. WILKINS, R. BARCLAY AND L. HAMILTON, *Nature*, 175 (1955) 834.

[15] M. WILKINS, *Cellular Biology, Nucleic Acids and Virus*, N.Y. Acad. Sci., 1957, p. 180.

[16] R. LANGRIDGE, W. SEEDS, H. WILSON, C. HOOPER, M. WILKINS AND L. HAMILTON, *J. Biophys. Biochem. Cytol.*, 3 (1957) 767.

[17] R. FRANKLIN AND R. GOSLING, *Nature*, 171 (1953) 740.

[18] C. BEEVERS AND W. COCHRAN, *Proc. Roy. Soc. (London) A*, 190 (1947) 257.

[19] S. FURBERG, *Acta Cryst.*, 3 (1950) 325.

[20] M. HUBER, *Acta Cryst.*, 10 (1957) 129.

[21] M. SPENCER, *Acta Cryst.*, 12 (1959) 59.

[22] D. MARVIN, M. SPENCER, M. WILKINS AND L. HAMILTON, *Nature*, 182 (1958) 387.

[23] D. RILEY AND G. OSTER, *Biochim. et Biophys. Acta*, 7 (1951) 526.

[24] A. RICH AND D. DAVIES, *J. Am. Chem. Soc.*, 78 (1956) 3548.

[25] A. RICH, in W. MCELROY AND B. GLASS, *The Chemical Basis of Heredity*, Baltimore, 1957, p. 557.

[26] A. RICH, *Rev. Mod. Phys.*, 31 (1959) 191.

[27] G. FELSENFELD, D. DAVIES AND A. RICH, *J. Am. Chem. Soc.*, 79 (1957) 2023.

[28] G. ZUBAY, *Nature*, 182 (1958) 388.

[29] A. RICH, *Ann. N.Y. Acad. Sci.*, 81 (1959) 709.

[30] A. RICH, *Biochim. et Biophys. Acta*, 29 (1958) 502.

[31] C. HALL, *Ann. N.Y. Acad. Sci.*, 81 (1959) 723.

[32] A. RICH, *Nature*, 181 (1958) 521.

[33] J. WATSON, in W. MCELROY AND B. GLASS, *The Chemical Basis of Heredity*, Baltimore, 1957, p. 552.

[34] F. CRICK, *Cellular Biology, Nucleic Acids, and Virus*, N.Y. Acad. Sci., 1957, p. 175.

[35] J. FRESCO AND E. KLEMPERER, *Ann. N.Y. Acad. Sci.*, 81 (1959) 730.

[36] A. RICH AND J. WATSON, *Proc. Natl. Acad. Sci. U.S.*, 40 (1954) 759.

Chapter 9

The Helix-Coil Transition for Polynucleotide Systems

THE THERMALLY INDUCED TRANSITION

We have already had occasion to describe several examples of the transition of a polynucleotide from an ordered to a disordered structure. As we have seen, such a transition may be induced by variations of pH, ionic strength, temperature, or solvent composition. In each instance there are many points of analogy to the corresponding process occurring in the case of native DNA. The sole major difference appears to be the absence of complete reversibility in the latter instance. For convenience such helix-coil transitions have been referred to as denaturation processes, irrespective of their reversibility.

An obvious and striking aspect of these transitions is the dramatically sharp character which they often assume. This is almost invariably the case when the molecular weight of the individual strands is large ($> 10^5$) and the helical content of the ordered state high. Intuitively it appears probable that some type of cooperative mechanism would be required to account for this degree of sharpening and that a helix disruption by a random breaking of hydrogen bonds is implausible.

The phenomena of this kind described earlier, whose quantitative discussion has been deferred to this chapter, have a parallel in the analogous processes occurring for α-helical polypeptides[1,2]. However, there are several basic differences.

In the polypeptide case the hydrogen bonding is *vertical* (in a direction parallel to the axis of the chain) and each amino acid residue of the intact helix is bridged by three hydrogen bonds, all of which must be ruptured to permit potential free rotation of the given residue[2,3].

Thus, for a sequence of m consecutive random subunits to be formed, $(m+2)$ hydrogen bonds must be broken. To anticipate, for the denaturation of a helical macromolecule to occur, the energy increment arising from the breaking of hydrogen bonds must be compensated for by the entropy gain occurring whenever a residue gains the rotational freedom accompanying random status and hence the ability to assume a variety of configurations. Since, in the polypeptide case, each sequence of random residues which does not include the terminal subunit is accompanied by an extra pair of ruptured hydrogen bonds for which there is no entropic compensation, it is obvious that the enlargement of a sequence already present is energetically favored over the initiation of a new random sequence. Once the constant *down payment* in free energy has been met, a random sequence can enlarge with relative ease[4].

In the doubly stranded polynucleotide case the hydrogen bonding is *horizontal* rather than *vertical*[1]. There is no bridging of residues by hydrogen bonds and the rupture of the bonding between a given nucleotide pair should, in the absence of steric hindrance, permit the assumption of complete rotational freedom by both members[1-7].

A further difference between the α-helical and the polynucleotide cases arises with respect to the nature of the random sequences in the interior of the molecule. In the polypeptide case these will be linear chains while in the doubly stranded polynucleotide case they will have the form of rings[1, 3]. This has for the latter type of system the important consequence of restricting the number of possible configurations, as only those configurations are permissible which are consistent with the junction of the termini of a random ring[8].

In either case two plausible alternative mechanisms can be invoked for the helix-coil transition. The first of these is by an *unzipping* process originating at the termini of the double strands. In the polynucleotide case such a mechanism would be energetically favored to some extent by the fact that in this case the random segments would be linear rather than ring-like and hence would be subject to no configurational restraint.

The alternative mechanism involves the production of intermittent unbonded, random regions along the length of the molecule. It may be stated in advance that neither mechanism has been definitely excluded in any instance. They are, of course, by no means mutually exclusive and it is entirely possible and even likely that both are operative. Intuitively, it would be expected that the "unzipping" mechanism would be dominant for very short chains and that the intermittent mechanism would become progressively more important for longer chains.

Despite the severe obstacles in the path of any comprehensive theoretical treatment, great progress has been made recently in the analysis of the helix-coil transition for polynucleotides. Statistical mechanical treatments have been made by Hill[1], by Rice and Wada[5], and by Gibbs and DiMarzio[3]. All of these are essentially variants of a basically similar approach.

Let us consider first the intermittent mechanism, assuming for simplicity that the chains are effectively of infinite length and that *unzipping* may therefore be disregarded as a mechanism of chain disruption.

Thus at a molecular state intermediate to the completely helical and the completely random configurations, the doubly stranded polynucleotide will on this model consist of alternating bonded regions and random rings. For the moment let us further restrict consideration to the case where all the residues of each strand are identical. The bonded regions must then, of course, be perfectly matched, that is, each nucleotide must be paired with a complementary nucleotide in the other strand. It is, however, possible for extensive mismatching to occur in the random rings.

The treatment will be developed explicitly for the case of the thermal denaturation of a doubly stranded helical molecule, each strand of which is a polymer of a single monomer unit. The two monomer units are not necessarily identical. For simplicity the chain lengths of the two strands are assumed to be equal and sufficiently large so that end effects are unimportant.

The situation in the intermediate state may be schematically represented as follows:

The energy gain occurring as a result of hydrogen bonding is opposed by the entropic gain occurring upon the release of a pair of residues from the rigid helical configuration, which enables them to assume a variety of configurations. Of the various treatments that of Hill is perhaps the most detailed and we shall therefore select it for explicit discussion[1].

In order to be realistic any theory must take into account at least two types of interaction. The first of these corresponds to *vertical* interactions between unbonded neighboring nucleotides in a direction parallel to the fiber axis. These will consist of electrostatic interactions superimposed upon Van der Waals interactions. While it is probably legitimate to consider the short range Van der Waals forces as important for nearest neighbors only, such an approximation may be inadequate for the electrostatic forces, which decay less rapidly with distance.

The second type of interaction corresponds to the *horizontal* interactions between mutually bonded nucleotides in the helical regions of the macromolecules. The energy of interaction will include contributions from the specific hydrogen bonding and from the non-specific Van der Waals interactions. No effort is made to differentiate the two in this and other theories.

The basic statistical mechanical approach common to all the current theories is as follows. First a partition function is defined and evaluated. Once the partition function has been evaluated it is possible to derive the equilibrium thermodynamic properties of the system, such as the fraction of non-helical nucleotide units as a function of temperature, by the standard methods of statistical thermodynamics.

The problem of setting up the partition function is simplified by the fact that only those energetic and entropic factors need be considered which depend upon the helical content of the molecule. The so-called configurational partition function, which is the quantity of interest, can be defined as

$$Q = \Sigma\, G_i \exp\left(-w_i/kT\right)$$

The summation is carried out over all possible states of the molecule from the completely helical to the completely random and unbonded. The parameter w_i is the free energy of the i th state, which can be realized in G_i ways.

For present purposes a particular state of the molecule may be defined as one for which there are:

n_0 groups of paired helical units containing one pair each

n_1 groups containing two pairs each

n_2 groups containing three pairs each

.

.

.

.

n_h groups containing $(h+1)$ pairs each

and

m_{00} rings of random units containing one unit from each strand

m_{01} rings containing one unit from the A strand and two from the B strand

.

.

.

m_{rs} rings containing $(r+1)$ units from the A strand and $(s+1)$ from the B strand

All configurations of each state will have the same energy. The number of ways, G_i, of realizing each state, will be equal to the number of ways of ordering the total of

$$\Sigma_h \, n_h + \Sigma_{r,s} \, m_{rs}$$

groups in a linear manner, subject to the obvious proviso that the sequence must be alternating and no two helical groups or two random rings can immediately follow each other.

The statistical problem is elementary and G_i is expressible in terms of a simple product of combinatorials. The evaluation of the partition function by direct summation would be a major undertaking, which fortunately is not necessary. A well-known theorem in statistical mechanics states that for practical purposes it is sufficient to replace the partition function by its maximum term, corresponding to the most probable state. This can be done by maximizing the generic term, introducing Stirling's approximation for the combinatorials. In evaluating the maximum term, due regard must be had for the requirement that for each state the following parameters must have definite and constant values:

$\Sigma_h\, n_h$ (=the total number of helical groups)

$\Sigma_{r,s}\, m_{rs}$ (=the total number of random rings)

$\Sigma_h\, (h+1)\, n_h$ (=the total number of helical pairs)

$\Sigma_{r,s}\, (r+1)\, m_{rs}$ (=the total number of random elements of type A)

$\Sigma_{r,s}\, (s+1)\, m_{rs}$ (=the total number of random elements of type B)

These constraining conditions are accounted for by the method of undetermined multipliers, thereby introducing a total of five unknown parameters. Upon maximizing the generic term of the partition function with respect to n_h and m_{rs} and combining with the terms accounting for the constraining conditions, a set of equations is obtained which is solvable for the fraction of non-helical units.

The detailed derivation of Hill is given in the following section. Readers interested only in the result may skip ahead to page 272 without interrupting the continuity.

It must be emphasized that the presence of a helical configuration *per se* is in no way essential to the argument. It would hold equally well for a linear combination of two polymers with bonded and unbonded sections. Basic to the derivation is the assumption that a nucleotide unit must be in either one state or the other, without intermediate gradations. In the helical or bonded state it is assumed to be held in an essentially rigid position, without rotational freedom.

Derivation of Hill's Theory[1]

A hydrogen-bonded nucleotide is referred to as in state H and an unbonded nucleotide as in state R. We let X_{RA}, X_{RB} represent the partition functions for unbonded nucleotides in chains A and B, respectively, and X_{HA}, X_{HB} represent the corresponding partition functions for bonded nucleotides. Four different kinds of nearest neighbor interactions must be taken into account. Corresponding to these Hill defines:

> w_{RH} =free energy of interaction of an RH nearest neighbor pair
> w_{rs} =free energy of a random ring containing $r+1$ "A" residues   (1)
>   and $s+1$ "B" residues in excess of that of $r+1$ single units
>   in chain A and $s+1$ single units in chain B
> w_h =free energy of a group of $h+1$ *pairs* of H units in excess of
>   that of $h+1$ *pairs* of isolated H units.

It should be noted that, when defined in this way, w_{rs} and w_h can include the contribution of second and higher order nearest neighbor interactions, as well as first nearest neighbor interactions. In what follows the approximation will be made of regarding the first nearest neighbor and higher order interactions of "A" and "B" subunits in the unbonded state as equal. Thus $v_{rs} = v_{sr}$. We also define:

$$\sigma'' = e^{-w_{RH}/kT}$$

$$y_h = e^{-w_h/kT}$$

$$v_{rs} = e^{-w_{rs}/kT}$$

If the two chains are of equal length, B: $\qquad\qquad\qquad\qquad$ (2)

$$N_{RA} = \text{number of } R \text{ units in chain } A$$
$$= N_{RB} = \text{number of } R \text{ units in chain } B \equiv N$$
$$= \text{total number of bonds broken}$$

If $N_{RH} =$ the number of RH pairs or the number of junctions between a group of R units and a group of H units, then $N_{RH}/2 =$ the number of *groups* of R units and the number of *groups* of H units in each chain.

As each of the $N_{RH}/2$ groups of H units in each chain contains at least one H unit, there remain $B - N - N_{RH}/2$ excess H units which can be distributed among the $N_{RH}/2$ groups in $(N_{RH}/2)!/\Pi_h n_h!$ ways, where n_h is the number of H groups containing $(h+1)$ H units.

Similarly, the number of ways of distributing the excess (over $N_{RH}/2$) R units in the two chains is given by $(N_{RH}/2)! \, \Pi_{r,s} \, m_{rs}!$, where m_{rs} is the number of rings of R units containing $(r+1)$ "A" units and $(s+1)$ "B" units. The above are subject to the restrictions:

$$\Sigma_h \, n_h = N_{RH}/2$$

$$\Sigma_h \, h n_h = B - N - N_{RH}/2$$

$$\Sigma_{r,s} \, m_{rs} = N_{RH}/2 \qquad\qquad\qquad (3)$$

$$\Sigma_{r,s} \, r m_{rs} = N - N_{RH}/2$$

$$\Sigma_{r,s} \, s m_{rs} = N - N_{RH}/2$$

We may then write for the partition function:

$$Q = \Sigma_N \, \Sigma_{N_{RH}} X_{RA}^N \, X_{HA}^{B-N} \, X_{RB}^N \, X_{HB}^{B-N} \, \sigma''^{N_{RH}} \Sigma_{m_{rs}} \, t_R \, \Sigma_{n_h} \, t_H$$

where $\qquad\qquad\qquad t_R = (N_{RH}/2)! \, \Pi_{r,s} \, (v_{rs} \, m_{rs}/m_{rs}!) \qquad\qquad (4)$

$$t_H \equiv (N_{RH}/2)! \, \Pi_h (y_h n_h/n_h!)$$

The summation is carried out over all possible states of the molecule, subject to the above restrictions. Although a direct evaluation of the summation is impractical, it is feasible to use the maximum term method. It is most convenient to do this for t_R and t_H independently. At constant N and N_{RH} we may set:

$$\frac{\delta \ln t_R}{\delta m_{rs}} = 0$$

$$\qquad\qquad\qquad\qquad\qquad\qquad (5)$$

$$\frac{\delta \ln t_H}{\delta n_h} = 0$$

The restrictive conditions embodied in equations (3) are taken into account by introducing the undetermined multipliers λ_H, ρ_H, λ_R, ρ_{RA}, ρ_{RB}, for the relationships given by equations (3) in that order. Upon evaluation, using Sterling's approximation, we find from (3), (4) and (5):

$$n_h = e^{-\lambda_H} \, y^h \, q^h; \quad \text{where} \quad q \equiv e^{-\rho_H} \tag{6}$$

$$e^{-\lambda_H} = (N_{RH}/2) \, \Sigma_H$$

and
$$\frac{\Sigma'_H}{\Sigma_H} = \frac{B - N - (N_{RH}/2)}{N_{RH}/2}; \quad \text{where} \quad \Sigma'_H \equiv \Sigma_h \, h y_h \, q^h; \quad \text{and} \quad \Sigma_H \equiv \Sigma_h \, y_h \, q^h \tag{7}$$

We also have:

$$m_{rs} = e^{-\lambda_R} \, v_{rs} \, p_A^r \, p_B^s; \quad \text{here} \quad p_A \equiv e^{-\rho_{RA}}; \quad p_B \equiv e^{-\rho_{RB}} \tag{8}$$

$$e^{-\lambda_R} = (N_{RH}/2)/\Sigma_R; \quad \Sigma_R \equiv \Sigma_{r,s} \, v_{rs} \, p_A^r \, p_B^s \tag{9}$$

and
$$\Sigma'_{RA}/\Sigma_R = \frac{N - N_{RH}/2}{N_{RH}/2}; \quad \Sigma'_{RA} \equiv \Sigma_{r,s} \, r \, v_{rs} \, p_A^r \, p_B^s \tag{10}$$

$$\Sigma'_{RB}/\Sigma_R = \frac{N - N_{RH}/2}{N_{RH}/2}; \quad \Sigma'_{RB} \equiv \Sigma_{r,s} \, s \, v_{rs} \, p_A^r \, p_B^s \tag{11}$$

From the above we obtain for the maximum terms of $\ln t_R$ and $\ln t_H$:

$$\ln t_R^{\text{max}} = - [N - (N_{RH}/2)] \ln p_A - [N - N_{RH}/2] \ln p_B + (N_{RH}/2) \ln \Sigma_R \tag{12}$$

$$\ln t_H^{\text{max}} = - [B - N - N_{RH}/2] \ln q + (N_{RH}/2) \ln \Sigma_H \tag{13}$$

Substituting the above in equation (4) and maximizing with respect to N and N_{RH} we obtain finally:

$$p_A \, p_B / X_{RA} \, X_{RB} = q / X_{HA} \, X_{HB} \equiv S \tag{14}$$

and
$$\sigma''^2 \, p_A p_B q \, \Sigma_R \, \Sigma_H = 1 \tag{15}$$

These, together with equations (6)–(11), furnish the required relationship between p_A, p_B, q, N and N_{RH}. By combining equations (7) and (10) we obtain for the fraction of broken bonds:

$$N/B = (N_{RH}/2B)\{1 + (\Sigma'_{RA}/\Sigma_R)\} = \{1 + (\Sigma'_{RA}/\Sigma_R)\}/\{(\Sigma'_{RA}/\Sigma_R) + (\Sigma'_H/\Sigma_H) + 2\} \tag{16}$$

From the identity of (10) and (11), as v_{rs} has been assumed to be equal to v_{sr}:

$$\Sigma'_{RA} = \Sigma'_{RB} \tag{17}$$

and hence $p_A = p_B \equiv p$.

In the most general case, very involved numerical computations would be required to obtain explicit values of N/B. However, the computation becomes relatively simple if the following approximations are made:

(a) Only first nearest neighbor interactions are important for H units. That is:

$$w_h = hw_{HH}; \quad y_h = y^h \tag{18}$$

and

$$\Sigma_H = (1-yq)^{-1}; \quad \Sigma'_H = yq/(1-yq)^2 \tag{19}$$

(b) The parameter v_{rs} may be placed in the form:

$$v_{rs} = v^{r+s}/(r+s+1)^{3/2} \tag{20}$$

where

$$v = e^{-w_{RR}/kT}$$

This corresponds to neglecting all but first nearest neighbor electrostatic and Van der Waals interactions between R units and to introducing a factor $(r+s+1)^{-3/2}$, of the Jacobsen–Stockmayer[8] type to account for the restriction upon the number of possible configurations assumed by the random sequences imposed by their ringlike nature. We then introduce:

$$p' = vp; \quad q' = yq$$

$$\sigma' = \sigma''/vy^{1/2} = e^{-w'_{RH}/kT} \tag{21}$$

where

$$w'_{RH} = w_{RH} - w_{RR} - 1/2\, w_{HH}$$

w'_{RH} is equal to one-half the free energy increment upon creating one new *group* of R units while leaving the total *number* of R units unchanged. The factor one-half occurs before w_{HH} in the definition of w'_{RH} because w_{HH} is defined as the free energy of nearest neighbor interaction for two pairs of H units while w_{RR} is the corresponding quantity for two *individual* R units. We have:

$$\Sigma_R = \Sigma_{r,s}\ p'^{r+s}/(r+s+1)^{3/2} \tag{22}$$

$$\Sigma'_{RA} = \Sigma_{r,s}\ rp'^{r+s}/(r+s+1)^{3/2} \tag{23}$$

$$= \Sigma_{r,s}\ sp'^{r+s}/(r+s+1)^{3/2}$$

Setting

$$q' = Kp'^2; \quad K = \frac{X_{HA}\, X_{HB}\, y}{X_{RA}\, X_{RB}\, v^2}$$

equation (15) reduces to:

$$\sigma'^2\ Kp'^4\ \{\Sigma_{r,s}\ p'^{r+s}/(r+s+1)^{3/2}\}/(1 - Kp'^2) = 1 \tag{24}$$

The above hold equally well if strands A and B are identical. The parameter w_{RH} is equal to the increment in free energy occurring upon the formation of a junction between a helical and a random sequence.

Application of Hill's theory to the thermal transition

The predicted temperature dependence of the fraction of random residues is contained in equations (16), (19), (22), (23), and (24). Equation (24) has the form:

$$\sigma'^{2}\,Kp'^{4}\Sigma_{r,s}\{p'^{\,r+s}/(r+s+1)^{3/2}\}/(1-Kp'^{2})=1 \qquad (24)$$

The parameter K, which is a ratio of the partition functions of a random and helical element, may be factored into entropic and energetic components and written in the form:

$$K=z^{2}\,e^{-\mathcal{E}/kT} \qquad (25)$$

where ε is the energy increment upon rupturing the hydrogen bonding between a pair of helical units and z is the effective number of configurations a *single* unbonded random unit can assume.

The parameter σ', which is of central importance, has been defined as $e^{-w'_{RH}/kT}$, where w'_{RH} is equal to one-half the free energy increment upon creating one new group of random units while leaving the total number of random units unchanged. When $w'_{RH}=0$ ($\sigma'=1$) there is no penalty in free energy imposed upon the creation of a new group and internucleotide bonds can be ruptured with equal ease by enlarging an existing random ring or creating a new one. When $w'_{RH}>0$ ($\sigma'<1$) there is an energetic bias in favor of enlarging existing breaks. As w'_{RH} becomes increasingly negative so that σ' approaches zero this bias becomes more and more pronounced. The converse situation when $w_{RH}<0$ ($\sigma'>1$) is probably not realizable physically.

For particular values of K and σ', the parameter p' may be computed from equation (24) by iterative machine computation. Once p' is available it is possible to compute N/B, the fraction of linkages which are ruptured, from equation (16).

$$N/B=\{1+(\Sigma'_{RA}/\Sigma_{R})\}/\{(\Sigma'_{RA}/\Sigma_{R})+(\Sigma'_{H}/\Sigma_{H})+2\} \qquad (16)$$

since

$$\Sigma_{R}=\Sigma_{r,s}\;p'^{\,r+s}/(r+s+1)^{3/2} \qquad (22)$$

$$\Sigma'_{RA}=\Sigma_{r,s}\;rp'^{\,r+s}/(r+s+1)^{3/2} \qquad (23)$$

$$\Sigma_{H}=(1-Kp'^{2})^{-1};\;\;\Sigma'_{H}=Kp'^{2}/(1-Kp'^{2})^{2} \qquad (19)$$

By introducing the value of p' into equations (19), (22), and (23), the parameters Σ_{R}, Σ'_{RA}, Σ_{H}, and Σ'_{H} can be computed. These can be inserted in equation (16) to find N/B.

In this manner N/B can be computed as a function of K and hence of temperature if values are assumed for z and E.

The temperature dependence of N/B is thus contained in K. Upon the above basis computations have been made of N/B as a function of kT/ε for several values of σ', using an arbitrary value for z. The results are shown in Fig. 90.

The most striking aspect of Fig. 90 is that, for a pronounced degree of sharpening to occur, σ' must be small compared with unity. This is true irrespective of the value chosen for z.

It is by no means obvious how σ' could attain such small values. In the analogous a-helical polypeptide case this follows naturally from the energy bias resulting from the fact that for every sequence of n random residues, $(n+2)$ hydrogen bonds must be broken. In the polynucleotide case a low value of σ' must reflect a large and positive value of w'_{RH}.

Perhaps the most feasible explanation is to consider w'_{RH} as largely entropic in origin, arising from the restriction upon the rotational freedom of the terminal nucleotides of a random ring sequence imposed sterically by their close proximity.

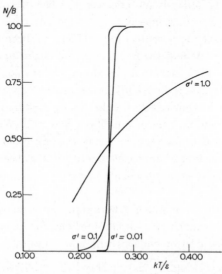

Fig. 90. Fraction of broken bonds as a function of kT/ε computed from eqns. (16) and (24). $(z^2 = 50)$.

In any event the observed sharpness of the thermal transitions in the $(A+U)$ and $(A+I)$ cases, as discussed in Chapter 7, indicates large and positive values of w'_{RH}, if the intermittent mechanism is valid.

Let us now consider the alternative mechanism of thermal denaturation by unzippering from the ends. This case has been treated by Gibbs and DiMarzio[3]. In this case there are only two random sequences which enlarge from each end. The problem of mismatching does not arise and the random sequences are linear rather than ringlike. In this model the partition function has the form

$$Q = \Sigma_{r,s}\, u^{r+s} + z^4 u^B$$

$$= \Sigma_{l=0}^{B-1} (l+1)\, u^l + z^4 u^B$$

$$= \frac{1 + Bu^{B+1} - (B+1)\, u^B}{(1-u)^2} + z^4 u^B \tag{26}$$

where

$$u = \frac{X_{RA}\, X_{RB}}{X_{HA}\, X_{HB}} = z^2\, e^{-\epsilon/kT}$$

r, s = the number of residues in the two random sequences originating at the two ends. The energy increment over the completely helical case is given by

$$U = kT^2 \frac{\delta \ln Q}{\delta T} \tag{27}$$

and the fraction of broken bonds by

$$N/B = U/\varepsilon B \tag{28}$$

Fig. 91 gives N/B as a function of temperature for varying values of B as computed from equations (26)–(28) using the unzippering model. In this case the number of junctions between bonded and unbonded sequences is constant and equal to two. Hence, in contrast to the intermittent model, the free energy of interaction between a random and a helical segment does not influence the results. The degree of sharpness of the transition is governed primarily by the chain length.

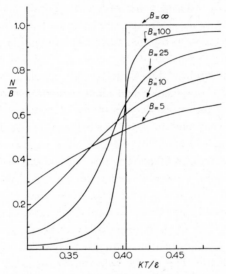

Fig. 91. Fraction of broken bonds as a function of kT/ε computed from equations (26)–(28). z is taken[3] as 12.

The preceding models appear to be adequate to describe, in a semiquantitative manner, the observed character of the thermally induced helix-coil transitions for the synthetic polynucleotide systems described earlier. However, it is worthwhile to dwell briefly upon some of the approximations required to place the theory in a tractible form for computation.

Among these is the implicit assumption that a nucleotide residue must be in either a completely helical or completely random state, with no intermediate gradations. In actuality there is considerable evidence that at sufficiently low temperatures a residue may retain its helical configuration even if its hydrogen bonding is partially or completely ruptured. However, this is probably unimportant in the case of the thermal transition as temperatures high enough to break hydrogen bonds would presumably be sufficient to overcome residual Van der Waals cohesive forces between nucleotide pairs as well.

The assumption that only nearest neighbor interactions are important is probably fairly severe, particularly at low ionic strengths where mutual electrostatic repulsion of the similarly charged phosphates becomes very important.

The manner in which the entropy gain arising from the liberation of a nucleotide pair from the helical state has been accounted for is rather artificial. It is clearly a quite crude approximation to introduce a discrete and constant number of possible configurations represented by the parameter z. However, it is possible to replace this kind of treatment by one more rigorous though less convenient[3].

The influence of ionic strength upon the position of the midpoint of the thermal transition, as discussed in the preceding chapter, can formally be accounted for in terms of a decrease in magnitude of ε with decreasing ionic strength. Thus, for a given value of kT/ε, a reduced value of ε corresponds to a lower value of T. The decrease in ε at low ionic strengths reflects the enhanced importance of the (positive) electrostatic term in the free energy of association of a base pair which arises from the mutual repulsion of the negatively charged phosphates.

The thermal denaturation of DNA can be only roughly accommodated by this kind of treatment. The presence of two kinds of hydrogen bonded base pairs of different stability and the probable occurrence of considerable heterogeneity of composition would be expected to result in a degree of broadening of the transition zone in excess of that predicted by the preceding treatment. Furthermore, the matching requirements of the DNA structure presumably hinder an exact reformation of any extensive unbonded sequence and thus introduce an intrinsic irreversibility into the denaturation process. This is counter to the assumption of thermodynamic equilibrium which is implicit in the preceding treatment.

It is clear, however, that the basic mechanism of DNA denaturation, the above complications aside, is almost certainly qualitatively analogous to that of the synthetic polynucleotide case. The similar behavior of the latter systems provides in fact a valuable confirmation of the accepted picture of DNA denaturation.

There remain to be discussed the thermal transitions of imperfectly helical systems including poly A, poly AU, and RNA. In contrast to the highly ordered systems discussed above, all of these display a relatively gradual loss with increasing temperature of the properties associated with appreciable helical content. In all probability this is a consequence of the small size of the helical regions present. The polynucleotide molecule thus behaves in this respect like a collection of small helical molecules which melt independently, probably by an unzipping mechanism. The broadening of the transition zone as a consequence of reduced effective chain length is predicted by equations (26)–(28), as Fig. 91 shows.

There has as yet been no published treatment of the helix-coil transition for a triply-stranded polynucleotide. While the algebra would certainly be very complicated in this case, the nature of the problem is similar in principle to the doubly stranded case.

THE EFFECT OF A HELIX-COIL TRANSITION UPON THE
HYDROGEN ION TITRATION CURVE

There remains to be considered the case of a helix–coil transition brought about as a result of a change in the state of ionization of the polynucleotide, as well as the influence of such a transition upon the shape of the hydrogen ion titration curve. It would certainly be excepted *a priori* that the influence would be profound since, for all four bases, the probable locus of proton attachment is to a site likely to serve as a donor or acceptor group in forming a hydrogen bonded base pair, such as has been postulated to account for the stability of doubly stranded helical polynucleotides.

Confining our attention for the moment to the synthetic polynucleotides, it may be recalled that a striking feature of the titration curves reported to date is the high degree of sharpening which they often display when a change in the state of ionization of a particular base is accompanied by a helix–coil transition. This is the case for the alkaline branch of the titration curve of the (A + U) equimolar complex[9], as well as for the titration curve of poly A itself[10].

The theoretical treatment of such a problem would be greatly simplified if it were legitimate to assume that only one state of ionization of each nucleotide base is consistent with its involvement in a helical configuration. According to this model, as each base bound a proton it would change from the helical to the random configuration (or *vice versa*). Unfortunately the evidence on whether this assumption is quantitatively valid is still somewhat ambiguous.

In the case of the alkaline branch of the titration curve of the (A + U) complex the close parallel between the dissociation of hydrogen ions and the loss of hypochromism suggests that the above is valid in this case[9, 11]. A similar statement may be made for the case[10] of poly A. However, even in these instances, the evidence is by no means conclusive. Moreover in the case of native DNA the calorimetric results of Sturtevant *et al.*[12] stand in direct contradiction to this assumption. In view of the above uncertainties the general theory will be developed without invoking this postulate.

For the sake of concreteness the treatment will be limited to the doubly stranded case for which each of the two (non-identical) strands is a linear polymer of B single nucleotide units. This model would correspond formally to the equimolar (A + U) and (A + I) cases.

The actual problem is considerably simplified by the fact that the pK's of the two different bases involved in each case are widely separated so that the two zones of titration can therefore be considered independently. The state of ionization of one of the strands can thus be regarded as constant and attention centered upon the other. It will also be assumed that the degree of polymerization (B) of the two strands is sufficiently large so that end effects may be disregarded. The treatment will be confined to the intermittent model and unzipping from the ends will be assumed to be unimportant as a mechanism of helix disruption.

If the temperature is well below the midpoint of the thermal transition, each nucleotide unit of the strand which is being titrated can exist in any of four states. These are:

RH^+ (random, with a bound proton)

R (random, without a bound proton)

HH^+ (helical, with a bound proton)

H (helical, without a bound proton)

At a molecular state intermediate to the completely helical and the completely random case the polynucleotide may, as in the case of thermal denaturation, be visualized as consisting of alternating regions of hydrogen-bonded pairs of helical subelements and rings of unbonded random subelements. For purposes of analysis it is convenient to divide the macromolecule into segments containing one or more pairs of helical residues on the left and one or more pairs of random residues on the right. For the reasons cited earlier we need consider the binding of protons by only one of the two strands. In the zone of titration of the "A" residues we may visualize the polynucleotide as follows:

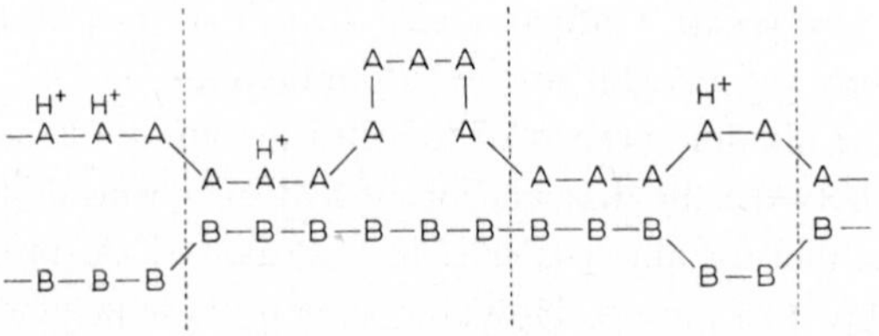

As was mentioned earlier, while identical pairing of "A" and "B" residues is required in the helical regions it is possible for mismatching to occur in the random, unbonded regions [1].

The problem is of a generalized Ising type and may be attacked readily, provided the assumption is made that only nearest (electrostatic) neighbor interactions are important for the bound protons. This degree of approximation is virtually essential in order to obtain tractible relationships, as the inclusion of higher order interactions results in very complicated relationships even when the problem is not complicated by the occurrence of a helix–coil transition [13].

Nevertheless, it should be made clear that the assumption that only nearest neighbor interactions of bound protons are important is basically inexact and will inevitably lead to errors in the computed titration curves. However, the computed results of Lifson et al. [13], indicate that for nearest neighbor interaction energies of the order of magnitude expected in this case ($<2kT$) the degree of distortion of the shape of the titration curve caused by neglect of higher order interactions is probably unimportant for the present purpose.

The additional assumption will be made that the first and higher order nearest neighbor Van der Waals interactions of the nucleotides themselves are not perturbed by the presence of bound protons.

The method is not too dissimilar from that outlined earlier for the thermal transition. In this case it is more convenient to use the completely helical form of the macromolecule as a reference state.

The partition function is set up as before and again is of the form

$$Q = \Sigma_i \, G_i \exp\left(-w_i/kT\right)$$

The definition of a particular state of the molecule is somewhat more complicated than in the previous case, as it is necessary to specify the number of protons bound to the helical and random portions of the A chain in each double segment as well as the number of nearest neighbor pairs of bound protons in each case.

In this case it is more convenient to work with the grand partition function which is defined as

$$\Sigma_j \, Q_j \, \lambda^j$$

where λ is the absolute activity of hydrogen ion. The summation is carried out over all possible values of j, the number of bound protons, from zero to B. The use of the grand partition function has a particular advantage in that the equilibrium number of bound protons is given by the derivative of its logarithm with respect to the logarithm of absolute activity.

The evaluation of the grand partition function by direct summation is impractical, but again it is permissible to replace it by its maximum term. As before, this may be done by maximizing the generic term, due account being taken of the constraining conditions by the method of undetermined multipliers.

A detailed derivation is given in the following section.

Derivation of the isotherm

Subject to the above we may write for the partition function, *in terms of the completely helical macromolecule as a reference state:*

$$Q = \Sigma\left\{(\Sigma \, N_{<m>})! \, \Pi \, \frac{X'^{N_{<m>}}}{N_{<m>}!}\right\} \tag{29}$$

where $N_{<m>} = N_{rshijkl}$

> = the number of segments (as defined earlier) containing h pairs of helical subelements with j bound protons and l nearest neighbor pairs of bound protons;
> r random residues of type "A", with i bound protons, and k nearest neighbor pairs of bound protons; and s random residues of type "B". forming an $(r+s)$ membered ring with the r residues of type "A",

The combinatorial $(\Sigma N_{<m>})!/\Pi N_{<m>}!$ is simply the number of ways of ordering the $\Sigma N_{<m>}$ segments.

The summation in equation (29) is carried out over all values of the subscripts r, s, h, i, j, k, l such that

$$k \leqslant i-1; \quad l \leqslant j-1$$

$$i \leqslant r; \quad j \leqslant h$$

$$1 \leqslant r, \ s, \ h \leqslant B$$

$$X_m' = \sigma C_{i-k-1}^{i-1} C_{i-k}^{r-i+1} C_{j-l-1}^{j-1} C_{j-l}^{h-j+1} f(r+s) x_R^i x_H^j a_R^k a_H^l \ \Phi_R(r+s) \ \Phi_H(h) \tag{30}$$

where C_{i-k-1}^{i-1}, etc. $=$ binomial coefficient

$$= \frac{(i-1)!}{(i-k-1)! \ k!}, \text{ etc.}$$

$$x_R, \ x_H =$$

partition function for a proton bound to a random and to a helical "A" subelement respectively. x_H includes a factor accounting for the free energy increment accompanying the formation (or rupture) of a hydrogen bond upon binding a proton

$$a_R, \ a_H = e^{-wii/kT}, \ e^{-wjj/kT}$$

respectively, where $w_{ii}, \ w_{jj} =$ free energies of interaction of nearest neighbor pars of protons bound to random and to helical "A" subelements, respectively.

$$\sigma = e^{-\left(2w_{RH} - w_{RR} - w_{HH}\right)/kT}$$

where $w_{RH}, \ w_{RR}, \ w_{HH} =$ free energies of interaction for nearest neighbor pairs of helical and random, random-random, and helical-helical subelements, respectively.

$$\Phi_R(r+s), \ \Phi_H(h) =$$

factors accounting for nearest neighbor interactions of order higher than the first for random and helical subelements, respectively

$$f(r+s) = z(r+s)e^{-(r+s)\mathcal{E}/kT}$$

where $\varepsilon =$ energy change per subelement upon rupturing a helically bonded pair $Z(r+s) =$ number of configurations available to a ring of $(r+s)$ random elements.

The product of the binomial coefficients $C_{i-k-1}^{i-1} \ C_{i-k}^{r-i+1} \ C_{j-l-1}^{j-1} \ C_{j-l}^{h-j+1}$ is the modified

Ising expression for the number of ways of ordering i protons upon r random residues and j protons upon h helical residues so that they possess k and l nearest neighbor pairs, respectively[14].

We may write for the grand partition function, summing over all possible numbers of bound protons:

$$\Xi = \Sigma \, Q \, \lambda^{(i+j) \, N_{<m>}}$$

$$= \Sigma \left\{ (\Sigma \, N_{<m>})! \, \Pi \, \frac{X_{<m>}^{N_{<m>}}}{N_{<m>}!} \right\} \tag{31}$$

where

$$X_{<m>} = X_{<m>}' \, \lambda^{i+j}$$

$$\lambda = \text{absolute activity of hydrogen ion}$$

This must be evaluated subject to the two subsidiary conditions:

$$\Sigma_{r,h} \, (r+h) \, N_{<m>} = B$$
$$\Sigma_{s,h} \, (s+h) \, N_{<m>} = B$$

Picking out the maximum term of Ξ (Ξ_*) and employing the method of undetermined multipliers, we have, using Sterling's approximation:

$$\text{in} \, \Sigma \, N_{<m>} - \ln N_{<m>} + \ln X_{<m>} + \ln \alpha \, (r+h) + \ln \beta \, (s+h) = 0 \tag{33}$$

where $\ln \alpha$, $\ln \beta$ = undetermined multipliers

or

$$N_{<m>} = (\Sigma \, N_{<m>}) \, X_{<m>} \, \alpha^{r+h} \, \beta^{s+h}$$

This yields for Ξ_*

$$\ln \Xi^* = \Sigma \{ N_{<m>} \, (\ln \Sigma \, N_{<m>} - \ln N_{<m>} + \ln X_{<m>}) \}$$
$$= -\ln \alpha \, \Sigma \, (r+h) \, N_{<m>} - \ln \beta \, \Sigma \, (s+h) \, N_{<m>}$$

or

$$\Xi^* = (\alpha\beta)^{-B} \tag{34}$$

and

$$N_a = \text{number of hydrogen ions bound}$$

$$= \frac{\delta \ln \Xi^*}{\delta \ln \lambda} = -B \frac{\delta \ln \alpha\beta}{\delta \ln \lambda}$$

or

$$\theta = \frac{N_a}{B} = -\frac{\delta \ln (\alpha\beta)}{\delta \ln\lambda} = \text{fraction of "A" sites occupied} \tag{35}$$

From equation (33) and the subsidiary relationships we have:

$$\Sigma \, X_{<m>} \, \alpha^{r+h} \, \beta^{s+h} = 1 \tag{36a}$$

$$\Sigma \, r X_{<m>} \, \alpha^r \beta^s = \Sigma \, s X_{<m>} \, \alpha^r \beta^s \tag{36b}$$

These furnish the required relationship between λ, α, and β. The exact form[3] of the equations depends, of course, upon the form chosen for $\Phi_R(r+s)$, $\Phi_H(h)$, and $Z(r+s)$. A number of cases of varying exactness (and complexity) can be treated. In order of increasing complexity we have:

I.
$$\Phi_R(r+s)=\Phi_H(h)=1$$

$$r=s$$

$$Z(r+s)=Z(2r)=z^{2r}$$

where $z=$ effective number of configurations available to a random residue. This model corresponds to ignoring all nucleotide interactions except first nearest neighbors, to excluding the possibility of mismatching of the strands, and to ignoring the ring-like nature of the random segments, which prohibits many configurations.

Subject to the above, the two parameters α and β may be replaced by the single parameter γ $(=\alpha\beta)$.

Thus
$$\theta=-\frac{\delta \ln \gamma}{\delta \ln \lambda} \tag{37}$$

Upon summing equation (36a) over all values of r, i, k and h, j, l, using the binomial theorem we obtain:

$$1=\sigma\left\{\frac{\gamma(1-\gamma\lambda''a_H+\lambda''+\gamma\lambda'')}{(1-\gamma)(1-\gamma\lambda''a_H)-\overset{2}{\gamma}\lambda''}\right\}\left\{\frac{\gamma'(1-\gamma'\lambda'a_R+\lambda'+\gamma'\lambda')}{(1-\gamma')(1-\gamma'\lambda'a_R)-\gamma'^2\lambda'}\right\} \tag{38}$$

where
$$\lambda'=\lambda x_r$$

$$\lambda''=\lambda x_h$$

$$\gamma'=\gamma z^2 e^{-2\varepsilon/kT}$$

The above yields a simple quadratic equation for λ as a function of γ. In the case for which the binding of a proton or its dissociation (regarded formally as the binding of a OH$^-$ion) is sufficient to rupture the internucleotide linkage, a further simplification is possible. We then have $\lambda''=0$ and equation (38) reduces to

$$1=\sigma\frac{\gamma}{1-\gamma}\left\{\frac{\gamma'(1-\gamma'\lambda'a_R+\gamma'\lambda'+\lambda')}{(1-\gamma')(1-\gamma'a_R)-\gamma'^2\lambda'}\right\} \tag{39}$$

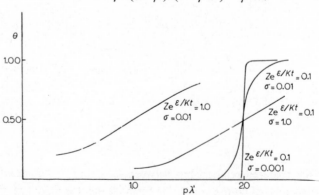

Fig. 92. Computed titration curves for varying values of σ, $ze^{-\varepsilon/kT}$
$(a_R=1,\lambda''=0)$. $p\lambda'=\log \lambda'$.

In actuality the evidence is strong that this latter condition may hold for several of the cases thus far studied[9,11]. Computations have been made for this simplest case. Figs. 92, 93 and 94 show the variation of θ with $p\lambda'$ as a function of σ, $ze^{-\varepsilon/kT}$, and a_R, respectively.

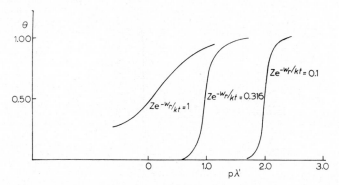

Fig. 93. Computed titration curves for varying values of $ze^{-\varepsilon/kT}$ ($a_R = 1$, $\lambda'' = 0$, $\sigma = 0.01$).

In general it can be stated that, for a pronounced sharpening of the titration curve to occur, σ and $ze^{-\varepsilon/kT}$ must both be $<< 1$. For a given value of σ the curve becomes sharper with decreasing values of $z^2e^{-2\varepsilon/kT}$ and *vice versa*. A value of σ less than unity means that it is less difficult to enlarge a sequence of broken bonds than to start a new sequence. A decrease in a_R has a broadening effect upon the titration curve, which also becomes asymmetric, as Fig. 94 shows. The midpoint of the curve is displaced to greater values of λ' as $ze^{-\varepsilon/kT}$ or a_R decreases.

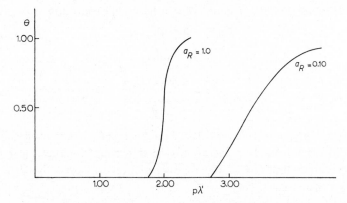

Fig. 94. Computed titration curves for two values of a_R ($\lambda'' = 0$, $ze^{\varepsilon/kT} = 0.1$, $\sigma = 0.01$).

Fig. 95 shows two titration curves computed from equations (37) and (38) for the case where a proton may be bound by either a helical or a random subunit. If the proton can be bound equally well by either ($\lambda' = \lambda''$) no sharpening occurs, irrespective of the values of σ and $ze^{-\varepsilon/kT}$. If binding by a helical subunit is much less favored ($\lambda''=0.0001\ \lambda'$) then considerable sharpening does occur. In the limit when $\lambda''=0$, the curves approach those shown in Figs. 92 and 93.

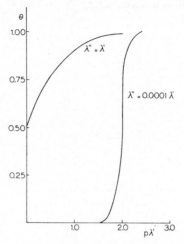

Fig. 95. Computed values of θ as a function of $p\lambda'$ for two values of λ''
$ze^{-\mathcal{E}/kT} = 0.1$, $\sigma = 0.01$, and $a_R = a_H = 1$ in each case.

The influence of temperature is also accounted for by equations (37)–(39) via the dependence upon $ze^{-\mathcal{E}/kT}$. An increase in temperature (corresponding to an increase in $ze^{-\mathcal{E}/kT}$) shifts the midpoint of the curve to lower values of λ', as has been observed experimentally[10].

Thus this crudest possible approximation appears capable of accounting for most of the features observed experimentally for the hydrogen ion titration curves of polynucleotides capable of undergoing a helix–coil transition.

II. $\Phi_H(h)=\Phi_R(r+s)=1$

$$r=s$$

$$Z(r+s)=\frac{z^{2r}}{(2r+1)^{3/2}}$$

This case is analogous to I, except that the refinement is made of introducing an expression of the Stockmayer–Jacobson type to account for the constraint upon the available configurations of the random sections imposed by their ring-like nature[8]. We then have

$$\theta=-\frac{\delta\ln\gamma}{\delta\ln\lambda} \tag{40}$$

and $$1=\sigma\left\{\frac{\gamma(1-\gamma\lambda''a_H+\lambda''+\gamma\lambda'')}{(1-\gamma)(1-\gamma\lambda''a_H)-\gamma^2\lambda''}\right\}\Sigma_{i,k,r}\ C_{i-k-1}^{i-1}\ C_{i-k}^{r-i+1}\ a_R^k\ \lambda'^i\ \frac{\gamma'^r}{(2r+1)^{3/2}} \tag{41}$$

If $\lambda''=0$ (as above)

$$1 = \frac{\sigma\gamma}{1-\gamma} \Sigma_{i,k,r} C_{i-k-1}^{i-1} \; C_{i-k}^{r-i+1} \; a_R^k \, \lambda'^i \left[\frac{\gamma''^r}{(2r+1)^{3/2}}\right] \tag{42}$$

Equations (41) and (42) give λ implicitly as a function of γ. Iterative machine computation would be required to obtain numerical values of λ' as a function of γ. If a_R can be set equal to unity, as may be roughly valid at high ionic strengths, we then have, corresponding to equation (41):

$$1 = \sigma \left\{\frac{\gamma(1 - \gamma\lambda''a_H + \lambda'' + \gamma\lambda'')}{(1-\gamma)\,(1 - \gamma\lambda''a_H) - \gamma^2\lambda''}\right\} \Sigma_r \frac{[\gamma'(1+\lambda')]^r}{(2r+1)^{3/2}} \tag{43}$$

If $\qquad\qquad$ $\lambda'' = 0$, the above becomes

$$1 = \sigma\frac{\gamma}{1-\gamma} \Sigma_r \frac{[\gamma'(1+\lambda')]^r}{(2r+1)^{3/2}} \tag{44}$$

Introducing $\Phi \; (\equiv \gamma(1+\lambda'))$ we have

$$\lambda' = \sigma \; \Phi \; \Sigma_r \frac{\Phi'^r}{(2r+1)^{3/2}} + \Phi - 1 \tag{45}$$

where $\qquad\qquad$ $\Phi' = \gamma \; z^2 \; e^{-2\epsilon/kT}$

and $\qquad\qquad$ $\theta = -\dfrac{\delta \ln \gamma}{\delta \ln \lambda'} = \dfrac{\lambda'}{1+\lambda'} - \dfrac{\lambda'}{\Phi}\dfrac{\delta\Phi}{\delta\lambda'} \tag{46}$

where $\qquad \dfrac{\delta\Phi}{\delta\lambda'} = \dfrac{1}{\delta\lambda'/\delta\Phi} = 1 / \left[\sigma \left\{\Sigma_r \dfrac{\Phi'^r}{(2r+1)^{3/2}} + \Sigma_r \dfrac{r\,\Phi'^r}{(2r+1)^{3/2}}\right\} + 1\right] \tag{47}$

The above is readily computable.

III. $\qquad\qquad\qquad \Phi_R(r+s) = \Phi_H(h) = 1$

$$Z(r+s) = z^{r+s}$$

This corresponds to ignoring the ring-like nature of the random segments. We then obtain, using the binomial theorem:

$$\beta' = \frac{a'}{\lambda' + [1 + a'\lambda'(1-a_r)]^2} \{[1 + a'\lambda'(1-a_r)]^2 + \lambda'(2 + \lambda'a_R + 2a'\lambda - 2a'\lambda'a_R)\} \tag{49}$$

where $\qquad\qquad$ $a' = aze^{-\epsilon/kT}; \; \beta' = \beta ze^{-\epsilon/kT}$

and $\quad 1 = \dfrac{\sigma a'\beta'(1 - a'\lambda'a_R + \lambda' + a'\lambda')\,(1 - a\beta\lambda''a_H + \lambda'' + a\beta\lambda'')a\beta}{(1-\beta')\,\{(1-a')\,(1 - a'\lambda'a_R) - a'^2\lambda'\}\,\{(1-a\beta)\,(1 - a\beta a_H\lambda'') - a^2\beta^2\lambda''\}} \tag{49}$

If $a_R = 1$ and $\lambda'' = 0$, the above reduce to:

$$\beta' = a'(1+\lambda') \tag{50}$$

and $\qquad\qquad$ $1 = \dfrac{\sigma \; a'\beta' \; (1+\lambda')a\beta}{(1-\beta')\,(1-\beta')\,(1-a\beta)} \tag{51}$

$$\lambda' = \frac{\sigma\beta'^2\beta^2}{(1-\beta')^2} + \beta^2 - 1$$

(52)

also
$$\theta = -\frac{\delta \ln \alpha\beta}{\delta \ln \lambda'} = \frac{\lambda'}{1+\lambda'} - \frac{2\lambda'}{\beta}\frac{\delta\beta}{\delta\lambda'}$$

(53)

Fig. 96 compares titration curves computed using equations (39) and (51). Similar values of σ and $ze^{-\mathcal{E}/kT}$ were assumed. As Fig. 96 shows, allowance for mismatching has no important effect upon the position of the midpoint, but does result in a slight broadening of the curve.

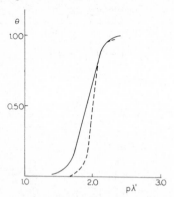

Fig. 96. Effect of mismatching upon the titration curve. In both cases $a_R = 1$, $\lambda'' = 0$, $ze^{-\mathcal{E}/kT} = 0.1$, and $\sigma = 0.01$. ——————— computed from equation (51), taking mismatching into account. – – – – – – – computed from equation (39).

IV. $\Phi_R(r+s) = \Phi_H(h) = 1$

$$Z(r+s) = \frac{z^{r+s}}{(r+s+1)^{3/2}}$$

We then have:

$$\sigma \Sigma_{r,i,k,s} C_{i-k-1}^{i-1} C_{i-k}^{r-i+1} \lambda'^i a_R^k \frac{\alpha'^r \beta'^s}{(r+s+1)^{3/2}} \Sigma_{h,j,l} C_{j-l-1}^{j-1} C_{j-l}^{h-j+1} \lambda''^j a_H^l (\alpha\beta)^h = 1$$

(54)

$$= \sigma \frac{\alpha\beta(1 - \alpha\beta\lambda'' a_H + \lambda'' + \alpha\beta\lambda'')}{\{(1-\alpha\beta)(1-\alpha\beta\lambda'' a_H) - \alpha^2\beta^2\lambda''\}} \Sigma_{r,i,k,s} C_{i-k-1}^{i-1} C_{i-k}^{r-i+1} \lambda'^i a_R^k \frac{\alpha'^r \beta'^s}{(r+s+1)^{3/2}}$$

and

$$\Sigma_{r,i,k,s} r C_{i-k-1}^{i-1} C_{i-k}^{r-i+1} \lambda'^i a_R^k \frac{\alpha'^r \beta'^s}{(r+s+1)^{3/2}} = \Sigma_{r,i,k,s} s C_{i-k-1}^{i-1} C_{i-k}^{r-i+1} \lambda'^i a_R^k \frac{\alpha'^r \beta'^s}{(r+s+1)^{3/2}}$$

(55)

In this most general case there is nothing for it but to solve numerically for λ as a function of α and β by machine computation. However, if $\lambda''=0$ and $a_R=1$, we have:

$$\beta' = a'(1+\lambda')$$

and
$$1 = \sigma \frac{\alpha\beta}{(1-\alpha\beta)} \Sigma_{r,s} \frac{[\alpha'(1+\lambda')]^r \beta'^s}{(r+s+1)^{3/2}} = \sigma \frac{\alpha\beta}{1-\alpha\beta} \Sigma_{r,s} \frac{\beta'^{r+s}}{(r+s+1)^{3/2}} \tag{56}$$

$$1 = \sigma \frac{\beta^2}{1+\lambda'-\beta^2} \Sigma_{r,s} \frac{\beta'^{r+s}}{(r+s+1)^{3/2}} \tag{57}$$

or
$$\lambda' = \sigma\beta^2 \Sigma_{r,s} \frac{\beta'^{r+s}}{(r+s+1)^{3/2}} + \beta^2 - 1 \tag{}$$

and
$$\theta = \frac{\lambda'}{1+\lambda'} - \frac{2\lambda'}{\beta} \frac{\delta\beta}{\delta\lambda'} \tag{58}$$

where
$$\frac{\delta\beta}{\delta\lambda'} = \frac{1}{\delta\lambda'/\delta\beta} = 1/[\sigma \left\{ 2\beta \Sigma_{r,s} \frac{\beta'^{r+s}}{(r+s+1)^{3/2}} + \beta \Sigma_{r,s} \frac{(r+s)\beta'^{r+s}}{(r+s+1)^{3/2}} \right\} + 2\beta] \tag{59}$$

This is readily evaluable.

Application of the theory of hydrogen ion binding

Certain generalizations can be made from the theory outlined in the preceding section. The general shape of the hydrogen ion titration curve and, in particular, its degree of sharpening are governed by the three parameters:

$$K (= ze^{-\mathcal{E}/kT}); \quad \sigma (= \sigma'^2); \quad \text{and} \quad \lambda''/\lambda'$$

which is equal to the ratio of association constants for the binding of a proton by a helical and a random A unit respectively.

While detailed computations for the most general case have yet to be made, it is possible to make certain conclusions from the limited calculations discussed above. If $ze^{-\mathcal{E}/kT}$ is small compared with unity so that the helical form of the polynucleotide is stable in the absence of any binding (or dissociation) of protons it can be stated that a definite sharpening of the titration curve is predicted if the following hold:

(*a*) The ratio λ''/λ' is small compared with unity, *i.e.* the binding of a proton (or its dissociation, represented formally as the binding of a hydroxyl ion) favors the rupture of the internucleotide bonding. In the case of the alkaline titration of the poly A plus poly U equimolar complex the available evidence appears to indicate that this is the case, in view of the close parallel of the spectral transition to the almost discontinuous titration curve. Indeed, the observed sharpening may be regarded as supporting evidence that this is the case. It should be noted that, as Fig. 95 shows, the binding of a proton by a helical subunit need not be prohibited absolutely for a high degree of sharpening to occur. Indeed, equations (37) and (38) predict a gradual increase in sharpness as binding by helical subelements becomes less favored.

(*b*) The parameter σ is small in comparison with unity or, in other words, the enlargement of a given sequence of ruptured bonds is energetically favored over the initiation of a new sequence. This is in complete analogy to the case of thermal denaturation and appears to be of central importance for all one dimensional transitions of this type. It is especially to be noted that if $\sigma = 1$ no sharpening occurs irrespective of the relative magnitudes of λ' and λ''. A similar conclusion has been reached for the thermal transition. Thus the frequently made assertion that a high degree of order in a linear array of hydrogen bonded subunits is sufficient in itself to bring about a sharp order-disorder transition is incorrect. It should furthermore be noted that, when nearest neighbor interactions of bound protons are negligible ($a_R = a_H = 1$) and a proton may be bound equally readily by a helical or a random subunit ($\lambda' = \lambda''$), the preceding equations reduce to the familiar Langmuir isotherm ($\theta = \lambda'/1 + \lambda'$).

However, both this treatment and the one outlined previously for the thermal transition should not be regarded as representing more than a first approximate attempt upon the problem. The removal of the simplifying assumptions which made this kind of approach feasible has the result of so inordinately complicating the mathematics that it seems likely that further progress will be attained only with difficulty.

The origin of a low value of σ is less obvious than for the case of α-helical polypeptides, where it follows naturally from the requirement that, to form a sequence of m random residues, $(m+2)$ hydrogen bonds must be broken. In the polynucleotide case, perhaps the most plausible explanation is that the effect is primarily entropic in origin and reflects the steric restriction upon the rotational freedom of the terminal nucleotides of a random ring imposed by their close proximity.

The introduction of nearest neighbor interactions of bound protons has the effect of broadening the titration curve and rendering it asymmetrical, with a tendency toward flattening at large values of θ. This effect has been observed in the synthetic polynucleotide case [10].

In general the preceding theory can account for most of the anomalous features of the titration curves observed for several synthetic polynucleotide systems. In particular the high degree of sharpening, the asymmetry, and the shifts with temperature (as reflected by changes in $ze^{-\mathcal{E}/kT}$) are all predictable in terms of this kind of treatment.

REFERENCES

[1] T. HILL, *J. Chem. Phys.*, 30 (1959) 383.
[2] J. SCHELLMAN, *Compt. Rend. Trav. Lab. Carlsberg, Ser. Chim.*, 29 (1955) 230.
[3] J. GIBBS AND E. DiMARZIO, *J. Chem. Phys.*, 30 (1959) 271.
[4] L. PELLER, *Ph.D. Thesis*, Princeton University, 1957.
[5] S. RICE AND A. WADA, *J. Chem. Phys.*, 29 (1958) 233.
[6] B. ZIMM AND J. BRAGG, *J. Chem. Phys.*, 28 (1958) 1246.
[7] J. GIBBS AND E. DiMARZIO, *J. Chem. Phys.*, 28 (1958) 1247.
[8] H. JACOBSEN AND W. STOCKMAYER, *J. Chem. Phys.*, 18 (1950) 1607.
[9] R. WARNER, *Proc. Fourth Int. Congress of Biochemistry*, Vienna, 1958, Vol. 9.
[10] R. STEINER AND R. BEERS, *Biochim. et Biophys. Acta*, 32 (1959) 166.
[11] R. STEINER AND R. BEERS, *Biochim. et Biophys. Acta*, 33 (1959) 470.
[12] J. STURTEVANT, S. RICE AND E. GEIDUSCHEK, *Disc. Faraday Soc.*, 25 (1958) 130.
[13] S. LIFSON, B. KAUFMAN AND H. LIFSON, *J. Chem. Phys.*, 27 (1957) 1356.
[14] Z. ISING, *Physik. Ber.*, 31 (1925) 253.

Chapter 10

The Binding of Molecules and Ions by Polynucleotides

While the available data on the binding properties of natural and synthetic polynucleotides do not approach in volume those obtained in the case of proteins, they nevertheless represent a sizeable number of extensive investigations which have yielded results of high interest. The available information includes hydrogen ion titration curves, the binding of metallic cations, and the binding of dyes. The first of these has already been discussed in detail in an earlier chapter.

A dominant factor in the binding of small cations by polynucleotides is, of course, the presence of a linear array of singly charged primary phosphates in the ribose-phosphate backbone. In many cases the adsorption process can be adequately described in terms of binding by these sites alone, for which electrostatic forces appear to be of primary importance. Indeed, whatever the site of binding, the negative electrostatic field arising from the phosphates must inevitably make a major contribution to the free energy of association for cations.

However, there are many instances, particularly in the case of dye-nucleic acid systems, where the possibility that the bases themselves may serve as binding sites is rather tempting. This is especially so for planar dyes, which could have extensive areas of Van der Waals contact with the flat purine bases. In particular, the hypothesis has often been advanced that such planar dyes can fit between the flat bases in a *sandwich* manner, with the locus of positive charge adjacent to the phosphates. However, no example of this has yet been conclusively shown to occur.

The interpretation of binding data for polynucleotides is simplified to some extent by their linear character and well established chemical composition. The simplest case is, of course, polymers of a single nucleotide which are singly stranded and devoid of secondary structure, such as poly U and the alkaline form of poly I. In this case the mutual interactions of bound adsorbate molecules will be exclusively *vertical* in character. All of the binding sites in the interior of the molecule are identical. As each monomer unit contains a negatively charged phosphate the electrostatic term in the free energy of association will be important for the binding of cations. It is thus to be expected that the binding of cations would be ionic strength dependent and that the free energy of association would decrease with increasing ionic strength. In addition each polynucleotide molecule will possess an atypical site at its terminus, which contains a doubly charged phosphate.

Unorganized polynucleotides of this type are flexible and hence will undergo some contraction upon binding a cationic adsorbate, as a consequence of charge neutralization. This will modify the mutual interactions of the bound material and thus will alter the effective free energy of association. The latter parameter will thus, for a given set of external conditions, be a complicated function of the fraction of available sites which are occupied by adsorbate[1,2].

If the polynucleotide is capable of undergoing a helix–coil transition and may possess varying helical content, as poly A, an additional complication is introduced. Not only will the *vertical* interactions of bound adsorbate be modified as a consequence of helix formation, but an additional set of *horizontal* interactions between molecules bound to the two strands of a helical region will be introduced. Since the helical content of such a system will often depend upon the number of bound adsorbate molecules or ions it is easy to see that a complete theoretical description of such a system would be very complicated. If more than one type of binding site is present, the difficulties are, of course, intensified.

We have already had occasion to discuss a particular example of a binding process complicated by the occurrence of a helix–coil transition. This was the hydrogen ion titration curve of a doubly stranded helical polynucleotide. A tractible solution was obtainable for the case for which the zones of titration of the two (non-identical) strands were sufficiently separated to permit their independent consideration. In general this will not be the case and *horizontal* as well as *vertical* interactions of bound adsorbate would have to be taken into account in any really comprehensive treatment.

Unfortunately, such a comprehensive treatment is not as yet in sight and the theoretical discussion to follow must consequently be confined to a vastly oversimplified model. The following drastic approximations will be made:

(*a*) Both the intrinsic binding constants and the mutual interactions of bound adsorbates are not influenced by any alteration in the secondary structure which may occur as a consequence of the binding process.

(*b*) Only *vertical* interactions of bound adsorbates are important.

(*c*) Of these *vertical* interactions only those involving first nearest neighbors need be taken into account.

(*d*) The polymer is sufficiently long so that end effects may be neglected.

The classical solution for this case is cited by Fowler and Guggenheim[3] who obtain:

$$\lambda x = \frac{(\beta - 1 + 2\theta)}{(\beta + 1 - 2\theta)} \, \mathrm{e}^{w/kT} \tag{1}$$

where
λ = absolute activity of adsorbate
$= \mathrm{e}^{\mu/kT}$
μ = the chemical potential of adsorbate
x = the partition function for a molecule of bound adsorbate
θ = the fraction of occupied sites
w = the free energy of interaction of a nearest neighbor pair of bound adsorbates

$$\beta \equiv \{1 - 4\theta(1 - \theta)(1 - \mathrm{e}^{-w/kT})\}^{1/2}$$

References p. 320

For dilute solutions λx is equivalent to $k_0 m$, where k_0 is the intrinsic association constant for one molecule of adsorbate with a single site and m is the molar concentration of free adsorbate.

If nearest neighbor interactions are negligible ($w=0$) equation (1) reduces to the familiar Langmuir form

$$k_0 m = \frac{\theta}{1-\theta} \tag{2}$$

In many cases the actual number of sites is not known. Equation (2) may be rewritten in a form which permits direct determination of the number of sites per molecule from the adsorption isotherm. Thus, upon replacing θ by r/B, where r and B are the number of occupied sites and the total number of sites per molecule, respectively, we have, upon rearranging[4]

$$\frac{r}{m} = k_0 B - k_0 r \tag{3}$$

or

$$\frac{\theta}{k_0 m} = 1 - \theta$$

If there is only one type of binding site and the Langmuir isotherm is valid, r/m should vary in a linear manner with r. From the limiting values of the slope and intercept at $r=0$, k_0 and B can be evaluated directly.

Equation (3) has been very widely utilized in studying the binding of small molecules and ions by proteins. Deviations from linearity of the plot of r/m versus r can arise either from a heterogeneity of binding sites or the presence of mutual interactions of the bound adsorbates. If the latter are purely electrostatic in origin the following corrected form of equation (3) is often used[5]:

$$\frac{r}{m} \exp(2 \omega r) = k_0 B - k_0 r \tag{4}$$

For a spherical macromolecule, with the net charge assumed to be *smeared* uniformly over the surface, ω is given by:

$$\omega = \frac{\varepsilon^2 z^2}{2 DkT} \left(\frac{1}{b} - \frac{A}{1+Aa} \right) \tag{5}$$

where $\varepsilon=$ electronic charge; $z=$ valence of adsorbate; $D=$ dielectric constant; $k=$ Boltzman's constant; $T=$ absolute temperature; $b=$ radius of the macromolecule; $a=$ distance of closest approach of adsorbate to the macromolecule; and

$$A = (4\pi N_0 \varepsilon^2 / 1000 DRT)^{1/2} \Gamma^{1/2}$$

where N_0 is Avogadro's number and Γ is twice the ionic strength of the medium.

In practice ω is usually regarded as an adjustable empirical parameter, the best value of which is chosen by direct curve fitting. In applying equation (4) it should be kept in mind that its use becomes progressively more dubious as the actual system deviates from the assumed uniformly charged rigid spherical model. The occurrence of important non-electrostatic interactions or a change in shape of the macromolecule can render it inapplicable. For linear macromolecules the more exact approach represented by equation (1) is probably preferable, although it involves relatively tedious curve fitting.

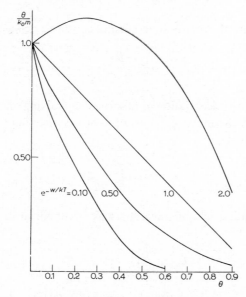

Fig. 97. Theoretical plots of θ/k_0m versus θ for several values of $e^{-w/kT}$.

Fig. 97 shows plots of θ/k_0m versus θ for several values of $e^{-w/kT}$, as computed from equation (1). When w is not equal to zero, pronounced curvature is obtained. Values of $e^{-w/kT}$ less than unity, corresponding to positive values of w, result in curvature convex toward the abscissa, while values greater than unity, corresponding to negative values of w, give rise to curvature concave toward the abscissa.

As is clear from the alternative form of equation (3) the above plot is equivalent to a plot of r/m versus r. It is easy to see that, when w is appreciably different from zero, correct values of the limiting slope and intercept of the latter will be very difficult to attain. In particular when w is negative the kind of variation predicted is qualitatively different from that expected on the basis of equations (3) or (4).

The Langmuir isotherm may also be rearranged into the following alternative form (4):

$$\frac{1}{r} = \frac{1}{B} + \frac{1}{k_0 \, Bm} \tag{6}$$

This equation likewise provides a basis for obtaining B and k_0 by extrapolation of $1/r$ *versus* $1/m$ to $1/m=0$. It suffers from the disadvantage of dangerously minimizing the apparent distance of the extrapolation.

Still another approach permits a direct determination of consecutive association constants without requiring any knowledge of B or any assumptions about the relative magnitude of the binding constants[6]. If a parameter $f(m)$ is defined by:

$$f = 1 + k_1 m + k_2 m^2 + k_3 m^3 + \ldots \tag{7}$$

where k_1, k_2, etc., are the consecutive binding constants defined by:

$$k_i = \frac{m_i}{m^i m_A} \tag{8}$$

where m_i is the molar concentration of absorbent containing i molecules of bound adsorbate and m_A is the molar concentration of free macromolecular adsorbent. It has been shown that[6]:

$$\ln f(m) = \int_0^m \frac{r}{m}\, dm \tag{9}$$

By graphical evaluation of this integral f may be obtained as a function of m. We then have:

$$k_1 = \left(\frac{df}{dm}\right)_{m=0} \tag{10}$$

$$k_2 = \frac{1}{2m}\frac{d}{dm}(f - 1 - k_1 m)_{m=0}$$

The method is, of course, limited to the first few association constants.

Finally, if two distinct types of binding sites are present in numbers B_1 and B_2 the following expression has been shown to hold, if mutual interactions of bound adsorbate may be neglected:

$$\frac{r}{m} = \frac{B_1 k_1}{1 + k_1 m} + \frac{B_2 k_2}{1 + k_2 m} \tag{11}$$

where k_1 and k_2 are the intrinsic binding constants characteristic of the two types of site.

Whatever equation is employed to interpret binding data, it is highly desirable to bear in mind the severe nature of the approximations involved in all the relations cited previously. For the polynucleotide case equation (1) is probably the most nearly adequate. However, it appears to have been employed only rarely.

Electrostatic interactions of bound adsorbate are always present if the latter is an ion, and appear to be dominant in many cases. They will, of course, have the effect of favoring binding of adsorbate ions on non-adjacent sites. However, in many cases, encountered especially frequently for the binding of dyes by polynucleotides, attractive Van der Waals forces may be important. In some cases they appear to overshadow electrostatic effects and favor the formation of linear clusters of bound dye on adjacent sites.

There are many instances where it is useful to know the fraction of combined adsorbate molecules which are bound with one or more nearest neighbors. This will, of course, be governed by the sign and magnitude of w in equation (1). The problem is a purely statistical one and has been solved for the case of a linear array of sites by Botts and Morales[7].

These authors find for the fraction of bound adsorbates with zero, one, or two nearest neighbors on adjoining sites, respectively, for a large number of sites:

$$Y_0 = \frac{(\theta - \theta_{aa})^2}{\theta^2} \tag{12a}$$

$$Y_1 = \frac{2\,\theta_{aa}\,(\theta - \theta_{aa})}{\theta^2} \tag{12b}$$

$$Y_2 = \frac{\theta_{aa}^2}{\theta^2} \tag{12c}$$

where

$$\theta_{aa} = \frac{n_{aa}}{B}$$

n_{aa} = the number of first nearest neighbor pairs

B = the total number of sites

The quantity θ_{aa} is obtainable from the quasichemical expression for the number of first nearest neighbor pairs of bound adsorbate which is cited by Fowler and Guggenheim:

$$\theta_{aa} = \theta - \frac{2\,\theta\,(1-\theta)}{\beta + 1} \tag{13}$$

Thus, by combining equations (1), (12), and (13), the fraction of all bound adsorbate molecules with zero, one, or two nearest neighbors may be computed as a function of m, k_0, and w. For the case where k_0 is very large, so that binding is quantitative if the total number of sites is greater than the number of adsorbate molecules, Y_0, Y_1, and Y_2 become equal to the fraction of *total* adsorbate which is bound with zero, one, or two nearest neighbors. Thus we have, from (12a) and (13):

$$Y_0^{1/2} = \frac{2(1-\theta)}{\beta + 1} \tag{14}$$

or

$$\theta = \frac{1 - Y_0^{1/2}}{1 - Y_0\,(1 - e^{-w/kT})} \tag{15}$$

Under conditions where binding is quantitative θ is equal to the ratio of adsorbate molecules to the total number of available sites.

Fig. 98 shows curves of the fraction of occupied sites as a function of λx, as computed from equation (1) for various values of $e^{-w/kT}$. As would be expected, increasingly large values of the latter parameter lead to predicted isotherms which are progressively sharpened and displaced to lower values of λx.

Fig. 99 shows values of $(1 - Y_0)$ as a function of θ for a series of values of $e^{-w/kT}$. As is intuitively obvious, $(1 - Y_0)$, or the fraction of bound adsorbate molecules with one or more nearest neighbors, decreases with decreasing values of θ. As $e^{-w/kT}$ becomes larger, the range of values of θ at which $(1 - Y_0)$ begins to decrease appreciably from unity is displaced progressively to smaller values of θ.

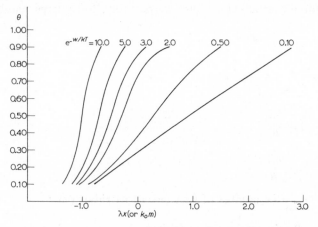

Fig. 98. Theoretical curves of θ as a function of log λx for several values of $e^{-w/kT}$.

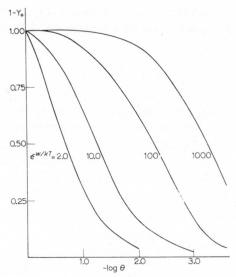

Fig. 99. Theoretical plot of $(1 - Y_0)$, the fraction of occupied sites with one or more nearest neighbors, as a function of θ.

It is important to note that if some quantity which depends upon pairing of bound adsorbate is being measured, such as fluorescence quenching in some cases, $(1 - Y_0)$ will be a direct measure of the expected extent of the effect.

A wide variety of experimental techniques has been applied to the problem of the binding of small ions or molecules by macromolecules. A few of these which have found application in the case of polynucleotides are as follows:

(a) *Equilibrium dialysis*. In this procedure a vessel is divided into two compartments by a semipermeable membrane which permits passage of the small adsorbate molecules, but retains the macromolecules. If the latter are confined to one compartment, then, at equilibrium, the number of adsorbate molecules in this compartment will exceed that in the other chamber. The difference in concentration is a direct measure of the concentration of bound adsorbate.

This concentration difference may be measured directly, or may be computed from the difference between the total amount of adsorbate added and that present in the adsorbate chamber at equilibrium, after correcting for binding by the membrane itself.

A major drawback of the equilibrium dialysis method is the necessity for addition of neutral electrolyte to suppress the Donnan effect. This often reduces the extent of binding and may thereby complicate interpretation of the results.

(b) *Conductiometric analysis*. As the binding of a diffusible ion by a macromolecule invariably reduces its conductivity, measurements of this parameter provide a measure of the concentration of free adsorbate ion. This method is rapid and precise. However, it suffers from the disadvantage of being practically confined to very low concentrations of supporting electrolyte. Furthermore, as the macromolecule itself, together with its counter ions, makes a finite contribution to the conductivity and as the extent of this contribution will itself be, in general, dependent upon the concentration of adsorbate, this method cannot yield the concentration of free adsorbate directly. However, when binding is quantitative, a conductiometric titration can determine the number of binding sites per macromolecule.

(c) *Partition analysis*. When an aqueous phase containing adsorbate is equilibrated with an immiscible organic solvent, the adsorbate will be distributed between the two phases. The concentration ratio will depend upon temperature, ionic strength, and pH. The addition of a macromolecule which binds adsorbate to the aqueous phase will cause a competitive removal of adsorbate from the organic phase. A redetermination of the equilibrium concentration in the latter phase permits a direct computation of free adsorbate in the aqueous phase and hence, by difference, the amount of adsorbate bound.

This procedure has the advantages of being free from complications arising from the Donnan effect or the binding of adsorbate by a membrane. However, the organic solvent generally has a finite solubility in water and may modify the adsorption process.

THE BINDING OF DIVALENT CATIONS BY POLYNUCLEOTIDES

It was early recognized that divalent cations, including Mg^{++}, Ca^{++}, and Mn^{++}, were strongly bound by the naturally occurring nucleic acids. Most of the investigations of this process have utilized conductiometric titration. This technique offers several practical advantages, including high precision and ease and rapidity of measurement. On the other hand, it suffers from a number of disadvantages in interpretation of the results. Measurements must be made at very low ionic strengths, at which many of the ordered polynucleotide structures are unstable. Moreover, the measured conductivity represents the summation of the contributions of the divalent cation, the polynucleotide itself, and the counter ions. In practice it is almost impossible to sort out these components quantitatively, especially as the latter two will in general depend upon the concentration of added cation.

Nevertheless, information of considerable usefulness has been obtained in this manner. The usual method of procedure has been to make parallel additions of the divalent cation to distilled water and to a solution of the polynucleotide. The difference between the two curves provides a measure of the extent of binding of the cation at a particular net concentration, but is not necessarily directly proportional to it.

Since divalent cations are known to complex with organic phosphates, an obvious choice for the sites of binding is the negatively charged phosphate groups of the pentose-phosphate backbone. If this were the case it would be expected that the end point of the titration would occur sharply when one equivalent of divalent cation per phosphate group was present (or one mole of cation per two phosphate groups), provided that the binding was quantitative or almost so.

Among the earliest measurements of this type were those of Shack et al.[8] upon the binding of Ca^{++} and Mg^{++} by DNA in distilled water. These suffer from the drawbacks cited earlier and in addition from the fact (unknown at that time) that DNA undergoes spontaneous denaturation at very low ionic strengths ($< 10^{-4}$), the extent of which is dependent upon the time of exposure, the temperature, and very likely upon the concentration of divalent cation. The system observed was therefore somewhat indeterminate.

Nevertheless, the results of these workers appear to give a definite indication of a sharp upward break in the curve of conductivity *versus* Mg^{++} concentration when only about 0.80 equivalents per phosphate had been added. If this were taken as the endpoint, one would be forced to the conclusion that either not all the phosphates were accessible or that binding occurred preferentially to some other group.

Zubay and Doty[9] in a more recent publication likewise observed a sharp break in the conductivity curve when less than one equivalent of Mg^{++} per phosphate was bound. As their results for denatured DNA were identical to those of Shack and co-workers they concluded that the latter observations actually were obtained with this kind of material. Identifying the observed break with the true endpoint of the titration, they suggested that binding occurred preferentially to the purines through a chelation process. As these groups would presumably be accessible for denatured DNA this conclusion appeared plausible. Supporting evidence for this point of view came from the observation by these workers that DNA which had not been previously denatured showed markedly less affinity for Mg^{++} than completely denatured DNA.

However, Felsenfeld[10] has recently challenged this conclusion upon the basis of new observations upon poly A and poly U. The two polynucleotides were found to behave in an identical manner despite the different character of the bases. Furthermore, by extending the range of Mg^{++} and Mn^{++} addition, it was found that the conductiometric titration curve consisted of three approximately linear regions separated by sharp breaks. It thus appears that there were two breaks rather than one (Figs. 100 and 101). The first of these occurred at about 0.6 equivalents Mg^{++} or

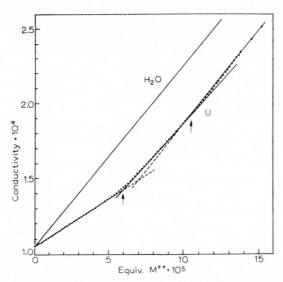

Fig. 100. The conductiometric titration[10] of $1.0 \cdot 10^{-4}$ M poly U with $2.0 \cdot 10^{-3}$ M $MnCl_2$.

Mn^{++} per phosphate and could evidently be identified with the pseudo-endpoint observed by Shack and co-workers and by Zubay and Doty. The second break occurred sharply at 1.0 equivalents cation per phosphate. The ratio of slopes of the three linear regions of the curve was 1 : 1.7 : 1.95. Since the slope of the third region beyond 1.0 equivalents Mg^{++} or Mn^{++} per phosphate was identical to that of the (linear) curve for the addition of cation to water, the second break was identified with the true endpoint.

Felsenfeld also found that denatured DNA behaved in an equivalent manner, thereby resolving the anomalies observed by earlier workers. The different behavior of undenatured DNA was attributed to secondary effects arising from its greater rigidity and the consequent presence of stronger electrostatic repulsion between bound cations.

The results of Felsenfeld indicate clearly that it is unnecessary to postulate the direct involvement of the purine bases to account for the Mg^{++} binding properties of DNA and the synthetic polynucleotides. Indeed, all the above data can now be accommodated on the basis of the simple model cited earlier which identifies the phosphate groups with the sites of binding.

However, the results of Felsenfeld also indicate that binding of divalent cations is almost quantitative under these conditions of very low ionic strength. Thus, if the affinity of the purines for the cations were of the same order of magnitude or greater than the affinity of the phosphates, no difference in behavior of poly A and poly U would be detectable. However, preliminary equilibrium dialysis experiments at an ionic strength of 0.1, where binding is not quantitative, have failed to show any important difference in behavior between native poly A and formaldehyde-treated poly A[11]. Since formaldehyde pretreatment should eliminate the capacity of the adenine base to chelate with divalent cation, this result is certainly inconsistent with any direct involvement of the former.

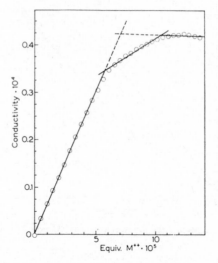

Fig. 101.   The difference between the conductiometric titration curves[10] for H_2O and for poly U. The data are those of Fig. 100.

All in all it can be stated that there is conclusive evidence that the phosphates can serve as binding sites, that there is no compelling evidence for any direct involvement of the bases, and that it is very highly probable that the phosphates are the only important binding sites.

There remains to be discussed the nature of the first break in the conductiometric titration curve. Since it clearly is not a true endpoint, it must represent either some structural change in the polynucleotide which causes an alteration in mobility or else a competitive release of bound counter ion which partially cancels the effect of divalent cation binding.

THE BINDING OF AMINO ACIDS AND PEPTIDES

Zubay and Doty[9] have examined the interaction of natural RNA from TMV with threonine, glutamic acid, and proline by means of equilibrium dialysis. The results were negative in each case. While no parallel experiments with synthetic polynucleotides have been reported, it would be most surprising if different results were obtained.

The above authors have also attempted to measure the binding of several amino acids by native and denatured DNA. In the case of serine and glutamic acid the results were clearly negative. Arginine, however, was found to be bound to a slight extent.

In the case of the basic polypeptide polylysine a definite effect has been observed by Felsenfeld[10]. If, to an equimolar poly A plus poly U mixture with a small excess of Mn^{++} present, is added a solution of polylysine hydrobromide, the ultraviolet absorption curves show only a linear dilution effect at most ratios of polynucleotide to polylysine in the spectral region 230–300 mμ, as polylysine has negligible absorption in this region. However, at ratios of about 1 : 1 there is a considerable elevation of the curve, probably arising from an enhanced scattering factor due to aggregation.

These results are fairly conclusive in indicating that interaction occurs between the polynucleotide and the polypeptide. Additional information was sought by means of conductiometric titration with polylysine of a 1 : 1 (A + U) complex in the presence of a slight excess of Mn^{++}. The curve consisted of two linear regions with a single sharp break at a lysine-nucleotide mole ratio of 1 : 1. The first linear region had a slope equal to that for the addition of Mn^{++} to water, and the second had a slope equal to that for the direct addition of polylysine to water.

These results were consistent with, and suggested, that one equivalent of divalent cation was displaced for each mole of lysine added. The occurrence of the sharp endpoint at a 1 : 1 lysine : nucleotide mole ratio suggests that the complex formation between polylysine and the (A + U) complex is stoichiometric. This in turn suggests that each cationic lysine residue is associated with a negatively charged phosphate.

THE BINDING OF DYES BY POLYNUCLEOTIDES

Most of the investigations of nucleic acid interactions with small molecules are concerned with dyes. This subject has acquired considerable importance as a consequence of the very extensive studies upon the identification of nucleic acids in the intact cell with the use of dyes and stains.

References p. 320

Unfortunately, most of the investigations to date have been inconclusive on both the nature of the site of binding and the basic mechanism of binding, and even on the total number of sites in many cases. Thus it is difficult to make logical groupings of the dye binding studies.

In what follows we shall group together for discussion purposes the dye–polynu-cleotide systems which have definitely been shown to exhibit the phenomena known generally as metachromatic effects. The balance of the systems studied will be discussed separately.

Cavalieri and Angelos[12] studied the binding of rosaniline by DNA, using the equilibrium dialysis method. Measurements were carried out at pH 5.6 and pH 6.7 in 0.05 M phosphate buffer.

Efforts were made to analyze the data upon the assumption of a single set of homogeneous binding sites, using equation (4). However, it proved impossible to obtain linear plots with any reasonable value of ω. Nevertheless, it was found that the curves of r/m versus r could be fitted by assuming the existence of two different kinds of site with different binding constants, utilizing equation (11) with an appropriate choice of parameters. The ratio of the apparent numbers of the two sites was usually of the order of 100 : 1 although the apparent value of the ratio was dependent upon conditions. The sites occurring with greater frequency were identified with the primary phosphates, and the less frequently occurring sites with the secondary phosphates.

Nevertheless, several severe anomalies remained. The apparent total number of binding sites was in all cases very much less than the known total number of phosphates. Indeed, if taken at face value, the results would indicate that only about 18% of the phosphates are available for binding at pH 6.7 in 0.05 M phosphate and about 15% at pH 5.6. This was attributed to the inaccessibility of most of the phosphates as a consequence of their involvement in some form of hydrogen bonding.

It was also observed that the apparent number of available sites increased sharply upon exposure of the DNA to a pH of 3.0.

Subsequent investigations of the above group of workers extended the obser-vations upon DNA to low ionic strengths using the method of partition analysis[13–15]. Similar measurements were made upon yeast ribonucleic acid.

The over-all qualitative features of the binding process were similar for all the systems studied. In no case could the results be well represented by an equation of the type of (3) or (4). In each instance this was interpreted as reflecting the presence of two kinds of sites corresponding to different binding constants, which were identified as before with the primary and secondary phosphates. In most cases the apparent total number of sites did not approach the total number of phosphate groups.

Both the apparent ratio of the numbers of sites of the two types and the apparent total number of sites were ionic strength-dependent. The total number of sites increased markedly with decreasing ionic strength.

The observations of Cavalieri and co-workers bring out clearly the inadequacy, when applied to DNA, of the approach conventionally used in the case of binding by globular proteins. In the light of our current knowledge of DNA structure, the suggestion that any major fraction of the phosphate groups could be inaccessible must certainly be rejected. In all probability the varying apparent values obtained for the number of rosaniline binding sites under various conditions may equally well be attributed to difficulties in making an accurate extrapolation of r/m to $r=0$, especially in view of the marked curvature displayed at low values of r. In any event there is no supporting evidence for the major changes in configuration with ionic strength that would be required to account for the greatly increased apparent number of binding sites in 0.005 M phosphate as compared with 0.1 M phosphate.

In view of the inexactness of equations (3) and (4) as applied to this problem, the invocation of a heterogeneity of sites to account for curvature in the r/m versus r plots is probably unnecessary. Certainly the identification of one of these with the secondary phosphates leads to unrealistically large values for the number of the latter.

Peacocke and Skerrett[16] have made an intensive investigation of the interaction of three dyes of the acridine series with bacterial and herring sperm nucleic acid. As this work dealt with many features repeatedly encountered in studies of dye-nucleic acid interactions, it will be discussed in some detail.

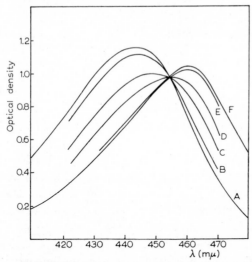

Fig. 102. The spectral effect of the progressive addition of DNA to proflavine solutions[16]. The dye concentration is $3.0 \cdot 10^{-5}$ M. The pH is 6.9 and the ionic strength 0.10.

Curve	DNA concentration (moles nucleotide/l)
A	0
B	$1.7 \cdot 10^{-5}$
C	$8.5 \cdot 10^{-5}$
D	$15.3 \cdot 10^{-5}$
E	$38.3 \cdot 10^{-5}$
F	$115 \cdot 10^{-5}$

References p. 320

The progressive addition of herring sperm DNA to a proflavine solution at neutral pH results in a pronounced alteration in the visible spectrum of the dye, as Fig. 102 shows. The maximum shifts from about 440mμ to 460mμ. It is especially to be noted that, to a first approximation, all of the curves have a single isobestic point at about 454mμ. This suggests that only a single spectrally distinct dye–nucleic acid complex is formed, at least at this low dye concentration.

Furthermore, as Fig. 103 shows, the spectral alteration attains a plateau with the continued addition of DNA, and shows no indication of a subsequent change even at quite high nucleotide: dye mole ratios.

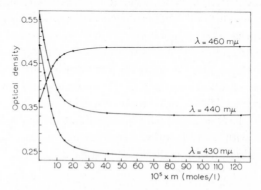

Fig. 103. The variation of the absorbency of proflavine at three wavelengths as a function of added DNA concentration[16]. The pH is 6.9 and the ionic strength 0.10. The total dye concentration is $1.3 \cdot 10^{-5}$ M.

The spectral change thus provided a convenient means of obtaining the fraction of dye which was bound, and thus of studying the influence of various factors upon the binding process.

At neutral pH (6.9) the binding of proflavine by herring sperm DNA was found to be profoundly ionic strength dependent, as Fig. 104 shows. The extent of binding fell off markedly with increasing ionic strength. Magnesium ion was roughly one hundred times as effective as sodium in reducing the extent of binding. As the pK of proflavine is about 9.7, the dye is overwhelmingly in the cationic state at pH 6.9. The influence of ionic strength upon binding is thus readily predictable in terms of a reduction in the magnitude of the electrostatic term in the free energy of association with increasing ionic strength.

The degree of binding was found to be independent of pH for pH's above 3.7, as would be anticipated from the fact that extensive binding of hydrogen ions by DNA does not commence until about this pH.

At a low nucleic acid concentration the extent of dye binding was found to be much less for the RNA from *A. aerogenes* than for the DNA isolated from the same organism. Rather surprisingly, the DNA from *A. aerogenes* was found to be considerably less effective than herring sperm DNA. However, the visible spectrum of the dye in the presence of a very large excess of nucleic acid was the same in all three cases.

For proflavine concentrations greater than about 10^{-5} molar the direct spectrophotometric method was impractical and recourse was had to equilibrium dialysis. The resulting rather anomalous results are shown in Fig. 105. The sigmoidal nature of the complete isotherm does not fit well into the family of curves discussed in the first section of this chapter. However, this discrepancy is probably a consequence of the inadequacy of the model utilized there.

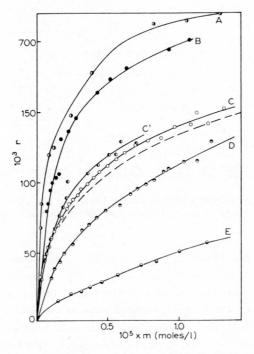

Fig. 104. The dependence of the extent of binding of proflavine by DNA upon the ionic strength[16]. The dye concentration is $1.4 \cdot 10^{-5}$ M except for curves A and C', for which is it $1.7 \cdot 10^{-5}$ and $0.80 \cdot 10^{-5}$ respectively.

Curve	NaCl concentration	MgCl₂ concentration
A	—	—
B	0.01	
C	0.09	
C'	0.09	
D	0.09	0.005
E	2.0	

The isotherm has three distinct regions. These are: an initial very rapid rise $(r < 0.22)$, an almost flat region $(r \cong 0.22)$, and a subsequent more gentle rise $(0.22 < r < 1)$. These results are impossible to explain in terms of the mutual interaction of single dye molecules bound to a linear array of sites. The authors were, therefore, driven to invoke the occurrence of two distinct binding processes. The first of these, which predominated at concentrations of free proflavine less than 10 mg/l, was believed to consist of the binding of monomeric proflavine cations. The leveling off of the isotherm at proflavine concentrations of 10–20 mg/l presumably reflects the occurrence of important repulsive nearest neighbor electrostatic interactions of the bound proflavines.

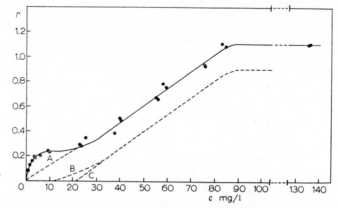

Fig. 105. Isotherm for the binding of proflavine by DNA. The pH is 6.9 and the ionic strength 0.1[16]. The DNA concentration is $1.05 \cdot 10^{-2}$ moles nucleotide/l.

The subsequent rise in r at higher proflavine concentrations was believed by Peacocke and Skerrett to reflect the binding of dye in the form of micelles or aggregates which retain their identity in the bound form. Since the deviations from Beer's law displayed by proflavine solutions at concentrations above about 7 mg/l point to the formation of such aggregates, there is some experimental support for this view. If this explanation were correct it would be expected that a different visible spectrum would be observed at high values of r. Unfortunately the spectrophotometric measurements were not extended into this range.

While the explanation cited above is probably the best available, it clearly must remain tentative pending more direct information or else a quantitative fitting of the data in terms of the above model.

Peacocke and Skerrett were led to reject explicitly an explanation of the type cited by Cavalieri et al. in terms of the binding of single dye molecules to two different types of site, in view of the unrealistic relative numbers of such sites computed on this model.

Whereas electrostatic forces unquestionably play a very important role in this process, some further results of the above authors indicated that electrostatic factors alone were inadequate to explain all of the data. Thus apurinic acid formed a complex with proflavine which showed a quite different visible spectrum from that formed by DNA. Moreover, there was some spectral evidence of interaction between proflavine and the purine deoxymononucleotides but not the pyrimidine deoxymononucleotides. Peacocke and Skerrett therefore suggested that Van der Waals interactions between the planar purine and dye molecules might be important. The relatively open character of intact DNA makes this plausible. This question will arise again in connection with the binding of acridine orange by purine polynucleotides.

Oster[17] has studied the interaction of the related dye acriflavine with thymus DNA. In the presence of a sufficient excess of DNA at neutral pH the visible dye spectrum is displaced to longer wave-lengths, the maximum shifting from about 440 mμ to 460 mμ. However, spectrophotometric measurements were not extended over a sufficient range of dye concentrations to permit a decision on whether only one or more than one spectrally distinct complex was formed.

The progressive addition of DNA to an acriflavine solution at neutral pH resulted in a pronounced quenching of the characteristic green fluorescence of the dye. Oster was able to eliminate the possibility that this reflected a collisional quenching, and attributed it to the formation of a non-fluorescent complex.

Heilweil and Van Winkle[18] have extended the measurements of Oster upon the DNA-acriflavine system. Determinations of fluorescence quenching were supplemented with direct measurements of the extent of binding, using the method of partition analysis.

Plots of r/m versus r were highly curved, and qualitatively resemble those obtained for the rosaniline–DNA system by Cavalieri and co-workers. As in the latter case the data could formally be fitted by assuming two kinds of binding site with an appropriate choice of parameters. The extent of binding was found to be very ionic strength-dependent, and decreased with increasing ionic strength. The apparent number of binding sites varied with conditions.

As in the case of the investigations cited earlier, the unassessed factor of the nearest neighbor interactions of bound dye may well be enough to cause a definite departure from linearity of the r/m versus r plots. Until this probability can be eliminated, an interpretation of the data in terms of two kinds of sites is probably premature. As in the case of the results with rosaniline, these misgivings are reinforced by the absence of any obvious correlation between the apparent numbers of sites and the known structural features of DNA.

If it is correct to assume that the ratio, P, of the quantum yields of fluorescence for bound and free dye is constant, then the following relationship should hold:

$$\frac{F_0}{F} - 1 = \frac{(1-P)\,m_b}{m + P\,m_b} \tag{16}$$

where F_0, F are the fluorescence intensities in the absence and presence of DNA; and m_b is the concentration of bound dye. If $P < 1$, equation (16) predicts a monotonous decrease in fluorescence intensity with increasing DNA concentration if the total dye concentration is held constant. However, it was observed by Heilweil and

Van Winkle that the fluorescence intensity actually passed through a minimum with increasing DNA concentration. Thus P must be dependent upon the fraction of sites which are occupied. As in the case of the binding data themselves, this result might reflect either a heterogeneity of binding sites or a dependence of fluorescence efficiency upon nearest neighbor interactions of bound dye.

Morthland, De Bruyn, and Smith[19] have made spectrophotometric studies on the interaction of a series of aminoacridines with natural DNA and RNA. The spectral changes observed at neutral pH in the presence of a large excess of DNA or RNA are shown in Table 28.

In the presence of excess nucleic acid all of the dyes cited in Table 28 displayed qualitatively similar spectral changes. In each case there was a shift in position of the major absorption peak to longer wavelengths, accompanied by a relatively small increase or decrease in magnitude. RNA and DNA were not completely equivalent, definite quantitative differences being observed between the two.

TABLE 28

CHANGES IN THE MAJOR ABSORPTION BAND OF VARIOUS DYES IN
THE PRESENCE OF EXCESS NUCLEIC ACID[19].

Dye	Buffer alone $\lambda^*_m(m\mu)$	ε^{**}	0.5 per cent RNA		0.5 per cent DNA	
			$\Delta\lambda$	$\Delta\varepsilon$	$\Delta\lambda$	$\Delta\varepsilon$
2-aminoacridine	357	6,200	+ 3	— 1,700	+ 15	— 2,500
3-aminoacridine	366	14,000	+ 4	— 5,400	+ 7	— 6,400
9-aminoacridine	402	9,700	+ 6	— 3,400	+ 6	— 4,800
2,8-diaminoacridine	430	3,600	+ 130	— 1,400	+ 130	— 1,100
3,6-diaminoacridine	443	29,000	+ 19	— 200	+ 21	— 100
3,7-diaminoacridine	368	9,500	+ 14	— 3000	+ 17	— 3500
	490	8900	+ 28	— 1500	+ 32	— 1800
4,5-diaminoacridine	405	4500	+ 19	— 1900	+ 30	— 3100
4,6-diaminoacridine	400	9300	+ 18	+ 3100	+ 25	+ 2400
4,8-diaminoacridine choride	405	4800	+ 15	+ 400	+ 20	+ 400
corephosphine	462	5000	+ 15	+ 1200	+ 12	+ 1200
3,6-diamino-10 methylacridine chloride	452	38,000	+ 16	+ 4600	+ 18	+ 2400
safranine 0	521	33,100	+ 22	+ 2700	+ 20	+ 700
rhodamine 6 G	529	77,500	+ 4	— 7000	+ 7	— 9500
rhodamine B	555	109,550	0	0	0	0
thionine	602	12,700	+ 15	— 1900	+ 17	— 3300
neutral red	525	25,500	+ 31	— 2900	+ 29	— 2700
rivanol	362	12,200	+ 14	— 500	+ 13	— 1700
berberine sulfate	345	31,700	+ 6	— 8800	+ 11	— 10,800
	420	7300	+ 15	— 2300	+ 24	— 2700

The solvent is 0.1 M phosphate, pH 7.0, in each case.
 * Position of the absorption maximum.
** Molar extinction coefficient.

Enzymatic degradation of the DNA had the expected effect of reducing the extent of the spectral shift.

We turn now to the interaction of metachromatic dyes with polynucleotides. The metachromatic effect has been the basis for a well-known cytological staining technique and refers to the property shared by a large group of dyes of undergoing a major shift in position of their visible absorption band to lower wave-lengths upon being bound by many polyelectrolytes. In some cases the wave-length shift is sufficiently large to produce a visually perceptible color change. This effect has often been used to differentiate nucleic acids in the intact cell.

The dyes which exhibit metachromasy generally belong to the class of polymerizable dyes and show extensive concentration-dependent aggregation. The metachromatic effect is not limited to the solid or gel state but can also arise upon the binding of a dye of the above class by a polyelectrolyte in solution.

Most of the known examples of polymerizable dyes which exhibit the metachromatic effect are planar molecules consisting of three fused six-membered rings (Fig. 106). In solution at least two and sometimes three distinct absorption bands, whose relative height depends upon concentration, have been observed in each case. In the order of decreasing wave-length, they have been referred to as the $\alpha, \beta,$ and γ bands. The α band is characteristic of the monomer and decreases in magnitude with increasing concentration. At extreme dilutions only the α band is observed. With increasing dye concentration first the β band and then, in some cases, a broad γ band make their appearance. In view of the nature of their concentration dependence the β band has generally been attributed to dimer formation and the γ band to high polymers.

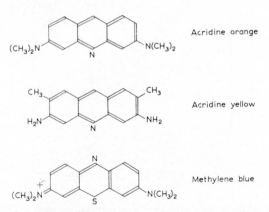

Fig. 106. The structural formulae of several metachromatic dyes.

A plausible explanation for the association process is that it results from the Van der Waals interaction of the planar fused ring systems. The planar nature of the latter would permit the close contact of a relatively large area.

It was early observed by Michaelis that the polymerizable dye toluidine blue displayed a pronounced metachromatic effect with both RNA and DNA at low ionic strengths[20]. The new observation was made that continued addition of nucleic acid until high nucleotide: dye mole ratios were attained was accompanied by the production of a new absorption band displaced to slightly *longer* wavelengths than the monomer band.

The fluorescent dye acridine orange is of particular interest for this type of study, as its fluorescent character provides effectively another dimension to studies of its interaction with biological macromolecules both in solution and in tissues. This dye is of especial cytological interest because, in addition to exhibiting the usual metachromatic effect, it has been found by several workers to possess the capacity to differentiate between DNA and RNA in the intact cell by virtue of its fluorescence properties[21]. Thus under the proper conditions a green fluorescence has been obtained with DNA and a red fluorescence with RNA[21].

Acridine orange belongs to the class of polymerizable dyes. Its association in aqueous solution, which has been intensively studied by Zanker, is reflected by a drop in intensity of the monomer band ($\lambda_m = 495$ mμ) and a shift in position of the absorption maximum to 465 mμ[22]. This is paralleled by the disappearance of the characteristic green fluorescence of the monomer species ($\lambda_t = 530$ mμ), and its replacement by a red fluorescence (or possibly phosphorescence).

It was naturally of considerable interest to ascertain whether the high degree of

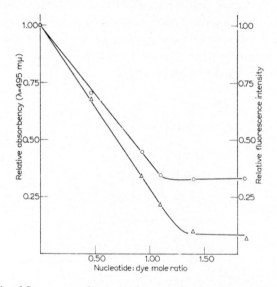

Fig. 107. Spectral and fluorescence changes[11] accompanying the addition of poly A to an acridine orange solution in 0.0001 *M* NaOAc, pH 6.5. The molarity of dye is 1.5 · 10^{-5}.
○ absorbency: △ fluorescence.

specificity exhibited by this dye for staining in the intact cell was paralleled by a corresponding specificity in interactions with polynucleotides in solution and to what extent this could be correlated with their known chemical and physical structures. Investigations in several laboratories have indicated that specificity in binding is indeed present, although it has proved to be of a quantitative rather than qualitative nature[23-25].

The acridine orange monomer is a univalent cation[22] at pH's acid to about 10. The loss of a proton is accompanied by pronounced spectral changes and by the disappearance of fluorescence. The results cited here refer, unless otherwise stated, to the singly charged form[22] prevailing at neutral and acid pH's.

As in the case of the nucleic acid-dye interactions discussed earlier, the binding process is, in general, pronouncedly ionic strength-dependent. At ionic strengths of the order of 10^{-3} or less all the polynucleotides examined show rather similar behavior at nucleotide to dye mole ratios of one or less.

When the dye concentration is of the order of 10^{-5} molar or less, so that the free dye is predominantly in the monomer state, the progressive addition of polynucleotide results in a linear drop in absorbency at the wave-length corresponding to the maximum of the monomer band ($\lambda = 495$ mμ). The decrease in height of the monomer band, which attains its limiting extent at a nucleotide: dye mole ratio of 1 : 1, is accompanied by a decrease in intensity of green fluorescence which likewise is linear with respect to the nucleotide: dye mole ratio[23-25]. When the mole ratio is 1 : 1 the intensity of green fluorescence is less than 10 per cent of that for the free dye and is replaced by a red fluorescence similar to that observed for the polymeric form of the free dye by Zanker. For convenience the red fluorescent complex at low nucleotide: dye mole ratios will be referred to as complex I. Fig. 107 shows the variation in height of the monomer band and in green fluorescence intensity with nucleotide: dye mole ratio for the case of poly A.

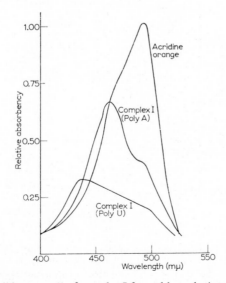

Fig. 108. Visible spectra[11] of complex I formed by poly A and by poly U

At ionic strengths of 10^{-3} or less the formation of complex I, as judged by the decrease in green fluorescence intensity, is virtually quantitative for all the polynucleotides examined so far, provided that their molecular weight is greater than about 10^5. However the detailed nature of the visible spectrum of complex I varies from system to system and, in the case of polymers of a single nucleotide, is dependent upon the nature of the purine or pyrimidine base.

In the case of the purine polynucleotides poly A and poly I, as well as natural DNA and RNA, the position of the new absorption maximum is at 465 mμ. In the case of the pyrimidine polynucleotides the peak is broader and the maximum is displaced to lower wavelengths, being at 435 mμ and 440 mμ for poly U and poly C respectively (Fig. 108). In the language of earlier workers, a β band appears in the case of the purine polynucleotides and a γ band in the case of the pyrimidine polynucleotides.

The visible spectra of all the dye–polynucleotide systems cited above show but a single isobestic point upon varying the nucleotide: dye mole ratio from zero to 1 : 1 [24]. This suggests that only a single complex species is present in each case.

The extent of formation of complex I is sensitive to such experimental parameters as pH, ionic strength, temperature, and the concentration of added organic solvents [24]. Only the charged form of acridine orange appears to interact with poly A. Thus complex I dissociates at alkaline pH's. A rise in temperature likewise results in a reversal of the spectral and fluorescence alterations characteristic of the forma-

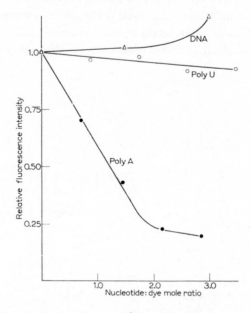

Fig. 109. Quenching of the fluorescence of acridine orange by poly A, poly U, and DNA at a high ionic strength [11]. The solvent is 0.50 M KCl, 0.01 M NaOAc, pH 6.5. The molarity of dye is $1.0 \cdot 10^{-5}$. The ordinate is the ratio of the fluorescence intensity at 550mμ to the corresponding intensity for the free dye. The activation wavelength is 490 mμ.

tion[24] of complex I. The presence of dioxane in high concentrations also prevents formation of this complex[24].

As mentioned above, the extent of formation of complex I is quantitative in each case at sufficiently low ionic strengths. An increase in ionic strength results in a decrease in the extent of formation of complex I in all cases. Moreover, pronounced differences in behavior of the various polynucleotides become evident under these less favorable conditions. Thus at neutral pH and an ionic strength of 0.5 the formation of complex I by poly A still proceeds almost to completion, while the interaction with poly U, native DNA, or formaldehyde-treated poly A is greatly reduced (Fig. 109). At this ionic strength the order of increasing stability of complex I is: poly U, DNA < poly C, poly AU (1 : 1) < poly A ([24]). That these differences in stability persist at low ionic strengths is indicated by an examination of the visible spectrum in 0.001 M NaOAc of a mixture of acridine orange, poly A, and poly U, at a mole ratio of 1 : 1 : 1. The complex I spectrum corresponds in this case to that produced by poly A alone.

The variation in the extent of formation of complex I at high ionic strengths for the various polynucleotide systems shows no very obvious correlation with what is known of their secondary structure. Thus the extent of interaction is least in the case of poly U and DNA, which represent the two extremes of helical content. The relatively low stability of the complex I formed by DNA raises the possibility that this may be a general characteristic of ordered helical structures.

This view is confirmed by observing the effect of prior addition of poly U upon

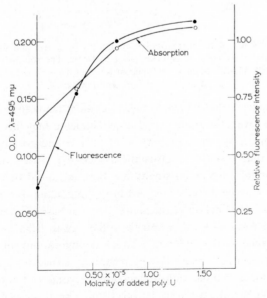

Fig. 110. The effect[11] of the prior addition of poly U upon the formation of complex I by poly A. The solvent is 0.50 M KCl, 0.01 M NaOAc, pH 6.5. The molarity of poly A is 6.4 · 10⁻⁵. The molarity of dye is 4.0 · 10⁻⁶.

the acridine orange–poly A interaction at an ionic strength of 0.5. As Fig. 110 shows, the addition of poly U results in a progressive reversal of the spectral and fluorescence effects accompanying the formation of complex I. The implication is that the involvement of poly A in a multi-stranded helical complex with poly U reduces its tendency to form complex I.

Furthermore, as Fig. 111 shows, the thermal denaturation of DNA, which largely disrupts its ordered helical structure, greatly increases the extent of formation of complex I at high ionic strengths.

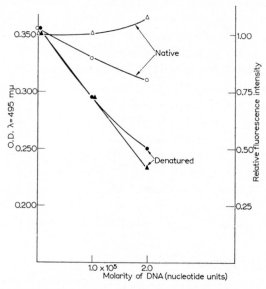

Fig. 111. A comparison[11] of the formation of complex I by native and thermally denatured (1000 seconds at 100° C in 0.001 M NaOAc, pH 6.5) DNA. The solvent is 0.01 M NaOAc, 0.05 M KCl, pH 6.5. The concentration of dye is $7.0 \cdot 10^{-5}$.
o, ● absorbency: △, ▲ fluorescence.

In general it appears that increased helical content tends to lower the stability of complex I. However, the results cited above indicate that this is by no means the only factor operative, as a comparison of poly U and poly A shows. Clearly something more than a simple electrostatic association of dye cations and phosphate groups is involved. The possibility has been advanced that the purine and pyrimidine bases may be directly involved in the interaction process, conceivably thru Van der Waals interaction of the planar dye and base residues.

The alternative possibility exists that the difference in behavior of the various polynucleotides reflects the different mutual configurations of the phosphate groups as a consequence of their varying secondary structures.

If the nucleotide:dye mole ratio is increased beyond 1 : 1 there occurs in all cases a gradual second alteration in the spectrum. The absorbency in the vicinity of the monomer band increases again and a new absorption band arises with its maximum at a wavelength (502 mμ), slightly greater than that for the original

monomer band of the free dye. This is reminiscent of the results of Morthland and
co-workers for other dyes of the acridine series[19]. This process is accompanied
by an increase in intensity of green fluorescence which attains ultimately a value
over three times that for monomeric acridine orange. The green fluorescent complex formed at high nucleotide: dye mole ratios has been referred to as complex II.
These points are illustrated by Figs. 112 and 113 and by Table 29.

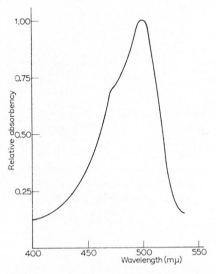

Fig. 112. Visible absorption spectrum of complex II formed by poly A and acridine orange[1]

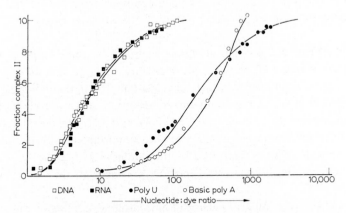

Fig. 113. The fraction of bound dye which is in the form of complex II as a function of the
nucleotide: dye ratio for several polynucleotides[25]. The solvent is 0.0001 M NaOAc. The ordinates
were computed from the equation $x_{II} = e_p - e_I/e_{II} - e_I$, where e_p, e_I, e_{II} are the molar
absorbencies at 500 mμ for the mixture, complex I, and complex II, respectively.

Bradley has observed that the range of nucleotide: dye mole ratios over which the
transition to complex II occurs is very dependent upon the nature of the polynucleo-

TABLE 29

EFFECT OF LARGE EXCESSES OF POLY A UPON THE ACRIDINE ORANGE SPECTRUM

The solvent is 0.01 M NaOAc, 0.5 M KCl, pH 6.6[24].

Molarity of Acridine orange	Molarity poly A (AMP units)	No. dye molecules per poly A*	d_{495}	d_{500}	Relative fluorescence intensity ($\lambda_a = 490\ m\mu$; $\lambda_f = 550\ m\mu$)
$7.2 \cdot 10^{-6}$	0		0.359	0.319	1.0
$7.2 \cdot 10^{-6}$	$1.0 \cdot 10^{-5}$	2050	0.134	0.121	0.33
$7.2 \cdot 10^{-6}$	$6.4 \cdot 10^{-5}$	320	0.134	0.121	0.38
$7.2 \cdot 10^{-6}$	$1.3 \cdot 10^{-4}$	158	0.141	0.129	0.46
$7.2 \cdot 10^{-6}$	$2.6 \cdot 10^{-4}$	79	0.165	0.158	0.65
$1.6 \cdot 10^{-6}$	0		0.092	0.081	1.0
$1.6 \cdot 10^{-6}$	$1.4 \cdot 10^{-3}$	3	0.086	0.090	2.4
$1.6 \cdot 10^{-6}$	$1.4 \cdot 10^{-3**}$	3	0.085	0.089	2.5

* This quantity was computed using a number-average molecular weight, M_n, of $1.0 \cdot 10^6$ for this poly A sample. This was obtained from the weight-average molecular weight, M_w, obtained from light scattering by assuming a "random" or most probable distribution of particle sizes, for which $M_w/M_n = 2$.

** Pretreated with formaldehyde.

tide[25]. At an ionic strength (10^{-4}) sufficiently low so that the formation of complex I proceeded to completion, the nucleotide: dye mole ratio at which the formation of complex II appeared to be half complete, from the spectral criterion, was found to increase in the order DNA, RNA < poly U < poly A as Fig. 113 shows.

In the case of poly A and poly U the nucleotide: dye mole ratios at which the formation of complex II becomes prevalent are so large that only a few dye molecules can be bound per polynucleotide chain under these conditions. It is very probable that complex II represents the contribution of dye molecules bound in an isolated manner without nearest neighbors and that complex I reflects that existence of linear clusters of bound dye with important nearest neighbor interactions. This hypothesis is reinforced by the similarity of the phenomena accompanying the formation of complex I to those produced by the association of the free dye.

As Fig. 113 shows, complex I persists at nucleotide: dye ratios very much greater than the above model would predict, if the fraction of dye molecules bound in an isolated manner were governed solely by statistical factors. As a comparison with Fig. 99 shows, the persistence of clusters of bound dye to this range requires the presence of attractive nearest neighbor interactions which are unusually large in magnitude and which must, moreover, depend upon the nature of the polynucleotide.

By this model the extent of formation of complex I would be a function of both the intrinsic association constant, k_0, and the free energy of nearest neighbor interaction, w, both of which would be dependent upon the nature of the polynucleotide and upon external parameters, such as ionic strength and temperature.

Under conditions where the binding of dye is quantitative, the results at nucleotide: dye ratios of 1:1 or greater may qualitatively be accommodated by this model if the fraction of dye bound as complex I is taken as proportional to $(1 - Y_0)$. Bradley has attempted to make the correlation quantitative[25]. Using an equation similar to equation (15) he was able to fit the spectral data fairly well over the entire range of nucleotide: dye mole ratios, except in the case of poly A[25].

In the case of several of the synthetic polynucleotides, especially poly A, the formation of complex II becomes important only at such high nucleotide: dye mole ratios that the possibility arises of an alternative controlling mechanism. If there were a *preferential* binding of dye by the terminal nucleotide groups such bound dye would inevitably be isolated. Such a preferential adsorption is rendered plausible by the doubly charged character of the terminal phosphates.

It is important to realize that, on either model, the characteristic features of complex I are attributed to the presence of nearest neighbor interactions of bound dye. The question is whether such nearest neighbor interactions are disrupted as a consequence of simple *dilution* of the linear clusters of bound dye by a large excess of unoccupied sites, or whether the breakup of such clusters occurs through the favored binding of dye to the necessarily isolated terminal sites. Which of these two mechanisms is the controlling factor in a particular instance would be determined by the relative magnitudes of w and the intrinsic binding constants for the chain termini and the interior of the molecule.

In the case of DNA and RNA the formation of complex II becomes prevalent at much too low nucleotide: dye mole ratios to be consistent with the terminal phosphate mechanism. It does, however, remain a possibility in the case of poly A.

In any event it is clear that both k_0 and w depend upon the nature of the polynucleotide. From the results at low ionic strengths, where binding is quantitative, it appears that the order of increasing magnitude of w is the same as that of increasing k_0, as determined by the results at high ionic strength.

The detailed reasons for the very wide variations observed in k_0 and w remain somewhat obscure. Other things being equal, a high helical content appears to favor complex II over complex I, as mentioned earlier. However, in view of the pronounced differences observed between poly A, poly U, and poly AU it is obvious that the nature of the particular bases involved is important.

Bradley has suggested that the absence of helical content favors the formation of complex I by virtue of the flexibility of the molecule thereby acquired. This might permit more readily the attainment of the configuration which is optimal for Van der Waal's contact of the bound dye. However, this explanation fails to account for the major differences between RNA and the alkaline form of poly A, which have about the same helical content.

Another obscure point is the quantitatively different spectra observed for complex I formed by poly A, poly U, and poly C. There is as yet no very obvious explanation in terms of the known structures of these polymers.

It is clear that the green fluorescence displayed by the DNA of intact cells which have been treated with acridine orange reflects the formation of complex II and that the red fluorescence of their RNA arises from complex I. However, as Fig. 113 shows, this difference in behavior in the cell is not reflected by any major difference between DNA and RNA, in solution. Apparently there must be additional factors operative in the former case.

That the phenomenon of metachromasy is not confined absolutely to dyes which polymerize in the free state is shown by the work of Lawley[26], who found that rosaniline displayed, at sufficiently low ionic strengths, a spectral shift in the presence of DNA which was of the metachromatic type described above. Since free rosaniline obeys Beer's law over the entire range of accessible concentrations, it probably does not associate in solution. At an ionic strength of 10^{-3} the progressive addition of DNA to a rosaniline solution results in the appearance of overlapping β and γ bands which attain their maximum extent of formation at a nucleotide: dye mole ratio of 1 : 1. The addition of a large excess of DNA results in the disappearance of these bands and the reappearance of the monomer band, displaced to slightly longer wavelengths. At ionic strengths of 0.1, or higher, the metachromatic effect was largely lost.

Lawley attributed these results to the occurrence of nearest neighbor interactions of the bound dye. In many respects it offers a parallel to the behavior of acridine orange, except that fluorescence effects are absent.

COMPLEX FORMATION BETWEEN DEOXYRIBONUCLEIC ACID AND PROTEINS

It was reported by Greenstein and Hoyer[27] that DNA could prevent the thermal coagulation of serum albumin when present in quantities as low as 0.5 to 1 per cent of the latter (by weight). This effect was only observed under rather restricted conditions, which included a salt-free solution at a pH (5.3), which was close to the isoionic point of bovine serum albumin.

This observation suggested that complex formation between the two macromolecular species occurred and that, furthermore, the complexing was not mediated by electrostatic forces exclusively, as the net charge on the albumin molecule is close to zero under these conditions.

Subsequently, Geiduschek and Doty[28] made a study of the interaction of bovine serum albumin and DNA at room temperature by means of light scattering. At pH 6.5, where the two components are similarly charged, no interaction occurred. However, at pH 5.5, a limited interaction was observed, corresponding to a binding by DNA of up to 35 per cent of its own weight of albumin.

The relatively limited extent of complex formation between the two native species under these conditions did not appear adequate to account for the ability of the DNA to prevent coagulation and suggested that the stronger binding which such protection appeared to require might occur with parts of the protein structure which were made accessible by thermal denaturation.

This hypothesis was borne out by subsequent experiments of Zubay and Doty[29]. It was found by these investigators that exposure of a 15 : 1 (by weight) mixture of albumin and DNA in 0.0015 M citrate, pH 5.5, to 100° for 10 minutes gave rise to a system which showed only one component upon ultracentrifugal analysis. It was concluded that extensive complex formation had occurred between the two thermally denatured species and that the prevention of the coagulation of the albumin could be attributed to this process.

The completeness of the binding under the above conditions indicated that at least 1800 molecules of albumin could be bound by one molecule of DNA. The molecular weight of the complex species, as determined by light scattering, was in close agreement with that predicted for a complex of the above composition, which contained only one DNA molecule. Thus extensive cross-linking of the DNA molecules by the albumin did not appear to occur.

It was further found that exposure of the complex to 8 M urea resulted in a drastic fall in molecular weight. Thus it is likely that some form of hydrogen bonding serves to stabilize the complex. The detailed nature of this bonding is still unknown.

A distinction must be drawn between complex formation of the above type and that occurring between native DNA and native proteins, under conditions where the two components are oppositely charged. Such complexing has been observed between DNA and the basic protein lysozyme[6]. Since the complexes in this case appear to dissociate at high ionic strengths, it is probable that electrostatic factors alone are adequate to account for this process.

References p. 320

REFERENCES

[1] S. LIFSON, B. KAUFMAN AND H. LIFSON, *J. Chem. Phys.*, 27 (1957) 1356.

[2] R. STEINER, *J. Chem. Phys.*, 22 (1954) 1458.

[3] R. FOWLER AND E. GUGGENHEIM, *Statistical Thermodynamics*, Cambridge, 1952.

[4] I. KLOTZ, in H. NEURATH, *The Proteins*, Vol. 2B, New York, 1953.

[5] G. SCATCHARD, *Ann. N. Y. Acad. Sci.*, 51 (1949) 660.

[6] R. STEINER, *Arch. Biophys. Biochem.*, 46 (1953) 291.

[7] J. BOTTS AND M. MORALES, *Trans. Faraday Soc.*, 49 (1953) 696.

[8] J. SHACK, R. JENKINS AND J. THOMPSETT, *J. Biol. Chem.*, 203 (1953) 373.

[9] G. ZUBAY AND P. DOTY, *Biochim. et Biophys. Acta*, 29 (1958) 47.

[10] G. FELSENFELD AND S. HUANG, *Biochim. et Biophys. Acta*, 34 (1959) 234.

[11] R. STEINER, unpublished.

[12] L. CAVALIERI AND A. ANGELOS, *J. Am. Chem. Soc.*, 72 (1950) 4686.

[13] L. CAVALIERI, A. ANGELOS AND M. BALIS, *J. Am. Chem. Soc.*, 73 (1951) 4902.

[14] L. CAVALIERI, *J. Am. Chem. Soc.*, 74 (1952) 1242.

[15] L. CAVALIERI, S. KERR AND A. ANGELOS, *J. Am. Chem. Soc.*, 73 (1951) 2567.

[16] A. PEACOCKE AND J. SKERRETT, *Trans. Faraday Soc.*, 52 (1956) 261.

[17] G. OSTER, *Trans. Faraday Soc.*, 47 (1951) 660.

[18] H. HEILWEIL AND Q. VAN WINKLE, *J. Phys. Chem.*, 59 (1955) 939.

[19] F. MORTHLAND, P. DE BRUYN AND N. SMITH, *Exptl. Cell Res.*, 7 (1954) 201.

[20] L. MICHAELIS, *Cold Spring Harbor Symposia on Quantitative Biology*, 12 (1947) 131.

[21] J. ARMSTRONG AND J. NIVEN, *Nature*, 130 (1957) 1335.

[22] V. ZANKER, *Z. physik. Chem.*, 199 (1952) 225.

[23] R. STEINER AND R. BEERS, *Science*, 127 (1958) 335.

[24] R. STEINER AND R. BEERS, *Arch. Biochem. Biophys.*, 81 (1959) 75.

[25] D. BRADLEY AND M. WOLF, *Proc. Natl. Acad. Sci., U.S.*, 45 (1959) 944.

[26] P. LAWLEY, *Biochim. et Biophys. Acta*, 19 (1956) 328.

[27] J. GREENSTEIN AND M. HOYER, *J. Biol. Chem.*, 182 (1950) 457.

[28] E. GEIDUSCHEK AND P. DOTY, *Biochim. et Biophys. Acta*, 9 (1952) 609.

[29] G. ZUBAY AND P. DOTY, *Biochim. et Biophys. Acta*, 23 (1957) 213.

Chapter 11

Inter-Relationships between DNA, RNA and the Synthesis of Proteins

Ideally this chapter would represent a culmination of the pattern of research in the nucleic acid area and would provide a link to the related discipline of genetics. Unfortunately the current state of the subject is very far from permitting so optimistic a description. At present we have at best the bare speculative skeleton of the theory.

Basic to most of the speculation in this field has been the notion that a unitarian approach is justified. We shall unavoidably follow this convention and shall not hesitate to combine evidence obtained for a variety of diverse systems.

We may as well begin by citing what has become the central dogma in this field. This is as follows:

(a) The basic genetic information which determines the identity and characteristics of a particular living system [1,2] is carried by DNA. Here of course an exception must be made in the case of several very primitive systems, as tobacco mosaic virus.

(b) The DNA does not organize the synthesis of the various enzymes and other proteins of the system directly. Instead it directs the synthesis of RNA which serves as a secondary carrier of genetic information [2,3].

(c) The RNA directs the synthesis of the enzymes and other protein constituents of the living organism [3-5].

Unlike most of the material discussed in this monograph, the preceding scheme cannot be said to be firmly established as the result of a large body of experimental evidence which has decisively refuted all competing mechanisms. It is rather a plausible and widely accepted working hypothesis, which is primarily useful as a guide to experiment.

The experimental justification and quasi-justification of the general scheme is much too voluminous to permit inclusion here of more than a few of the highlights in the first two sections of this chapter. The final two sections will discuss the actual molecular models and coding schemes which have been proposed, subject to the warning in advance that none of these stands on a very firm foundation as yet.

NUCLEIC ACIDS AS CARRIERS OF GENETIC INFORMATION

Part (a) of the general scheme has perhaps the most extensive experimental grounding. As usual the evidence is most clearcut in the case of the simpler organisms. For a number of these there is now overwhelming evidence that nucleic acids can act as the *exclusive* bearers of genetic information [1].

The first chemically simple material to be isolated which was shown to be endowed with genetic continuity was of course the transforming principle of pneumococcus, whose existence was established by the classical investigations of Avery and co-workers[6]. Earlier investigators had succeeded in extracting cell-free material from a particular encapsulated strain of pneumococcus which had the ability to induce a transition of the properties of a second unencapsulated strain to those characteristic of the original strain from which the transforming principle was obtained[7-9]. The induced change in properties was inherited by successive generations of the altered strain.

The first conclusive investigations of the chemical nature of transforming principle were made by Avery, MacLeod, and McCarty[6] upon purified transforming principle from pneumococcus Type III. The deproteinated samples were found to have a chemical composition typical of DNA. The material was treated with several peptidases, including trypsin and chymotrypsin, without any effect upon the activity. This rendered unlikely the possibility that a residual protein contaminant was the active ingredient. Further evidence against this came from the failure of the purified preparations to evoke any serological response.

Exhaustive treatment with ribonuclease likewise failed to abolish activity. This eliminated RNA as a contributing factor.

In contrast, treatment of these preparations with agents expected to degrade or denature DNA resulted in rapid and complete inactivation of the transforming principle. Thus incubation with deoxyribonuclease resulted in abolition of activity. This was virtually conclusive in identifying the active principle as DNA. Subsequent findings reinforced this conclusion. Thus the inactivation of transforming principle at elevated temperatures or extremes of pH parallels the denaturation of DNA.

It emerged clearly from this work that these pneumococcal DNA preparations had induced at least one inheritable property (capsule synthesis) and had initiated their own replication. They had thus performed two functions previously thought to be confined to genes.

Subsequent studies have consistently confirmed and extended these early conclusions[1]. Over a score of induced transformations have now been recognized for various micro-organisms, including other pneumococcus strains[10], E. coli[11], H. influenzae[12], and H. meningititis[13]. In all the cases in which the chemical nature of the transforming principle has been investigated, it has been identified with DNA. The recognition of the first transforming principle to be isolated depended upon an induced change in serological characteristics. Additional changes mediated by DNA have included alterations in drug resistance, enzymic capability, and cell morphology[1].

Induced transformations of this kind are very analogous in many ways to mutations and the similarity in function of transforming principles and genes is pronounced. The fact that many identified genes can be collected in one cell is paralleled by the introduction of several independent transforming abilities into the DNA of a single bacterial strain. The transforming agents, like the genes, undergo reduplication when the cells acquiring them reproduce.

It is natural to suppose that the induction of altered characteristics by the transforming principle is basically similar to the analogous genetic processes in higher organisms. Since the recognition of a transformation usually depends upon only a few properties of the system there is no reason to believe that the transforming DNA does not include a host of normal determinants as well. In fact, the entire genetic information characteristic of the system is probably present, including as a minor component that leading to the altered property.

Additional basis for the belief in DNA as a direct genetic determinant is derived from our knowledge of the bacterial viruses or bacteriophages. The life cycle of these is now fairly well understood, largely as a consequence of combined genetic and biochemical studies of their reproduction. Of the numerous examples of this type of organism the phages which attack *E. coli* are perhaps the most intensively studied.

The T coliphages, which are lytic for the host *E. coli*, are small rounded or hexagonal organisms possessing tails and containing protein, DNA, and some lipid. If the T2, T4, or T6 coliphages are subjected to osmotic shock their constituent DNA is released into solution and is vulnerable to deoxyribonuclease action[14]. The residual protein "ghosts" retain the serological characteristics of the intact phage but do not possess the capability of reproduction[15].

The T-even coliphages initiate infection of the host cell by first anchoring themselves, probably by their tails. This is followed by the passage of most of the phage DNA into the cell, together with a small amount of protein. The entry of the DNA into the host has been clearly demonstrated by isotopic marking[15] with ^{32}P. After an incubation period, extensive reproduction of the phage occurs within the host, followed ultimately by the lysis of the host and the release of the phage into solution.

The post-infection metabolism of the host cell is largely confined to phage reproduction[16, 17]. The normal processes of protein synthesis remain largely static while the phage multiplies several hundredfold.

The infection cycle includes several distinct stages[16, 17]. In the first of these, the *eclipse* period, no infectivity is present in the contents of artificially disrupted cells. The rate of synthesis of the normal host RNA falls very rapidly to a low value. While total protein synthesis remains at a high level it soon comes to be largely diverted to the production of phage-related material. Total DNA synthesis decreases sharply at first and then revives after an interval.

Early in the eclipse period and prior to the revival of extensive DNA synthesis, some RNA which differs in base composition from the host RNA, begins to be synthesized. Unlike the host RNA, it undergoes a rapid metabolic turnover. It appears likely that this RNA plays a definite role as an intermediary in phage production, although it is not incorporated into mature phage.

Soon after the appearance of the RNA, phage precursor DNA begins to be synthesized rapidly. At about the same time, new protein, which includes phage-specific antigens, begins to be produced. At an early stage of the eclipse period there appears to be a definite interdependence of DNA and protein synthesis. Thus, the blocking of protein synthesis by chloramphenicol shortly after infection inhibits the production of phage DNA. At longer times the two processes become relatively independent.

The end of the eclipse period is accompanied by a rapid multiplication of intact phage and finally by the rupture of the host cell wall and the release of fresh phage into solution.

Isotopic labeling studies have shown that the phage DNA is produced primarily from material present in the growth medium, although the host DNA also makes a minor contribution[16,17]. In the case of the T-even coliphages, the phage DNA shows a major chemical difference from that of the host, in that cytosine is replaced entirely by 5-hydroxymethylcytosine.

The phage protein appears to be synthesized exclusively from the growth medium[16,17]. In particular, it has been shown that the phage protein makes no contribution to the composition of its progeny. In contrast, experiments with phage labeled with ^{32}P have shown that at least half of the DNA of the original infecting unit is found in the progeny[20]. This is consistent with the concept that the replication of phage is mediated entirely by DNA and that the original phage protein has no genetic role.

Considerable work has been devoted to the problem of the molecular size of the injected DNA, in particular whether the entire DNA content of the infecting unit occurs as a single large particle or as several pieces[21,22]. If all of the phage DNA occurred as a single unit, it would have a molecular weight close to 100,000,000.

Levinthal and Thomas have applied the technique of β-ray track counting to ^{32}P-labeled DNA of T-2 coliphage[21]. A comparison of the "stars" formed in an electron-sensitive emulsion by intact labeled phage and by osmotically shocked phage revealed that the DNA of the latter disintegrated system occurred as a single large piece containing about 40% of the phage DNA, plus a number of much smaller fragments. One large DNA particle occurred per phage unit.

The invariance of the size of the large unit to urea treatment and to the action of trypsin and chymotrypsin and its sensitivity to deoxyribonuclease attack led Thomas to the conclusion that it represented a true molecular unit rather than a secondary aggregate of smaller DNA particles. If this is the case it is certainly tempting to identify it with the true genetic carrier. However, the failure of density gradient ultracentrifugation banding measurements to confirm these results introduces some uncertainty about their validity.

There is also some uncertainty about the size of the parental DNA unit which is transferred to the first generation of progeny and about the manner of distribution among the progeny. Current evidence from tracer experiments indicates that about half of the parental DNA is transferred to the progeny. It is possible that this figure is really a lower limit because of technical difficulties, and that the actual efficiency of transfer may be much higher. The available evidence indicates that the distribution of parental DNA is far from uniform and that a few first-generation filial particles contain a disproportionate fraction of the original material[16]. It thus appears that fairly large pieces of DNA can be transferred as intact units. This result is of course more consistent with a template role of the parental DNA than is a uniform distribution.

There is, of course, a well-known exception to the general rule that only DNA carries genetic information. In the case of a number of plant viruses the genetic role of DNA is taken over entirely by RNA, which thus assumes full responsibility for the guided production of new virus in the host[23, 24].

The best studied example is the infectious RNA from tobacco mosaic virus (TMV)[23]. It has been found that the careful deproteinization of virus preparations by means of phenol or sodium lauryl sulfate can produce protein-free systems with a residual infectivity amounting to several per cent. of the original.

In contrast to that of intact TMV, this residual infectivity is highly sensitive to ribonuclease action and to prolonged storage in salt solution. Infectivity is also pronouncedly inhibited by many metallic cations, including Sn^{++++}, Fe^{++}, Cu^{++}, and Hg^{++}.

There remains some question on what fraction of these RNA preparations is active. The observation that infectivity can be greatly enhanced by reconstitution with virus protein suggests that a major fraction is at least latently active. It is possible that the low level of infectivity of the protein-free material is a result of its greater susceptibility to degradation by the plant ribonucleases.

The available data indicate fairly conclusively that the TMV protein is devoid of infectivity. Furthermore, reconstitution of the ribonucleoprotein with RNA and virus protein from two different strains of TMV results solely in replication of the strain from which the RNA was obtained. Interestingly enough, the available evidence indicates that all the RNA of tobacco mosaic virus occurs as a single molecule, thus providing the first definite example of a molecule capable of mediating its own reproduction.

It is a long step from the rudimentary systems just discussed to the genetic processes of higher organisms. Yet a large body of evidence indicates that, except for the virus systems already mentioned, the basic genetic role of DNA is probably universal. This view obtained wide acceptance prior to the dramatic developments with the coliphages and with the transforming principle.

The existence of the morphological units called chromosomes in the cell nucleus and their intricate behavior during mitosis had been recognized and studied long before their genetic function had been postulated. It remained for Morgan and co-workers to demonstrate convincingly the correlation between chromosome movements and movements of the then hypothetical Mendelian genes[25, 26]. Since Morgan's time the role of the chromosomes as gene carriers has been consistently confirmed and reinforced. Among the most important pieces of evidence were the correspondence of the number of homologous chromosomes to the number of linked genetic units, the genetic consequences accompanying chromosome breakage, and the genetic effects of the chromosome redistribution occurring when a pair fail to divide[1, 27, 28].

Cytochemical evidence soon showed that DNA was a major constituent of chromosomes, the balance being histones and other proteins. The idea that DNA rather than protein was the genetic determinant gained momentum from the work of Boivin and co-workers and of Mirsky and Ris, who demonstrated the constancy in amount of DNA present in the diploid somatic nuclei of several tissues within a single species and its occurrence in half quantities in the haploid sperm cells[29, 30]. In contrast the residual protein did not have the distribution expected for gene material.

Further evidence was obtained from a consideration of the action of mutagenic agents upon DNA. Thus the action spectrum corresponding to the production of mutations by ultraviolet irradiation of fungi corresponds to the absorption spectrum[31] of DNA. The subsequently observed reversal of ultraviolet mutational and lethal effects by exposure to visible light have, however, shown that mutation production by this agent is not a simple process, although the observations are certainly consistent with a genetic function[32] for DNA.

A number of chemical mutagenic agents have also been shown preferentially to attack DNA. Prominent among these are the sulfur and nitrogen mustards, which have been shown to combine chemically with DNA, to cause alterations in chromosomes, and to produce mutations[33-35].

Less direct evidence for the genetic function of DNA includes its relative metabolic stability. Thus in tissues where extensive mitosis is not occurring, labeled metabolic intermediates are not introduced as readily into DNA as they are into RNA or protein. Furthermore, the extent of production of DNA usually obeys a fairly direct relationship to growth. In most investigations of this kind it has been found that, when once labeled, tissue DNA tends to retain its markers thru long periods of growth. All of these facts fit into the general picture of DNA as a genetic material.

In summary it can be stated that in the case of several primitive systems there is conclusive evidence that DNA serves as the exclusive carrier of genetic information. In the case of the higher organisms there is very strong circumstantial evidence that this is so. In general the available information certainly warrants the incorporation of this postulate into any comprehensive theory of cell reproduction.

The actual mode of duplication of parental DNA remains very much an open question. The possible schemes of replication can be grouped into three types. Mechanisms which preserve the integrity of the parental helical duplex and do not involve any separation of the two strands are referred to as *conservative*. This kind of model would not permit any transfer of parental DNA to the progeny.

The *semi-conservative* mechanism postulates that the single strands remain intact but become physically separated during the replication process. The original

Watson-Crick scheme, according to which the individual strands direct the synthesis of their complements, falls into this category.

In contrast to both of the above, a *dispersive* mechanism involves the redistribution of the parental DNA among the progeny by some form of fragmentation. The atoms of the original DNA would thus be shared in a more or less uniform manner by the progeny DNA molecules.

Questions of the above kind reoccur in connection with the transfer of genetic information from DNA to RNA, which will be discussed later in this chapter. It is, of course, also uncertain whether the new DNA is assembled directly on the parental template, or whether an RNA intermediate is involved.

Meselson and Stahl have made an ingenious effort to decide between the various replication schemes[36]. By growing *E. coli* for 14 generations in a medium containing $^{15}NH_4Cl$ as the source of nitrogen, they were able to obtain cells whose DNA contained the ^{15}N isotope almost exclusively. The culture was then transferred to an ^{14}N medium. Samples were withdrawn at intervals after transfer. Their DNA was isolated and examined by means of density gradient ultracentrifugation in CsCl solution (see Chapter 6).

The density of the bacterial DNA may be expected to vary directly with the fraction of ^{15}N labels which it contains. If a dispersive type mechanism were dominant, it would be anticipated that, when banded in CsCl solution, the DNA of each successive generation would show a continuous downward shift in density and that resolution into two or more bands corresponding to distinctly different densities would not occur. If a conservative mechanism were dominant it would be predicted that two, and only two, species would be observed for each generation. One of these would correspond to the original ^{15}N-labeled DNA. The second would represent the freshly synthesized DNA and would contain the ^{14}N isotope exclusively.

The observations of Meselson and Stahl showed that, after the lapse of one generation time, the DNA contained only *hybrids*, whose density was that expected for a half-labeled molecule. Subsequent generations contained only hybrids and completely unlabeled DNA. It was of particular interest that at no time did material accumulate in the interband region. This precluded the operation of a mechanism of the dispersive type.

The Meselson-Stahl experiment is clearly more consistent with a semi-conservative mechanism of DNA replication than with either of the other two alternatives. However, efforts to apply this technique to the problem of phage replication have yielded only inconclusive results[16].

RNA AND PROTEIN SYNTHESIS

Let us now examine the evidence for the second part of the general hypothesis cited earlier, namely, that RNA rather than DNA is the direct organizer of protein synthesis. To establish this theory conclusively it would be necessary to show that DNA is not involved *directly* in protein synthesis and that RNA is.

It is certainly well established from the observations with the infectious RNA's of several plant viruses that RNA *can* serve as the exclusive guiding agent for protein synthesis. Whether this is invariably the case for more complicated systems has yet to be conclusively proved or disproved.

The general idea that protein synthesis must involve some kind of template arose naturally from the recognition that the amino acid sequence in naturally occurring polypeptides was not random but highly specific. It is rather difficult to conceive of a mechanism other than the template which would be capable of bringing about such an ordered linear sequence.

A direct experimental test of the template idea is difficult to devise. One approach proceeds from the plausible surmise that a template mechanism would require the synthesis of an entire polypeptide chain as a unit. If the synthesizing enzymes drew upon an amino acid pool containing labeled amino acids, it would thus be expected that labeling would be uniform for different regions of the polypeptide.

Experimental tests of this approach have yielded varying results[37, 38]. The observation that non-uniform labeling can occur[38] does not strengthen the template hypothesis, but can be reconciled with it if it is postulated that different parts of a given protein are assembled on different templates and then combined in a final step. There also exists the possibility that the non-uniform labeling may actually reflect an unequal ease of exchange at different parts of the protein molecule.

A powerful argument for the template model is the failure so far of efforts to isolate small peptide intermediates as precursors of complete proteins[39]. To date there is no evidence for the existence of any immediate precursors larger than the individual amino acids, or their activated derivatives.

If it is granted that some form of template is required, the choice is virtually limited *a priori* to protein, RNA, or DNA, as the known polysaccharides and lipids do not possess sufficient chemical diversity of sequence to be feasible.

The idea that protein itself might serve as a template is difficult to exclude rigorously. However, several considerations make this rather unlikely. The problem of how the template itself was organized could be circumvented by postulating that there exists a particular class of proteins which can not only serve as templates for other proteins but also direct their own synthesis. Suffice it to say that there is not a shred of evidence for this hypothesis, which has rarely been put forward seriously.

The original suggestion that protein synthesis requires the mediation of RNA was brought forth by Caspersson[40] and by Brachet[41]. The earliest evidence was largely cytochemical in nature and was based upon both ultramicrospectrophotometry and staining by basic dyes. In this manner it proved possible to correlate the concentration of RNA in tissues with certain aspects of their function..

It was shown by Caspersson and Schultz[42] and by Brachet[43] that RNA is especially abundant in cells where extensive protein synthesis is known to be occurring, such as rapidly growing cells, cells producing enzyme, nerve cells, and liver cells. Cells where protein synthesis is occurring at a much slower rate have relatively low RNA contents, irrespective of their physiological activity. Thus it has been shown both by cytochemical techniques and by direct analysis that glandular organs which synthesize large amounts of protein, including intestinal mucosae, liver, and pancreas are rich in RNA while heart, brain, and lung tissues are relatively poor in RNA.

It has furthermore been demonstrated by Davidson and co-workers[44-46] that, in the case of embryonic material, the synthesis of RNA appears to precede that of protein.

Another example occurs in the case of liver, where administration of a protein-poor diet is reflected by a drop in RNA content[47]. In contrast, the DNA content is unaffected.

Growing cultures of micro-organisms likewise display a relationship between RNA content and protein synthesis. It has been reported that the RNA content of bacteria is proportional to the growth rate, irrespective of the culture medium[47].

There exists a wide variety of evidence collected from a number of diverse systems which tends to dissociate DNA metabolism from protein synthesis. It has been known for some time that irradiation of micro-organisms with ultraviolet light of wavelength about 2600 Å can result in pronounced changes including inhibition of growth, increased mutation, and death of the cell.

Kelner[48] has studied the effect of ultraviolet radiation upon the metabolism of *E. coli*, comparing the effect of sublethal doses upon DNA synthesis and net cell growth. The synthesis of DNA was found to be particularly sensitive to irradiation, while RNA synthesis and net growth were affected to a much less important extent. Indeed it proved possible to block DNA synthesis quantitatively while permitting a continued rapid net growth and hence protein synthesis. The rate of RNA synthesis paralleled the growth rate in all cases. Under conditions where DNA synthesis had been abolished, growth consisted of cellular enlargement, without cell division.

Siminovitch and Rapkine[49] found that lysis-inducing ultraviolet dosage of *B. megaterium* inhibited DNA synthesis while permitting growth, oxygen consumption, and RNA synthesis to continue unimpaired.

Similarly, Baron, Spiegelman and Quastler[50] have found that yeasts whose capacity to synthesize DNA has been eliminated completely by X-ray irradiation can still form enzymes in a normal manner.

Cohen and Barner[51] have described a thymine-less *E. coli* mutant which can synthesize xylose isomerase in the absence of an external supply of thymine. As this mutant cannot produce DNA without an added supply of thymine, this finding provides strong evidence of an uncoupling of DNA and protein metabolism.

Lester[52] found that cells of *M. lysodeikticus* which had been lysed by lysozyme in the presence of sucrose retained the ability to incorporate amino acids into protein. These systems were judged to be free from intact cells on the basis of direct microscopic observation and streaking on nutrient agar. Whereas neither deoxyribonuclease nor ribonuclease had any effect on the activity of intact cells, their influence upon the disintegrated system was profound. Ribonuclease treatment virtually eliminated the protein synthetic ability while the addition of deoxyribonuclease actually enhanced it. Lester used the incorporation of labeled leucine as a measure of protein synthesis.

Similar findings were obtained by Beljanski[53] for the same system, using labeled glycine. In conformity with the results of Lester he observed stimulation by deoxyribonuclease treatment and inactivation by ribonuclease treatment.

Gale and Folkes[54, 55] have carried out extensive studies upon protein synthesis by sonically ruptured cells of *Staphylococcus aureus*. In the initial phases of the work the incorporation of labeled glutamic acid was used as an index of activity. By varying the time of exposure to ultrasonic irradiation and by the use of differential centrifugation and salt extraction it was possible to obtain cell fractions which were virtually free of viable cells and most of whose nucleic acid (both RNA and DNA) had been removed.

The properties of these preparations depended markedly upon the degree of depletion of their nucleic acid content. As much as 60 per cent of the total nucleic acid could be removed without markedly reducing activity. However, the continued removal of nucleic acid resulted in preparations which exhibited a dramatic increase in activity upon the addition of either DNA or RNA from the same organism. Of the two, DNA appeared to be somewhat more effective on a dry weight basis.

A definite species specificity was observed. Nucleic acid preparations from other micro-organisms and from wheat germ, herring roe, and calf thymus were ineffective, as was also a mixture of purines and pyrimidines.

Some paradoxical aspects of these studies also emerged. If staphylococcal nucleic acid preparations were digested with ribonuclease (or deoxyribonuclease) and then reprecipitated and dialyzed, their entire activity was lost. However, if the complete digest was added to the cell fraction, the stimulating effect remained.

It was concluded by Gale and Folkes, on the basis of comparative experiments with several labeled amino acids, that the rate of incorporation of any one of these was not necessarily correlated with total protein synthesis. In view of this it was felt that measurements of the rate of incorporation of only a single amino acid were inadequate for the exploration of the effect of nucleic acids upon over-all protein formation.

The alternative procedure of following the production of particular enzymic activities was therefore introduced. The enzymes for which assays were made included glucozymase, catalase, and β-galactosidase. The progressive removal of RNA and DNA from the disrupted cell preparations resulted in a major loss of the capacity to form all three enzymes. The relative stimulating effect of added DNA or RNA varied from enzyme to enzyme. In the case of glucozymase, staphylococcal

DNA and RNA were about equally effective, irrespective of the stage of nucleic acid depletion. In the case of catalase, the relative effectiveness of DNA in comparison with RNA increased with the increasing removal of total nucleic acid. As in the case of amino acid incorporation only RNA or DNA from the same species was effective. In the case of β-galactosidase, only DNA was effective and its effectiveness was confined to preparations with initially very low nucleic acid content. Most significantly, however, the effect of DNA was abolished by the addition of *ribonuclease*.

It is possible to fit the results of Gale and Folkes into the postulated mechanism of protein synthesis, at lease roughly. However, the interrelationship of DNA and RNA activity remained incompletely resolved.

Pardee[56] has studied the formation of β-galactosidase by several mutant strains of *E. coli* which require for growth an external source of nucleic acid components. In each case the formation of enzyme did not occur in the absence of the essential purine or pyrimidine. If a limited amount was present the synthesis of enzyme ceased upon its exhaustion. The presence in excess of an amino acid mixture was without influence.

In contrast, the blocking of DNA synthesis by treatment with mustard gas permitted the formation of enzyme to proceed unimpeded. It was suggested by Pardee that the continuous formation of RNA, but not DNA, was essential for enzyme synthesis.

This general account would be incomplete without the inclusion of a set of experiments which are not particularly consistent with the hypothesis that DNA has no direct role in protein synthesis. Allfrey, Mirsky and Osawa[57] have isolated calf thymus cell nuclei by differential centrifugation in sucrose solutions and studied their rates of incorporation of labeled amino acids as a function of prior treatment.

The time course of uptake of labeled glycine, alanine, and methionine was used as a direct measure of protein synthesis. These workers were able to demonstrate that the amino acid uptake did not reflect merely a non-specific binding or exchange but represented an actual incorporation into protein. This followed from the ability of the nucleic acid to differentiate between the two optical isomers of alanine, only the L-isomer being incorporated.

The treatment of isolated nuclei with deoxyribonuclease was found to impair seriously the rate of amino acid incorporation. A definite correlation was found between DNA loss and the change in the amino acid uptake, up to the point where about 70 per cent of the DNA had been removed. Beyond this point the rate of uptake remained constant at a level about 20 per cent of that of the untreated nuclei.

Efforts were then made to ascertain whether the capacity of the nuclei to synthesize protein could be restored by the addition of DNA. It was indeed found that the addition of thymus DNA raised the rate of amino acid incorporation to levels approaching those of the original system. However, it was also found that alkali-denatured DNA and a non-dialyzable *core* remaining after deoxyribonuclease digestion were equally effective. It was furthermore shown that DNA's from other sources were quite comparable to thymus DNA in effectiveness. Moreover, calf liver and yeast RNA could replace thymus DNA in restoring protein synthesis.

In view of the non-specific character of the restorative action of the various additives examined by Allfrey and co-workers it can be concluded that these experiments neither confirm nor invalidate our central hypothesis. They do accentuate the need for caution in accepting any unitarian scheme of the role of either RNA or DNA in protein synthesis.

A more direct method of assessing the necessity for the presence of DNA for protein synthesis is to examine the results of the absence of a nucleus. Such experiments are difficult to carry out and to interpret. Mazia and co-workers[58] have found that, in the case of *Amoeba proteus*, enucleation results in some RNA loss and a decrease in, but not a complete elimination of, the capacity of this system to incorporate labeled amino acids.

Brachet[59], working with the same system, has found basically similar results. Nucleus removal produced a sharp drop in RNA content. The enzyme constitution of the cytoplasm was differentially modified.

A refinement of this approach is to work with discrete cytoplasmic fractions. Siekevitz and Zamecnik[60] prepared and studied a crude rat liver homogenate which retained the capacity to incorporate amino acids. This work was extended by Zamecnik and Keller[61].

Spiegelman has compared the effects of selective removal of DNA and RNA from protoplasts of *B. megaterium* upon their capacity to synthesize the enzyme β-galactosidase. The two nucleic acids were separately removed by incubation with ribonuclease or deoxyribonuclease during the actual formation of the protoplasts. It was found that a major portion of the DNA, up to 99 per cent, could be removed without seriously impairing protein synthesis. However, depletion of the RNA content by 30 per cent or more resulted in an extensive loss of synthetic capacity. In some cases the rate of enzyme synthesis could be reduced to zero under conditions where nearly all the DNA was still present.

These experiments do not preclude absolutely a direct role of DNA in enzyme synthesis as degraded fragments of DNA would remain in the intact protoplast and might conceivably possess some synthetic capability. In an effort to eliminate this uncertainty Spiegelman resorted to the use of osmotically shocked protoplasts, from which it proved possible to remove the residual fragments. In harmony with the results obtained with protoplasts the ability to form enzyme was lost upon RNA removal but retained after extraction of DNA.

Unfortunately, these results were complicated by the discovery that extensive resynthesis of DNA occurs during the period of incubation required for the test of enzyme-forming capacity. Thus these results cannot be said to preclude absolutely a direct role of DNA for this system. However, the findings of Spiegelman are certainly consistent with the basic scheme described earlier.

Much of the RNA present in the cytoplasm occurs in the microsomal particles in a state of intimate association with protein. Recent work has shown that the amino acid content of the protein component of microsomes is similar for particles isolated from a number of sources, including rat liver, pea seedlings, and mammalian reticulocytes[62]. This suggests a common function for these particles.

Littlefield and co-workers investigated the microsome fraction of rat liver cells[63].

Experiments with cell-free systems indicated that labeled amino acids were incorporated into microsome protein. The extent of labeling of microsome protein was up to 18 times that of soluble cell protein[63]. The addition of a large excess of inert amino acids failed to displace the labeled residues already incorporated. This suggested that incorporation did not reflect merely a rapidly established equilibrium between free and incorporated amino acids. The implication was that incorporation into the microsome fraction was an essentially irreversible step in protein synthesis.

Nothing has been said as yet as to the possible modes of linkage of the amino acid residues to RNA. As has been mentioned in an earlier chapter, there is no evidence for the binding of native amino acids by RNA *in vitro*. However, there is now increasing evidence for the formation *in vivo* of activated acyl adenylate derivatives of amino acids and a possibility that these activated forms may be intermediates in protein synthesis[64]. Furthermore, there is definite evidence that RNA can serve as an acceptor for activated amino acids[65].

Hoagland and co-workers have recently reported that the soluble (non-microsomal) RNA of a particular fraction of the cytoplasm became labeled with ^{14}C-amino acids in the presence of ATP and the amino acid-activating enzymes and that this labeled RNA had the capacity of subsequently transferring the amino acid to microsomal protein under the proper conditions[65].

Cellular fractions of rat liver and mouse Ehrlich ascites tumor were separated and used in these investigations. The complete system required for the incorporation of labeled amino acid into microsomal protein included microsomes, soluble (non-microsomal) RNA, activating enzymes, ATP, GTP, a nucleoside triphosphate-generating system, and ^{14}C-amino acids. For the first stage of the process, the labeling of the soluble RNA, only the activating enzyme system and ATP were necessary. The amino acid labeling of the soluble RNA was abolished by treatment with ribonuclease.

Evidence that this labeling step could be on the direct pathway of protein synthesis was furnished by the observation that in the case of intact ascites cells the labeling of soluble RNA proceeded much more rapidly than that of microsomal protein.

The second step of the process, involving the transfer of RNA-bound amino acid to microsomal protein, could be followed separately by incubating the former with microsomes, a nucleoside triphosphate-generating system, and GTP. The over-all process could thus be represented by:

$$\text{ATP} + \text{amino acid} \xrightarrow[\text{enzyme}]{} \text{activated amino acid}$$

$$\text{activated amino acid} + \text{RNA} \xrightarrow{} \text{RNA-bound amino acid}$$

$$\text{RNA-bound amino acid} + \text{microsomes} \xrightarrow[\text{enzyme}]{\text{GTP}} \text{labeled microsomal protein}$$

The precise nature of the amino acid-RNA linkage is as yet uncertain. Among the possibilities are an acyl anhydride utilizing the phosphate groups, carboxyl bonding to the ribose C_2 hydroxyl, and bonding involving the nucleotide bases themselves. In any event it is not likely that any condensation of the amino acids occurs at this stage, since they may be recovered as the specific hydroxamic acids upon treatment with hydroxylamine[65].

A number of attractive, but as yet unproved hypotheses naturally arise from this work. Thus Hoagland has suggested that the soluble RNA serves as an adaptor molecule which establishes the position of its attached amino acid on the actual template, which is believed to be microsomal RNA[66]. There is believed to be a different RNA adaptor for each amino acid. On this model the specificity of amino acid sequence in the final polypeptide would be conferred via nucleotide-nucleotide interactions between the soluble, adaptor RNA and the microsomal, template RNA. Much more work will be required, however, before this hypothesis can be regarded as firmly established.

THE TRANSFER OF GENETIC INFORMATION FROM DNA TO RNA

We consider now what is probably the least well understood aspect of the entire scheme of directed protein synthesis. There is virtually no direct information, so that speculation has a clear field.

Implicit in all the mechanisms which have been put forward is the belief that the transfer of information must proceed via the use of DNA as a template for the guided synthesis of RNA. The newly formed RNA must thus be either partially or wholly in a state of intimate association with the DNA organizer.

To be realistic any molecular model for this process must permit specificity of information transfer and must be geometrically and energetically feasible.

Let us consider first those conservative models of replication which conserve the hydrogen bonding of the intact DNA molecule. A possible precedent for this type of model would appear to be furnished by the triply stranded complexes formed by poly A plus poly U and poly A plus poly I. In both these cases the evidence is strong that the second poly U or poly I strand is added in such a way as not to disturb the pairing of the (A + U) or (A + I) duplex.

However, on closer inspection, the results with the biosynthetic polynucleotides provide little encouragement for this kind of model. The available evidence is more consistent with a structure in which the second U or I strand is bonded to adenine alone, rather than with any type of cyclic structure. Complexes corresponding to (2A + U) or (2A + I) have not been observed. It is not sterically feasible to add a third polynucleotide strand to a DNA duplex in this manner. Thus the

(A + U) and (A + I) examples do not provide support for this mechanism.

Stent has outlined a conservative scheme of directed RNA synthesis which permits retention of the original Watson-Crick pairings of the intact DNA and does not require any dissociation of the parental DNA duplex[17]. According to this model, the basic genetic information of the DNA is coded by means of the specific sequence of base *pairs* rather than that of the individual bases in each primary strand.

In this scheme the RNA is formed as a third polynucleotide strand within the deep helical groove of the DNA double helix, giving rise to a transient, triply stranded helical structure. Each base pair of the DNA template positions a single RNA nucleotide unit and can form an additional pair of hydrogen bonds with one and only one base.

The triplets suggested by Stent were of the following form:

DNA pair	RNA
cytosine–guanine	guanine
guanine–cytosine	cytosine
thymine–adenine	adenine
adenine–thymine	uracil

These pairings are illustrated by Fig. 114. Fig. 115 shows the general form of the RNA + DNA intermediate.

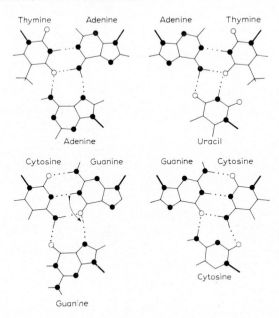

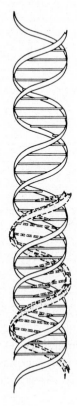

Fig. 114. The base triplets postulated for Stent's scheme[17] for the directed synthesis of RNA.

Fig. 115. The model of Stent for the growth of RNA within the helical groove of the DNA duplex[17].

References p. 345/346

Stent further suggested that the monomer units for the third strand might be amino acid–ribonucleotide complexes so that a polypeptide chain could grow on the outside of the triple helix simultaneously with the formation of the polyribonucleotide strand. This, however, is not essential to the model and the polypeptide chain could be synthesized on the RNA template after its separation from the parental DNA.

In either case the new synthesized strand could unwind by some process like that visualized in the Levinthal–Crane mechanism for the separation of the DNA duplex. This would allow a repetition of the process.

It was further suggested by Stent that two identical ribonucleoprotein strands might unite and form a doubly stranded helix via a pairing of identical bases, as shown in Fig. 116. The new duplex could serve as a template for the directed synthesis of fresh DNA by the inverse of the process described above. Only one of the two ribonucleoprotein strands would be active as a template. The growth of the new DNA duplex would require the unwinding of the two identical mated RNA chains, which would thus be freed to engage in further synthesis (Fig. 117).

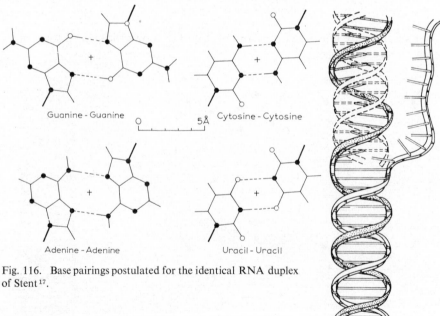

Guanine - Guanine   Cytosine - Cytosine

5Å

Adenine - Adenine   Uracil - Uracil

Fig. 116. Base pairings postulated for the identical RNA duplex of Stent[17].

Fig. 117. The growth of replica DNA on the RNA duplex[17].

The scheme of Stent has many attractive features. However, even if we confine attention to the first stage of the process, that involving the mediation of RNA synthesis by DNA, severe difficulties arise.

Thus Rich has criticized the above model on the grounds that it would involve an excessive distortion of hydrogen bond angles in order to form the two additional bonds required to stabilize the additional RNA strand[2]. In addition, an improbable tautomeric shift is postulated on the oxygen atom of guanine in the DNA.

Belozersky and Spirin have compiled some evidence in favor of a scheme of this general type[67]. They point out that for a number of bacterial nucleic acids there appears to be a general correlation between the ratio of $(G+C)/(A+T)$ in DNA to the ratio of $(G+C)/(A+U)$ in RNA. On this basis they propose that the adenine–thymine pair might be complementary to uracil and to adenine in the replicating system. However, this correlation is by means universal and is rather inexact at best.

There remains the alternative variant of this mechanism whereby the doubly stranded character of DNA is preserved, but the form of its base pairing is modified so as to permit hydrogen bonding of both members of each base pair with a base of the RNA molecule. The addition of the third strand would thus involve the formation of cyclic triplets.

Rich has reported that efforts to build this kind of model were unsuccessful[2]. However, Zubay[68] has succeeded in building a sterically feasible RNA+DNA model with cyclic triplets by tilting the DNA bases drastically (Fig. 118). This

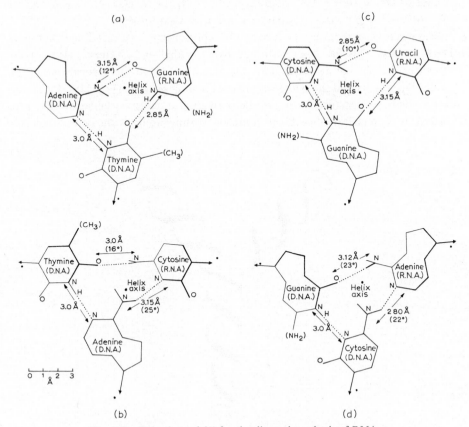

Fig. 118. Zubay's model[68] for the directed synthesis of RNA.

scheme, as was pointed out by its author, cannot possess specificity as there would be two equally acceptable modes of hydrogen-bonding the triplets, each of which would produce a different RNA molecule.

On the whole it can be said that models for the DNA-mediated synthesis of RNA which retain the DNA duplex structure have not been convincingly shown to be sterically or energetically feasible. At the present stage of development of the subject, however, it would be rash to preclude them absolutely.

Thus we are left with the single strand mechanism for the guided production of RNA. Since the stability of the equimolar (A+U) complex justifies us in dismissing the possibility that the 2'-hydroxyls of RNA might sterically interfere, such a model is clearly possible, on the same grounds as account for the stability of the DNA duplex itself. The only modification is the plausible substitution of uracil for thymine.

This model thus circumvents many of the problems faced by those discussed above. The transfer of genetic information proceeds in a readily comprehensible manner, without the need for invoking any new kind of base pairing. On this model the coding scheme would depend entirely on the nucleotide sequence in the two strands of DNA. New DNA could be produced by the inverse of this process, the two strands being produced separately and then combined.

This mechanism requires of course, a plausible scheme for unwinding the original DNA duplex. This has been furnished by Levinthal and Crane[69]. Their model visualizes the replicating DNA molecule as a Y in which the vertical part is the parent DNA helix and the two arms are the growing progeny (Fig. 119). If the new complementary structure forms on the individual threads as the separation proceeds, it is geometrically feasible to complete the unwinding of the parent molecule

Fig. 119. The unwinding mechanism of Levinthal and Crane[69].

and the formation of the replicas by a combination of rotations of the vertical part and the arms, each on its own axis. As the process continues the vertical part gradually shortens and the arms lengthen, in a manner somewhat analogous to the spinning of a speedometer cable.

Levinthal and Crane were also able to show that such a mechanism was energetically as well as geometrically possible. With the aid of a few plausible assumptions it was shown that the expected viscous drag for such a rotation was much too small to constitute an effective barrier to the unwinding process.

While the model of Levinthal and Crane was developed with the directed synthesis of new DNA in mind it would, of course, serve equally well for the guided synthesis of RNA. The RNA–DNA hybrids thereby produced could unwind by an analogous process.

Platt [70] has proposed an alternative mechanism of unwinding, in which the unwinding of the chains of the parent duplex and their replication are separate and alternating events. His scheme requires the assumption that the two halves of each strand of DNA are complementary so that the entire duplex has an inversion point in the middle. There is, of course, no independent evidence for this postulate.

The untwisting process is visualized as resembling the result of pulling sideways upon each strand at the inversion point. As the two strands are separated their two complementary halves are twisted upon themselves so that the ultimate result of the separation process is two molecules resembling twisted hairpins. Each of these can then undergo replication in a manner analogous to the model of Levinthal and Crane. During both separation and subsequent replication each arm of the four-or three-armed star will rotate as in the Levinthal and Crane model and will be subject to the same arguments.

The model of Platt does not appear to have any compensating asset to offset the disadvantage of requiring an as yet ungrounded postulate.

In any event it can certainly be stated that the problem of unwinding *per se* does not provide an insuperable obstacle to this kind of mechanism for replication. The results of Felsenfeld [71] and of Steiner and Beers [72] on the poly A plus poly U interaction have shown that the adenine-uracil linkage, at least, has the required ready reversibility.

The single stranded template model is by no means free from objections. Among these is the failure of any generalized correlation between the base composition of RNA and DNA of the same cell to emerge. If both strands of the parental duplex served equally for the synthesis of RNA, the Watson–Crick base ratios should be preserved in the latter.

Another rather severe objection to the single strand template model arises from experiments with the coliphages. If ^{32}P atoms are incorporated into the DNA of phage their radioactive decay must inevitably lead to rupture of the sugar-phosphate backbone. As would be expected this decay can result in a loss of the ability of the phage to reproduce itself.

However, the work of Stent and others has indicated that only a rather small fraction of the breakages produced by radioactive decay is actually lethal, about one in ten or less[20]. This does not accord with the extreme sensitivity to primary chain scission predicted for the single stranded template model. It is certainly difficult to visualize how single chain breaks could fail to lead to aborted RNA synthesis for any replication scheme of this general type.

In summary, it is possible to raise serious objections to all of the schemes for information transfer from DNA to RNA which have been proposed so far. It would certainly be hazardous to make a final choice at this time or to exclude the possibility of some drastically different mechanism.

TEMPLATES AND CODING

Let us turn now to the mechanism whereby the information stored in RNA is translated into the amino acid sequence of a given protein. We are now almost entirely in the realm of speculation. There has, however, been no shortage of such speculation, which has for the most part been confined to the purely formal aspects of the problem.

We are confronted with the problem of finding a coding mechanism whereby a linear sequential arrangement of only four different bases is enabled to guide the specific sequence of twenty different amino acids. Clearly a one-to-one arrangement is out of the question. An arrangement whereby an adjacent pair of nucleotides binds and aligns a single amino acid would also lack sufficient specificity, as there are only 4^2 or 16 different base pairs and 20 different amino acids.

However, an arrangement in which the specificity is conferred by nucleotide triplets would be adequate by this criterion as there are 4^3 or 64 such different triplets. However, a steric difficulty now arises. Such a triplet would have a linear displacement in the direction of the fiber axis of about 10 Å while the distance between two adjacent amino acids on an extended peptide chain is only about 3.7 Å.

This difficulty was circumvented by Gamow, Rich, and Ycas[73] by postulating a system of overlapping triplets. A sequence of m amino acids would be determined by $(m+2)$ or $(2m+1)$ nucleotides. Each pair of adjacent amino acids would share one or two nucleotides. Hence a sequence of two amino acids would be directed by a sequence of four or five nucleotides; the first amino acid by the first three

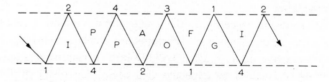

Fig. 120. Schematic diagram of the triangular code. The numbers stand for nucleotides and the letters for amino acids[73].

nucleotides and the second amino acid by the last three. This kind of model has, of course, been designed explicitly for the case of a singly stranded template.

The coding scheme devised by Gamow and co-workers for this case was called by them the triangular code. The arrangement is illustrated schematically in Fig. 120. In Fig. 120 the nucleotides are represented by the numbers 1, 2, 3, 4. The letters represent amino acids, of which there are a total of twenty to be coded.

There are a total of twenty possible different triangles, which are shown in Fig. 121, together with their respective letter assignments. It should be noted that

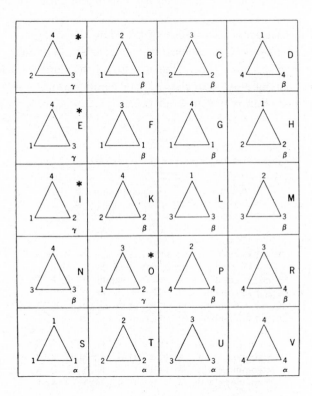

Fig. 121.   Possible triads of the triangular code[73].

rotation of a triangle, corresponding to a permutation of the sequence of three numbers, does not alter its specificity according to this scheme. The equivalence of the number of different triangles to the number of amino acids to be coded is a distinct asset to the model, although the assumptions involved in obtaining this equivalence may be somewhat artificial.

An inspection of Fig. 120 reveals that there are two possibilities for the arrangement of amino acids along the template. The first of these, called the compact triangular code, is obtained if the assumption is made that the amino acids unite in the direct order in which they are laid out along the template. In terms of Fig. 120

the peptide sequence thereby produced would be IPPAOFGI. For the compact code each pair of adjacent amino acids is guided by two adjacent triangles which have *two* numbers (or nucleotides) in common.

The alternative loose triangular code is obtained if it is assumed that peptide linkages are formed only between those amino acids occupying the upright triangles or those occupying the inverted ones of Fig. 120. A single template could thus synthesize two peptides corresponding to IPOG and PAFI. In the case of the loose triangular code the synthesis of a particular sequence is guided by sets of triangles, each adjacent pair of which has only *one* number (or nucleotide) in common.

Because of the overlapping character of the triangular code, not all sequential arrangements are possible. The compact triangular code has naturally much more restrictiveness than the loose code. Thus it is found that four triangles can combine with 10 different other triangles, 12 can combine with 7 others, and the remaining 4 can combine only with 4 others each.

TABLE 30

INTERSYMBOL RELATIONS FOR THE LOOSE TRIANGULAR CODE

A combines with all letters except: S
E combines with all letters except: T
I combines with all letters except: U
O combines with all letters except: D

B and H combine with all letters except: N, R, U, V
C and D combine with all letters except: C, M, T, U
F and L combine with all letters except: K, P, T, V
G and M combine with all letters except: D, G, S, V
K and P combine with all letters except: F, L, S, V
N and R combine with all letters except: B, H, S, T

S combines with: B, D, E, F, G, H, J, L, O, S
T combines with: A, B, C, H, J, K, M, O, P, T
V combines with: A, D, E, G, J, K, N, P, R, V
U combines with: A, C, E, F, L, M, N, O, R, U

The combination rules are somewhat relaxed in the case of the loose code. Any two triangles with at least one number in common can combine. Table 30 shows the possible combinations.

It is possible to make a choice between the two variants of the triangular code upon the basis of available data. Thus the compact triangular code predicts that no amino acid can have more than 10 different nearest neighbors. However, even the very restricted amino acid sequences which are known yield cases where a given amino acid has more than 10 different neighbors. Thus the compact code can be rejected leaving only the loose code as a possibility.

A general criticism of the triangular code and indeed of any coding scheme which invokes overlapping is that damage to the template should affect more than one amino acid. Hence it would be expected on this basis that mutations involving an alteration of two or more consecutive amino acids would be common. The limited available evidence has yet to produce an example of this .

A still more serious objection arises from the severely restricted character of the possible amino acid sequences permitted by this code. In fact, Brenner[74] has concluded that the observed sequences cannot be consistently analyzed by any code which invokes overlapping.

Crick, Griffith and Orgel[75] have outlined a non-overlapping triplet code which avoids the difficulties of those cited. The steric difficulties encountered with a code of this type could be obviated by postulating that each amino acid is attached to the template only in conjunction with an *adaptor* molecule which confers the proper dimensions, such as soluble RNA.

The model of Crick and co-workers assumes that all possible sequences of the amino acid may occur. It is further postulated that the code may be read unambiguously for any linear region in the template without need for reference to the ends. This requires that no meaningful triplets can be contained in the set of two pairs of nucleotides adjacent to the junction of any two meaningful triplets. In the language of the above workers the two overlapping triplets occurring at each such intersection must be *nonsense* triplets and must be clearly identifiable as such.

On this basis triplets composed of three identical nucleotides must be rejected, as a sequence of two such triplets would contain overlapping meaningful triplets. The 60 remaining triplets can be grouped into 20 sets of three triplets each. Each set of three consists of cyclic permutations of one another. Only one of these can be meaningful, as otherwise a sequence of two identical triplets would contain overlapping triplets which were meaningful.

The requirement of non-ambiguity thus reduces the total number of meaningful triplets to twenty. The fact that this is the number of amino acids which are to be coded is encouraging with regard to the applicability of the model.

The work of Ingram[76] upon abnormal human hemoglobin is quite relevant to the respective plausibilities of the several types of code which have been discussed. A study of several altered hemoglobins has shown that in each case only one amino acid has been changed. If each altered hemoglobin is the result of a mutation which has affected the template, it is clear that this result is not consistent with any type of overlapping code, as an alteration in a single base would have to affect more than one amino acid. It is, however, consistent with a code of the Crick, Griffith, and Orgel type.

Still another type of code has been proposed by Orgel[73]. In this code each amino acid has a particular nucleotide which acts as a major directing factor for that residue. Each nucleotide must, of course, serve as the major determinant for several amino acids.

In addition to the major determinant the adjacent nucleotides may also exert a directive influence. This might have the form of a steric blockage of one amino acid and a tolerance of a second. Thus corresponding to each amino acid there may be assigned a nucleotide triplet whose center member, corresponding to the major determinant, is invariant for that amino acid, but whose other two members may have more than one composition.

While of an overlapping character, this code has the advantage of permitting alterations in only one amino acid. However, efforts to apply it to known sequences have failed to produce a self-consistent correlation [73].

All of the RNA template models thus far discussed have been relatively vague on the precise manner in which the synthesis of protein is controlled. Jehle [77] has recently presented a scheme in which this process is made more explicit.

According to Jehle's model the transfer of information from RNA to protein occurs essentially in two stages. First a single polypeptide chain is formed which remains attached to the RNA. The synthesis of further protein molecules is mediated directly by this parental polypeptide, which proceeds to direct the formation of an exact duplicate of itself. It is supposed by Jehle that each amino acid of the parental chain preferentially attracts another like itself by virtue of specific Van der Waals interactions which favor the juxtaposition of two similar amino acid residues over that of two dissimilar ones.

Several alternative ways of bonding the parental polypeptide to the RNA were considered. These included bonding of the peptide carbonyls to the C_2 hydroxyls of ribose, bonding of the peptide NH groups to the RNA phosphates, and bonding of both the peptide NH and CO groups to the bases of RNA.

Jehle's proposal has at least the advantage of concreteness. However, it is by no means obvious how any of the proposed schemes of attachment of the parental polypeptide strand to the RNA would permit any specificity of amino acid sequence. Furthermore, it is difficult to see how Van der Waals' forces alone could be sufficient to confer the required uniqueness of sequence of the filial polypeptide chains. For example, it seems unlikely that two similarly charged glutamic acid residues would display a preferential mutual attraction.

Pending the availability of more direct information, it is clear that speculation can proceed almost indefinitely. The discussion in this section by no means exhausts the number of conceivable codes, of varying degrees of elaborateness, which could be devised.

To perform a completely unambiguous decoding it would really be necessary to isolate a single nucleic acid known to control the synthesis of a single protein and determine their nucleotide and amino acid sequence. Such an approach is clearly hopeless at present in the case of the higher organisms where the nucleic acids isolated are always heterogeneous collections of different molecules. However, in the case of the homogeneous infectious RNA of tobacco mosaic virus such an attack is at least conceivable, although hardly likely to be realized in the near future.

In general, perhaps the most encouraging aspect of the various schemes of information transfer discussed in this chapter is the demonstration that the subject has now advanced to a point where such speculation has become worthwhile.

REFERENCES

[1] R. HOTCHKISS, in E. CHARGAFF AND J. DAVIDSON, *The Nucleic Acids*, Vol. 2, New York, 1955, p. 435.

[2] A. RICH, *Ann. N. Y. Acad. Sci.*, 81 (1959) 709.

[3] G. BROWN, A. BROWN AND J. GORDON, in *Structure and Function of Genetic Elements, Brookhaven Symposia in Biology*, 12 (1959) 47.

[4] T. CASPERSSON, *Symposia Soc. Exptl. Biol.*, 1 (1947) 127.

[5] A. MEISTER, *Rev. Mod. Phys.*, 31 (1959) 210.

[6] O. AVERY, C. MacLEOD AND M. McCARTY, *J. Exptl. Med.*, 79 (1944) 137.

[7] M. DAWSON, *J. Exptl. Med.*, 51 (1930) 123.

[8] F. GRIFFITH, *J. Hyg.*, 27 (1928) 113.

[9] J. ALLOWAY, *J. Exptl. Med.*, 57 (1933) 265.

[10] M. McCARTY AND O. AVERY, *J. Exptl. Med.*, 83 (1946) 89.

[11] A. BOIVIN, A. DELAUNAY, R. VENDRELY AND Y. LEHOULT, *Experimentia*, 1 (1945) 334.

[12] H. ALEXANDER AND G. LEIDY, *J. Exptl. Med.*, 93 (1951) 345.

[13] H. ALEXANDER AND W. REDMAN, *J. Exptl. Med.*, 97 (1953) 797.

[14] R. HERRIOTT, *J. Bacteriol.*, 61 (1951) 752.

[15] A. HERSHEY AND M. CHASE, *J. Gen. Physiol.*, 36 (1952) 39.

[16] R. WILLIAMS, *Rev. Mod. Phys.*, 31 (1959) 233.

[17] G. STENT, *Adv. Virus Research*, 5 (1958) 95.

[18] A. DOERMANN, *J. Gen. Physiol.*, 35 (1952) 645.

[19] E. VOLKIN AND L. ASTRACHAN, *Virology*, 2 (1956) 149.

[20] M. DELBRUCK AND G. STENT, in W. McELROY AND B. GLASS, *The Chemical Basis of Heredity*, Baltimore, 1957, p. 699.

[21] C. LEVINTHAL AND C. THOMAS, *Biochim. et Biophys. Acta*, 23 (1957) 453.

[22] C LEVINTHAL, *Proc. Natl. Acad. Sci., U.S.*, 42 (1956) 394.

[23] G. SCHRAMM AND A. GIERER, *Cellular Biology, Nucleic Acids, and Viruses*, Special Publications, N.Y. Acad. Sci., 1957, p. 229.

[24] H. FRAENKEL-CONRAT, *ibid.*, 1957, p. 219.

[25] T. MORGAN, *J. Exptl. Zool.*, 11 (1911) 365.

[26] A. STURTEVANT, *J. Exptl. Zool.*, 14 (1913) 43.

[27] C. BRIDGES, *Genetics*, 1 (1916) 107.

[28] H. MULLER, *Science*, 66 (1927) 84.

[29] A. BOIVIN, R. VENDRELY AND C. VENDRELY, *Compt. rend.*, 226 (1948) 1061.

[30] A. MIRSKY AND H. RIS, *Nature*, 163 (1949) 666.

[31] A. HOLLAENDER AND C. EMMONS, *Cold Spring Harbor Symposia Quant. Biol.*, 9 (1941) 179.

[32] A. KELNER, *J. Bacteriol.*, 58 (1949) 511.

[33] R. HERRIOTT, *J. Gen. Physiol.*, 32 (1948) 221.

[34] J. BUTLER, L. GILBERT AND K. SMITH, *Nature*, 165 (1950) 714.

[35] C. AUERBACH AND J. ROBSON, *Nature*, 157 (1946) 302.

[36] M. MESELSON AND F. STAHL, *Proc. Natl. Acad. Sci.*, 44 (1958) 671.

[37] H. MUIR, A. NEUBERGER AND J. PERRONE, *Biochem. J.*, 52 (1952) 87.

[38] D. STEINBERG, M. VAUGHAN AND C. ANFINSON, *Science*, 124 (1956) 389.

[39] S. SPIEGELMAN, in W. McELROY AND B. GLASS, *The Chemical Basis of Heredity*, Baltimore, 1957, p. 232.

[40] T. CASPERSSON, *Cell Growth and Cell Function*, New York, 1950.

[41] J. BRACHET, in E. CHARGAFF AND J. DAVIDSON, *The Nucleic Acids*, Vol. 2, New York, 1955, p. 475.

[42] T. CASPERSSON AND J. SCHULTZ, *Nature*, 142 (1938) 294.

[43] J. BRACHET, *Arch. biol. (Liège)*, 44 (1933) 519.

[44] J. DAVIDSON, I. LESLIE AND C. WAYMOUTH, *Biochem. J.* 44 (1949) 5.

[45] I. LESLIE AND J. DAVIDSON, *Biochem. et Biophys. Acta*, 7 (1951) 413.

[46] J. DAVIDSON, *Cold Spring Harbor Symposia Quant. Biol.*, 12 (1947) 50.

[47] P. CALDWELL, E. MACKOR AND C. HINSHELWOOD, *J. Chem. Soc.*, (1950) 3151.

[48] A. KELNER, *J. Bacteriol.*, 65 (1953) 252.

[49] L. SIMINOVITCH AND S. RAPKINE, *Compt. rend.*, 232 (1951) 1603.

[50] L. BARON, S. SPIEGELMAN AND H. QUASTLER, *J. Gen. Physiol.*, 36 (1951) 631.
[51] S. COHEN AND H. BARNER, *Proc. Natl. Acad. Sci.*, 40 (1954) 885.
[52] R. LESTER, *J. Am. Chem. Soc.*, 75 (1953) 5448.
[53] M. BELJANSKI, *Biochem. et Biophys. Acta*, 15 (1954) 425.
[54] E. GALE AND J. FOLKES, *Biochem. J.* 59 (1955) 661.
[55] E. GALE AND J. FOLKES, *Biochem. J.*, 59 (1955) 675.
[56] A. PARDEE, *Proc. Natl. Acad. Sci.*, 40 (1954) 263.
[57] V. ALLFREY, A. MIRSKY AND S. OSAWA, in W. MCELROY AND B. GLASS, *The Chemical Basis of Heredity*, Baltimore, 1957, p. 200.
[58] D. MAZIA AND D. PRESCOTT, *Biochim. et Biophys. Acta*, 17 (1955) 23.
[59] J. BRACHET, *Biochim. et Biophys. Acta*, 18 (1955) 247.
[60] P. SIEKEVITZ AND P. ZAMECNIK, *Federation Proc.*, 10 (1951) 246.
[61] P. ZAMECNIK AND E. J. KELLER, *J. Biol. Chem.*, 209 (1954) 337.
[62] P. T'SO, J. BONNER AND H. DINTZIS, *Arch. Biochem. Biophys.*, 76 (1958) 225.
[63] J. LITTLEFIELD, E. KELLER, J. GROSS AND P. ZAMECNIK, *J. Biol. Chem.*, 217 (1955) 111.
[64] G. NOVELLI, *Proc. Natl. Acad. Sci.*, 44 (1958) 86.
[65] M. HOAGLAND, M. STEPHENSON, J. SCOTT, L. HECHT AND P. ZAMECNIK, *J. Biol. Chem.*, 231 (1958) 241.
[66] M. HOAGLAND, in *Structure and Function of Genetic Elements, Brookhaven Symposia in Biology*, 12 (1959) 40.
[67] A. BELOZERSKY AND A. SPIRIN, *Nature*, 182 (1958) 111.
[68] G. ZUBAY, *Nature*, 182 (1958) 1290,
[69] C. LEVINTHAL AND H. CRANE, *Proc. Natl. Acad. Sci.*, 42 (1956) 436.
[70] J. PLATT, *Proc. Natl. Acad. Sci.*, 41 (1955) 181.
[71] G. FELSENFELD, *Biochim. et Biophys. Acta*, 29 (1958) 133.
[72] R. STEINER AND R. BEERS, *Biochim. et Biophys. Acta*, 33 (1959) 470.
[73] G. GAMOW, A. RICH AND M. YCAS, *Adv. in Biol. and Med. Phys.*, 4 (1956) 23.
[74] S. BRENNER, *Proc. Natl. Acad. Sci.*, 43 (1957) 687.
[75] F. CRICK, J. GRIFFITH AND L. ORGEL, *Proc. Natl. Acad. Sci.*, 43 (1957) 416.
[76] V. INGRAM, *Nature*, 180 (1957) 326.
[77] H. JEHLE, *Proc. Natl. Acad. Sci.*, 45 (1959) 1360.

Appendix A

Table of Abbreviations

TABLE 31

Name	Abbreviation
adenosine-monophosphate	AMP
adenosine-diphosphate	ADP
adenosine-triphosphate	ATP
uridine-monophosphate	UMP
uridine-diphosphate	UDP
uridine-triphosphate	UTP
cytidine-monophosphate	CMP
cytidine-diphosphate	CDP
cytidine-triphosphate	CTP
guanosine-monophosphate	GMP
guanosine-diphosphate	GDP
guanosine-triphosphate	GTP
inosine-monophosphate	IMP
inosine-diphosphate	IDP
inosine-triphosphate	ITP
thymidine-monophosphate	TMP
thymidine-diphosphate	TDP
thymidine-triphosphate	TTP
ribonucleic acid	RNA
deoxyribonucleic acid	DNA
polyriboadenylic acid	poly A
polyriboinosinic acid	poly I
polyribouridylic acid	poly U
polyribocytidylic acid	poly C
polyriboguanylic acid	poly G
copolymer of adenylic and uridylic acids	poly AU
inorganic phosphate	P_i
ribonuclease	RNA ase
deoxyribonuclease	DNA ase

Appendix B

The Isolation of DNA from Calf Thymus

Methods for the separation of DNA from animal tissues generally involve two stages. The first step is the separation of the nuclear deoxyribonucleoprotein from the bulk of the cytoplasmic components, which contain most of the RNA. The second step is the removal of the basic proteins with which DNA occurs in combination. Most published procedures for the first step involve extensive washing of the ruptured cell suspensions with 0.9% NaCl, in which the DNA-containing chromatin is insoluble. A variety of methods have been utilized for the second, including salt extraction, $CHCl_3$ emulsification, and detergent treatment. We shall describe here only the last of these, which is at present the method of choice.

The most crucial aspect of any preparative technique is the avoidance of enzymatic degradation. While the problem is not as acute in the case of thymus as for many other tissues, extreme precautions are still necessary to obtain a highly polymerized product. These include the use of low temperatures whenever possible and the shortening of the time required for the various operations as much as possible. These are particularly important for the early steps of the procedure, prior to the extensive denaturation of the protein.

The following procedure is that of Kay, Simmons, and Dounce[1].

(*i*) Freshly excised calf thymus gland is frozen in liquid nitrogen and stored therein until use, which should be as soon as possible.

(*ii*) 50 g of frozen thymus is broken into chunks and blended at 0° with 200 ml of 0.9% NaCl in a Waring Blendor. The homogenate is centrifuged to bring down the insoluble chromatin. About 30 min are required at 2500 rpm and proportionately shorter times at higher speeds. The supernatant is discarded.

(*iii*) The sediment from step (*ii*) is subjected to the same treatment three additional times.

(*iv*) The sediment from step (*iii*) is homogenized at 0° with one liter of 0.9% NaCl.

(*v*) The homogenate from step (*iv*) is brought to room temperature. To it is added 90 ml of a 5% solution of purified sodium lauryl sulfate in 45% (by volume) ethanol. The mixture is stirred vigorously for 3 h during which time it sets to a fairly stiff gel.

(*vi*) 55 g of solid NaCl are added, bringing the NaCl concentration to 1 *M*. After complete solution of the NaCl the material is centrifuged for one hour at 10,000 rpm in a Servall centrifuge.

(*vii*) To the supernatant from step (*vi*) is added, with stirring, an equal volume of ethanol. The crude thymus DNA comes out of solution as a gelatinous mass which slowly loses water to form a white fibrous precipitate, which can be readily wound around a glass stirring rod. The fibers are pressed to free them from entrapped solution and are then washed twice with 80% ethanol. They may then be washed repeatedly with acetone until the supernatant is clear and then dried overnight. Some workers prefer to omit the acetone washing and instead redissolve the fibers at once.

(*viii*) The crude DNA fibers from step (*vii*) are cut with a pair of scissors into as small pieces as possible. They are then added to 700 ml of 0.0001 *M* NaCl and stirred vigorously at room temperature until solution is complete. This usually requires several hours. 63 ml of 5% sodium lauryl sulfate are added and stirring continued for one hour. 45 g of solid NaCl are then added, bringing the NaCl concentration to 1 *M*. After complete solution of the NaCl, the mixture is centrifuged for one hour at 25,000 rpm in a Spinco model L preparative ultracentrifuge. If a clear supernatant is not obtained centrifugation may be continued for longer periods.

(*ix*) The supernatant is treated exactly as in step (*vii*).

(*x*) The DNA is dissolved as before in 700 ml of 0.0001 *M* NaCl. 6.3 g of solid NaCl are added to bring the NaCl concentration to 0.9%. The solution is then centrifuged for one hour at 25,000 rpm in the Spinco model L. To the supernatant is added 35 g solid NaCl.

(*xi*) The DNA is precipitated and washed as in step (*vii*). It may be either washed with acetone and stored in the dry state or stored as an alcohol precipitate under 80% ethanol. In either case the temperature of storage should be low ($-5°$ or less).

It should be noted that the freezing of the thymus in step (*i*) appears to be essential. The omission of this step invariably results in a degraded product.

The sodium lauryl sulfate employed should be purified prior to use by recrystallization from boiling ethanol.

Variants of the above method may also be used for the preparation of DNA from other tissues, although in no other case yet examined do the conditions appear to be as favorable as in the case of the calf thymus gland. In general considerably larger amounts of starting material are required to obtain a comparable yield of product. In the case of calf spleen the weight of frozen material should be increased fourfold.

It has been reported that the drying of DNA is deleterious[2]. In the experience of the authors this has not been the case for thymus DNA. However, the drying steps in the procedure may easily be circumvented by washing the DNA fibers with 80% ethanol only and redissolving directly. The final precipitate may be redissolved in 0.0001 *M* NaCl, dialyzed, and stored in the frozen state.

Appendix C

The Isolation of a Bacterial DNA

The preparation of DNA from bacteria encounters problems similar to those which complicate its isolation from tissues. The example cited will be the preparation of active transforming DNA from pneumococcus. The existence of the subtle property of transforming activity provides a sensitive criterion for the absence of degradation or denaturation during the procedure. The process described is that of Hotchkiss[3].

(*i*) Pneumococci are grown in meat infusion–neopeptone medium. The latter is prepared by heating to 85° an aqueous infusion of ground beef hearts (450 g/l), filtering, and then adding 5 g NaCl, and 10 g Difco neopeptone per liter. The mixture is autoclaved and its pH adjusted to 7.5. The medium is placed in 2 l flasks in 1.5 l volumes. 3 ml of sterile 20% glucose and 15 ml of sterile 0.5 M K_2HPO_4 are added to each flask.

(*ii*) The medium-containing flasks are inoculated with 10 ml each of a *fresh* culture of the appropriate pneumococcus strain. Growth is usually heavy after about 16 hours.

(*iii*) After growth has proceeded to about its maximum extent the cells are harvested by centrifugation at 3000 rpm. The centrifuged cells are resuspended in 0.85% NaCl, 0.1 M Na citrate. About 1.0 ml per liter of original medium is used.

(*iv*) 1 ml of 0.5% sodium deoxycholate is added per 25 ml of suspension; lysis proceeds rapidly at room temperature, and is virtually complete in five minutes.

(*v*) One volume of chloroform, plus 1/40 volume of isoamyl alcohol are added. The mixture is shaken vigorously for 15 min. The emulsion is then centrifuged and the aqueous top layer pipetted off. The denatured protein is left as a layer at the water-chloroform interface.

(*vi*) To the aqueous solution is added 1.5 volumes of ethanol. The precipitate is centrifuged down and redissolved at once in 0.85% NaCl. About 7 ml per liter of original culture medium are usually required.

(*vii*) To remove RNA, 0.05 mg of crystalline ribonuclease are added per 10 ml. The mixture is incubated for 15 min at 37°.

(*viii*) To the solution 1.5 volumes of ethanol are added. The DNA comes down in fibrous form and may readily be wound around a stirring rod.

(*ix*) The DNA fibers are redissolved at once in about 80% of the volume of 0.85% saline from which they were precipitated. The chloroform emulsification of step (*v*) is repeated until no protein is found at the H_2O–$CHCl_3$ interface.

(*x*) To the aqueous layer is added 1.5 volumes of ethanol. The DNA fibers are wound around a stirring rod, squeezed dry, and washed repeatedly with 80% ethanol. The DNA may be redissolved in 0.001 *M* NaCl and frozen, or stored as an alcohol precipitate under 90% ethanol. It has been reported that complete drying results in a loss of activity.

Appendix D

Preparation of RNA from Yeast

If it is desired to obtain RNA in fairly large yield, yeast is the most favorable source. The difficulties encountered in the preparation of DNA reoccur in intensified form because of the greater lability of the ribose phosphodiester linkage. The following procedure is that of Crestfield, Smith, and Allen[4].

(*i*) 150 g of *fresh* yeast *(S. cerevisiae)* are added to 500 ml of a boiling aqueous solution containing 2% sodium lauryl sulfate, 4.5% ethanol and 0.025 *M* phosphate, pH 6.8. The yeast is cut into very small pieces prior to addition. Immediately after addition the temperature of the solution drops to about 85°. The temperature of the solution is then allowed to rise to about 93°. The mixture is then immediately poured into a beaker immersed in a dry ice–acetone bath and stirred until the temperature drops to about 3°.

(*ii*) The above solution is centrifuged for 30 min at 0° at 2000 rpm. The supernatant is poured into two volumes of ethanol, which has been precooled to 0°. The resultant suspension is centrifuged for 15 min at 2000 rpm at 0°.

(*iii*) The precipitate from (*ii*) is resuspended in 150 ml of 67% ethanol. About 10 drops of 2 *M* NaCl are added. The suspension is centrifuged for 15 min at 2000 rpm. The precipitate is resuspended and recentrifuged. The final precipitate is suspended in 80% ethanol and left overnight at 0°.

(*iv*) After centrifugation, the precipitate is dissolved in 150 ml H_2O. The pH is adjusted to 7 by the dropwise addition of 1 *N* acetic acid. The turbid solution is centrifuged for one hour at 25,000 rpm in a Spinco model L preparative ultracentrifuge.

(*v*) To the supernatant from (*iv*) are added 8.3 g of solid NaCl, bringing the NaCl concentration to 1 *M*. The solution is allowed to stand at 0° for one hour.

The RNA separates out as a gel. This is centrifuged down for one hour at 0° at 2000 rpm.

(*vi*) The gel is washed with 150 ml of 67% ethanol, to which 1 ml of 2 *M* NaCl has been added, and then centrifuged down as before. This washing is repeated twice.

(*vii*) The precipitate is dissolved in 100 ml of 0.001 *M* NaCl and dialyzed *vs.* solvent for 24 h at 0° with frequent changes.

(*ix*) The solution is clarified by one hour of centrifugation at 25,000 rpm at 0° in a Spinco model L preparative ultracentrifuge. The clear solution is lyophilized. The final yield is about 1.4 g.

Appendix E

Preparation of RNA from E. coli

The following procedure is that of Littauer and Eisenberg[5].

(*i*) *E. coli* (strain B) is grown in a medium containing:

1%	Difco dehydrated yeast extract
1%	Glucose
2.18%	K_2HPO_2
1.7%	KH_2PO_4
pH	7

(*ii*) To a series of 4 l Erlenmeyer flasks containing 1 liter each of autoclaved medium are added a small amount (0.3 ml) of surface growth from a 5 h culture grown on nutrient agar. The inoculum is suspended in 0.9% NaCl.

(*iii*) The growing cultures are incubated for 14 h at 37° with vigorous aeration. It is important to harvest just after the end of the logarithmic growth phase. Thus it is advisable to follow the optical density increase with time directly.

(*iv*) The cells are centrifuged down. A Sharples supercentrifuge is convenient. About 5 grams of cells are obtained per liter of medium. The cells are washed twice with chilled 0.05 *M* tris, pH 9.0.

(*v*) From the washed cells the protoplasts are isolated by the following procedure: Ten gram portions of cells are suspended in 40 ml each of 0.05 *M* tris buffer, pH 9.0, and incubated for 3 min at 37°. The temperature is then lowered to 4° and 20 ml of 2 *M* sucrose, 12 ml H_2O, and, 8 ml of a lysozyme solution containing

2 mg/ml are added. After 10 min, 4 ml of 1 M tris buffer, pH 7.4, are added. The protoplasts are centrifuged down for 6 min at 5000 g in a Servall centrifuge at 4°. They are then washed twice with 30 ml portions of cold 1 M sucrose.

(*vi*) The washed protoplasts are lysed by suspension in cold 10^{-4} M versene, pH 8.0 (80 ml per 10 g of cells).

(*vii*) To the viscous lysate is added an equal volume of 90% phenol. Steps (*vi*) and (*vii*) should be completed as quickly as possible, preferably within 5 min.

(*viii*) The mixture is stirred for one hour at 20°. It is then chilled and centrifuged at 4° in a Servall centrifuge for three minutes at 10,000 g. The centrifugation breaks the phenol emulsion and two layers separate. The upper aqueous layer contains the RNA and is removed with a separatory funnel.

(*ix*) The RNA is precipitated from the aqueous phase by the addition of two volumes of cold 96% ethanol containing 2% potassium acetate. After standing 30 min at 4° the precipitate is removed by centrifugation for 10 min at 10,000 g, washed with cold 75% ethanol containing 2% potassium acetate, and then with 75% ethanol.

(*x*) The precipitate is dissolved in 25 ml of 0.01 M tris, pH 7.4, and clarified by centrifugation at 10,000 g for 20 min.

(*xi*) The clear supernatant is dialyzed for 24 h *vs* 10^{-3} M NaCl at 4°.

(*xii*) The solution is again clarified by centrifugation for 20 min at 10,000 g and then lyophilized. About 100 mg of RNA are obtained from 10 g of cells.

It is important that the phenol used in step (*vii*) be as pure as possible. The commercial product should be redistilled.

Appendix F

Acid and Alkaline Hydrolysis of Polynucleotides
for Analytical Purposes

Hydrolysis to nucleotides

Polyribonucleotides are readily hydrolyzed by alkali, under fairly mild conditions to a mixture of isomeric nucleoside-2' and 3'-phosphates. Acid hydrolysis has also been used, but is less reliable, because of the tendency of the purines to be split off. Among the conditions which have been used successfully are:

> 0.3 M KOH at 37° for 18 hours[6]
> 1 M NaOH at 30° for 24 hours[7]
> conc. NH_3 ($D°$ = 0.925) at 45° for 8 days[8]
> 0.1 M NaOH at 100° for 2 hours[9]
> 0.5 M NaOH at 20° for 18 hours[8]

Some deamination of cytosine has been reported to occur under more drastic conditions, such as 1 M NaOH at 100°.

The polydeoxyribonucleotides are relatively resistant to acid or alkaline degradation, except under conditions so drastic as to break down the nucleotides. In general, enzymatic methods are the only practical means of splitting DNA quantitatively into nucleotides. For purposes of analysis it is usually more convenient to determine the purine and pyrimidine bases directly.

Hydrolysis to purines and pyrimidines

Quantitative yields of the free bases from RNA are difficult to achieve. Among the more satisfactory procedures is hydrolysis with 70% perchloric acid at 100° for one hour[10].

The purine bases of RNA may be selectively split off in 1 N HCl at 100° for one hour[11].

The bases of DNA are split off with relative ease. Among the conditions which have been found to be satisfactory are:

> 70% perchloric acid at 100° for 1 hour[12]
> 98% formic acid at 175° for 2 hours in a sealed tube[13]

The purine bases of DNA may be selectively and quantitatively split off by very mild acid treatment, such as pH 1.6 at 37° for 24 hours[14].

Appendix G

The Separation of Nucleotides and their Components by Ion-Exchange Chromatography

Both cation- and anion-exchangers have been extensively used. The usual require-ment of a strongly acid elution system for the cation-exchangers limits their usefulness for the separation of nucleotides and polynucleotides, because of the acid-lability of the purine glycosidic linkages.

The resins which have been extensively used are all of the polystyrene bead type. The usual range of sizes is 200–400 mesh. The following resins are among the most satisfactory.

Cation-exchangers:	Dowex-50	(sulfonic acid)
	Amberlite-IRC-50	(carboxylic acid)
	Amberlite-120	(sulfonic acid)
Anion-exchangers:	Dowex-1	(quaternary ammonium)
	Dowex-2	(quaternary ammonium)
	Amberlite-IRA-400	(quaternary ammonium)

The column is customarily contained in a glass tube and supported by a sintered glass disk. The exit tube should be kept at a minimal diameter to reduce the danger of mixing the effluent.

The resin is converted into the desired salt form, washed with water, and poured into the column supporter in the form of a slurry.

The two experimental parameters whose variation is used to alter the relative distribution coefficients of the nucleotides are pH and ionic strength. Resolution of a mixture may sometimes be achieved adequately by elution with a single solvent, but in general a higher degree of selectivity is attained by the use of a stepwise or continuous alteration of pH or ionic strength.

The usual means of following the course of elution sequence is by ultraviolet absorption. This method is rapid and precise and in addition can often serve to identify the successive fractions directly.

Bases and nucleosides

Since each of the purine and pyrimidine bases has at least one ionizable group, all of them exist as charged forms under some conditions. In most cases both cationic and anionic forms can occur. Similar statements can be made in the case of the nucleosides.

Both cation- and anion-exchange have been used.

Uracil and thymine, as well as the corresponding nucleosides, do not occur in cationic form and are not bound appreciably by cation-exchangers. Hypoxanthine and inosine are also retained weakly. Thus, these bases are generally eluted first from a cation exchanger under acid conditions. However, the pK of the base is not the sole determinant. Thus, the order of elution of the bases of RNA from Dowex-50 by 2N HCl is: uracil, cytosine, guanine, and adenine[15]. Purines are generally retained more strongly than pyrimidines under comparable conditions of charge. Because of the acid lability of the glycosidic linkage of purine nucleosides, cation-exchange is not normally the method of choice for resolution of the nucleosides.

For elution from anion-exchangers the method of charge adjustment has often been used. A dilute solution, buffered in the zone of the pK's involved, replaces the concentrated acid employed in the cation-exchange technique.

The order of elution of the five bases occurring normally in the natural nucleic acids generally follows that of their enolic pK's, although inversions do occur as a result of the stronger binding of purines.

For example, the five bases may be resolved by elution from Dowex-1-Cl$^-$ with 0.2 M NH$_4$OH–NH$_4$Cl, pH 10.6[15]. The order of elution is: cytosine, uracil thymine, guanine, and adenine.

Nucleosides show generally similar behavior.

Nucleotides

Most of the work upon the separation of nucleotides has utilized anion-exchange. The relative strength of retention of the various nucleotides by the resin is primarily dependent upon their state of charge. Adenylic, cytidylic, and guanylic acids exist as zwitterions under moderately acidic conditions, while uridylic, thymidylic, and inosinic acids exist as anions over the entire range of pH. It would thus be expected that, at neutral or alkaline pH, all of the nucleotides would be strongly bound and that, under acidic conditions, the latter three nucleotides would be retained more strongly than the former three. However, superimposed upon the purely electrostatic factors, there is a pronounced influence of the character of the base. In general, the purine nucleotides are retained more strongly, under comparable conditions, than are the pyrimidine nucleotides.

The absorption of the nucleotide mixture by the column is usually carried out at neutral or alkaline pH. The resin is usually used in the chloride form. As a general rule the pH should be above 6 and the concentration of competing ions less than 0.02 M. If the initial solution is strongly alkaline it is desirable to wash the column with 0.01 M NH$_4$Cl until the pH of the effluent drops to 7 or less. This serves to remove absorbed carbonate, which can otherwise produce CO_2 under acidic conditions and thereby disrupt the column. The concentration of nucleotide should not be greater than about 5 mg/ml of the column.

There are available a number of elution systems. It is in general impossible to separate all of the nucleotides, including the various isomers, with a single influent. The concentration of hydrogen ion or of competing ions must generally be increased, either stepwise or continuously by a mixing device.

Elution with a series of dilute HCl solutions is adequate to resolve the different mononucleotides and even to separate the isomeric forms in some cases. A representative separation of the ribonucleotides of an RNA digest, as described by Cohn, is as follows[16,17]:

(*i*) The alkaline RNA hydrolysate (0.5 M NaOH at 37° for 17 h) is diluted with water to an NaOH molarity of 0.02 and a nucleotide concentration of 1–2 mg/ml.

(*ii*) The diluted digest is run through a Dowex-1-Cl⁻ column, of bed size 6 cm × 0.72 cm². Ammonium chloride (0.01 M) is passed through the column until the pH of the effluent reaches neutrality.

(*iii*) Elution is carried out with increasing concentrations of HCl. The order of appearance of the nucleotides in the effluent is as follows[16] (Table 32):

TABLE 32

Molarity HCl	Volume added (ml)	Nucleotide
0.001	400–600	cytidylic acids
0.003	0–400	2′-adenylic acid
	400–1000	3′-adenylic acid
0.005	0–600	uridylic acids
0.007	0–600	2′-guanylic
	600–1600	3′-guanylic

The flow rates may be as high as 3 ml/cm²/min.

A constant concentration of HCl has also been used for elution of the ribonucleotides by Cohn[17]. No resolution of the isomeric nucleotides occurs under these conditions. A Dowex-2-Cl⁻ column, of dimensions 2.5 cm × 0.94 cm², was used. The absorption of the mixture of nucleotides was brought about under conditions similar to those described above. The influent solution was 0.003 N HCl. It was passed through the column at a flow rate of 0.8 ml/min. The order of appearance of the nucleotides was as follows[17] (Table 33):

TABLE 33

Volume of 0.003 N HCl (ml)	Nucleotide
0–200	cytidylic acids
200–600	adenylic acids
1500–2100	uridylic acids
2500–4500	guanylic acids

The cytidylic and uridylic isomers are usually not well resolved by the HCl system. In general it is advantageous to use a somewhat higher pH for separation of the isomeric nucleotides. Formate and acetate systems are convenient with regard to pH control. It is usually preferable to make a preliminary separation of the nucleotides with an HCl system and then separate the groups of isomers in a separate operation.

Some systems which have been used successfully for resolution of isomeric ribonucleotides are cited[18,19] in Table 34.

TABLE 34

Ribonucleotide	Column	Solvent	Order of Appearance
cytidylic	Dowex-1	0.02 M formic acid	5'-, 2'-, 3'-
adenylic	Dowex-1	0.02 M NaCl, 0.01 M NaOAc, pH 5.5	5'-, 2'-, 3'-
	Dowex-1	0.15 M formic acid	5'-, 2'-, 3'-
uridylic	Dowex-1	0.0004 M formic acid, 0.04 M Na formate	5'-, 2'-, 3'-
guanylic	Dowex-1	0.1 M formic acid, 0.1 M Na formate	5'-, 2'-, 3'-

The separation of the deoxyribonucleotides is generally governed by entirely similar principles. Cohn[18] has utilized stepwise elution from Dowex-1 with 0.002–0.005 N HCl to separate the nucleotides of an enzymatic digest of DNA.

Appendix H

Preparation of Diethylaminoethyl Cellulose

Peterson and Sober have described a procedure for the preparation of diethylaminoethyl (DEAE) cellulose suitable for use in the chromatography of oligonucleotides[20]. Wood cellulose was found to be preferable as a starting material. The commercial material Solka-Floc, among other products, is convenient. The technique is as follows:

(*i*) 40 g of NaOH in 170 ml water is stirred into 60 g of Solka-Floc. The mixture is allowed to stand in an ice bath for 30 min, with occasional stirring.

(*ii*) A solution of 35 g of recrystallized 2-chlorotriethylamine hydrochloride in 45 ml water is added stepwise.

(*iii*) After thorough blending the mixture is immersed in an 80–85° oil bath for 35 min and stirred occasionally.

(*iv*) The product is then cooled in an ice bath. To it are added 250 ml of 2 *M* NaCl with stirring.

(*v*) The thick suspension is filtered and the filter cake washed with 1 *M* NaOH until the filtrate is no longer deeply colored.

(*vi*) The product is resuspended in 350 ml of 1 *M* HCl and immediately filtered.

(*vii*) The filter cake is washed successively with 250 ml portions of 1 *M* NaOH, 1 *M* HCl, and 1 *M* NaOH. It is then suspended in 250 ml of 1 *M* NaOH and diluted with water to 3 l.

(*viii*) After standing overnight the turbid supernatant is decanted and the sediment washed 6 times with water by decantation to remove the smaller particles.

(*ix*) The sediment is filtered and then washed with 200 ml each of 95% and then absolute ethanol.

(*x*) The product is ground into a powder, after partial drying, and then dried *in vacuo*. This material has about 1 mequiv. of substituent per g. The degree of substitution can, of course, be controlled by varying the amount of reagent added initially.

Appendix I

Fractionation of Oligonucleotides with DEAE Cellulose

Tener *et al.*, have described the fractionation of a mixture of thymidine (3′,5′) oligonucleotides on a column of DEAE cellulose (0.65 mequiv./g)[21]. The procedure was as follows:

(*i*) The DEAE-cellulose was washed successively with 0.1 *M* NaOH and then 0.1 *M* HCl (2 l per 50 g cellulose). This cycle was repeated twice and the exchanger then washed free of acid with water.

(*ii*) The sediment was poured into the column (8 cm × 0.9 cm²) as a slurry and allowed to settle.

(*iii*) The mixture of oligonucleotides (Na salts) was applied to the column in water solution. The total concentration was about 3 g/liter.

(*iv*) After a water wash, elution was carried out with a linear gradient technique, using 500 ml water in the mixing chamber and an equal volume of 0.4 *M* lithium chloride containing 0.04 *M* lithium acetate, pH 5.

(*v*) A flow rate of 1 ml/min was maintained. The order of elution was di-, tri-, tetra-, pentanucleotide.

Appendix J

Paper Chromatographic Separation of Nucleotides and Their Components

The general procedures of paper chromatography have been so extensively reviewed [26] that it is unnecessary to do more here than mention a few points of particular interest for the above systems.

Whatman No. 1 filter paper appears to be the most generally satisfactory for nucleic acid derivatives. Both ascending and descending chromatograms have been widely used.

The most convenient means of spot detection is based on the quenching of the characteristic ultraviolet light-excited fluorescence of the filter paper, as a consequence of the strong absorption of purine or pyrimidine derivatives. Thus, when exposed to short wavelength (< 260 mμ) ultraviolet radiation and observed in a darkened room, the spots appear as dark areas on a light background. In practice, a Mineralight S–L lamp is adequate for this purpose.

TABLE 35

R_F VALUES OF NUCLEOSIDES AND BASES

Solvent	a	b	c	d	e	f
Reference	22	23, 23	23, 26	22	22	24, 26
Direction	as.	des.	des.	as.	as.	as.
adenine		0.38	0.33			0.40
uracil		0.31	0.39			0.33
guanine		0.15	0.13			0.15
cytosine		0.22	0.26			0.28
thymine			0.56			0.50
hypoxanthine		0.26	0.30			0.19
adenosine	0.76	0.20	0.12	0.63	0.13	0.33
uridine	0.47	0.17	0.25	0.73	0.54	
guanosine	0.43	0.15	0.17	0.56	0.34	0.10
cytidine	0.59	0.12	0.18	0.65	0.56	0.15
inosine						0.08
deoxyadenosine		0.35				0.41
deoxyguanosine		0.21				0.18
deoxycytidine		0.23				0.26
thymidine		0.51				0.48

Solvents for bases and nucleosides

For these relatively non-polar compounds aqueous butanol, with or without added ammonia, is one of the most commonly used solvents. Other useful systems are based on isobutyric acid and on isopropanol.

Some frequently used solvent mixtures, with their characteristic R_F values (for Whatman No. 1) are as follows (Table 35).

Solvents for nucleotides

The charged nucleotides require relatively polar solvent mixtures to permit reasonably rapid movement. Some useful systems are cited below (Table 36).

TABLE 36

R_F VALUES FOR NUCLEOTIDES

Solvent	a	d	e	g	h	i	j
Reference	22	22	22	26, 25	26, 27	22	26
Direction	as.	as.	as.	des.	des.	as.	des.
5'-AMP	0.45	0.15	0.29	0.69			0.43
3'-AMP				0.67	0.16		0.48
2'-AMP				0.74	0.26		0.48
ADP	0.30	0.07	0.37	0.77			
ATP	0.20	0.04	0.48	0.83			
5'-CMP	0.28	0.13	0.67				
CDP	0.13	0.07	0.71				
CTP	0.07	0.04	0.77				
5'-UMP	0.23	0.18	0.64				
UDP	0.13	0.09	0.71				
UTP	0.08	0.04	0.77				
5'-GMP	0.13	0.09	0.50			0.31	
GDP	0.09	0.06	0.58			0.24	
GTP	0.05	0.03	0.61			0.18	

Solvents for oligonucleotides

Heppel and co-workers[28] have developed chromatographic techniques for separating the lower adenine and uracil oligonucleotides (Table 37). Some of the R_F values cited in Table 38 are relative to that for 3'-AMP.

References p. 379

TABLE 37

R_F VALUES OF SOME OLIGONUCLEOTIDES

Solvent	k
Reference	28
Direction	des.

R_F (rel. to 3'-AMP)	3'-AMP	1.0
	5'-AMP	1.98
	pApA	0.56
	pApApA	0.19
	pApApApA	0.09
	3'-UMP	4.8
	U (2' : 3')p	3.62
R_F	U (2' : 3')p	0.47
	UpU (2' : 3')p	0.28
	UpUpU (2' : 3')p	0.18
	UpUpUpU (2' : 3')p	0.10
	UpUp	0.49
	UpUpUp	0.31
	UpUpUpUp	0.22

TABLE 38

Solvent	Composition (by volume)	Solvent	Composition (by volume)
a	66% isobutyric acid 1% conc. NH₄OH 33% H₂O	g	5% (by weight) Na₂HPO₄, saturated wtih isoamyl alcohol
b	86% n-butanol 14% H₂O	h	79% saturated (NH))₂SO₄ 19% 0.1 M buffer, pH 6.0 2% isopropanol
c	77% n-butanol 10% formic acid 13% H₂O	i	57% isobutyric acid 4% conc. NH₄OH 39% H₂O
d	70% 95% ethanol 30% 1 M NH₄OAc, pH 7.4	j	68% isopropanol 16.4% conc. HCl (sp. gr. 1. 19) 15.6% H₂O
e	97% 0.1 M sodium phosphate, pH 6.8, plus 600 g/l (NH₄)₂SO₄ 3% n-propanol	k	80% saturated (NH ₄)₂SO₄ 2% isopropanol 18% 1 M NaOAc
f	99% n-butanol, saturated with H₂O 1% conc. NH₄OH		

Appendix K

Assays for Polyribonucleotide Phosphorylase

I. RELEASE OF INORGANIC PHOSPHATE

A. The following assay procedure was used by Grunberg-Manago and co-workers[29] for the polynucleotide phosphorylase of *A. vinelandii:*

reaction volume:	1 ml
temperature:	30°
reaction mixture:	0.01 M ADP
	0.005 M MgCl$_2$
	0.10 M tris (hydroxymethylamino) methane plus enzyme
pH:	8.1
reaction times:	5 and 15 min

The amount of enzyme in the reaction mixture should be adjusted so as to assure a linear time course of the reaction during the period of assay. The reaction is stopped by the addition of 0.1 ml of 40% trichloroacetic acid. After centrifugation to remove the acid-insoluble material, the amount of inorganic phosphate released is determined by the method of Lohmann and Jendrassik[30]. The rate of the reaction is determined by the difference in the amount of orthophosphate released in 5 and in 15 min.

The enzyme unit defined by Grunberg-Manago *et al.*, is the amount of enzyme in 1 ml which will catalyze the release of 1 micromole of orthophosphate in 15 min at 30°. This unit is equal to 1.1 microunits, as defined in Chapter 4.

B. Beers[31] has recommended the following procedure for the polynucleotide phosphorylase of *M. lysodeikticus:*

reaction volume:	3 ml
temperature:	37°
reaction mixture:	$6 \cdot 10^{-4}$, $1.4 \cdot 10^{-3}$, and $2 \cdot 10^{-3}$ M ADP
	0.0013 M MgCl$_2$
	0.2 M KCl
	0.02 M tris (hydroxymethylamino) methane plus enzyme
pH:	9.0
reaction time:	20 min

The reaction is stopped by the addition of 1 ml of 10% perchloric or trichloroacetic acid and the acid-insoluble material is removed by centrifugation. The amount of orthophosphate released is determined by the method of Fiske and Subbarow[32].

References p. 379

A control is run for each concentration of substrate by adding the acid prior to the addition of substrate.

The data are plotted according to the Lineweaver-Burk equation and the maximum velocity is obtained by extrapolation[33]. The enzyme unit, as has been defined in Chapter 4, is the amount of enzyme in 1 ml which will catalyze the release of 1 millimole of orthophosphate from ADP in one second. A milli- and a microunit have also been defined and are equal to 10^{-3} and 10^{-6} times the unit as defined above. The level of activity in the usual assay mixture will be of the order of microunits[29, 31, 34].

II. NUCLEOTIDE INCORPORATION

A. Beers[35] has employed the following procedure for the polynucleotide phosphorylase from *M. lysodeikticus:*

> reaction volume: 2 ml
> temperature: 37°
> reaction mixture: $6 \cdot 10^{-4}$, $1.4 \cdot 10^{-3}$, and $2 \cdot 10^{-3}$ M ADP
>   0.0013 M MgCl₂
>   0.2 M NaCl
>   0.02 M tris (hydroxymethylamino) methane plus enzyme
> pH: 9.0
> reaction time: 20 min

The reaction is stopped by the addition of 1 ml of 10% perchloric acid. The acid-insoluble material is collected by centrifugation, washed once with an additional 2 ml of 10% perchloric acid, and twice with 95% ethanol. The precipitate is suspended in 3 ml of 0.1 M tris, pH 8.0, and allowed to stand, with occasional shaking, for 15 min, to ensure complete solubilization of the polymer. Buffers of higher pH should be avoided, to prevent any solubilization of the denatured protein. The solution is clarified by centrifugation and the optical density is read at 257 mμ.

For highly purified enzyme preparations it is necessary to add, prior to the addition of the perchloric acid, approximately 0.1 ml of 0.2% casein recently precipitated with acid. An optical blank, which is dependent upon the polynucleotide present in the enzyme preparation, is determined by adding the acid prior to the addition of the substrate. The optical density of the blank should be less than 0.05.

The rate of formation of polymer may be determined from the rate of increase in optical density. The measured optical densities can be converted to concentrations (moles AMP/l) by the use of the extinction coefficient, ε_p, reported by Warner, which is 9,800. A more precise method involves the hydrolysis of the polymer in 1 N NaOH for 24 h at room temperature and the measurement of the optical density of the hydrolysate, a mixture of adenylic acids a and b, at 259 mμ. The molar extinction coefficient, ε_p, is 15,400.

B. A variant of the above procedure uses a direct analysis for phosphorus to determine the amount of polymer formed. In place of 0.2 *M* NaCl, 0.2 *M* KCl is used in the reaction mixture. After precipitation of the acid-insoluble material, the sediment is collected by centrifugation, washed again with acid, and digested with 0.2 ml of 70% perchloric acid over a bunsen flame (in the hood). The digest is diluted to 2.0 ml with water and the inorganic phosphate determined by the method of Fiske and Subbarow[32].

The method of treating the data is the same as in method I B.

C. Littauer and Kornberg[36] have employed the following method for the polynucleotide phorphorylase from *E. coli:*

reaction volume:	0.25 ml
temperature:	37°
reaction mixture:	0.0032 *M* ADP
	$1.8 \cdot 10^{-4}$ *M* ADP-8-[14]C
	(7.8 · 10⁵ c.p.m./micromole)
	0.004 *M* MgCl₂
	0.2 *M* glycylglycine plus enzyme
pH:	7.4
reaction time:	10 min

The reaction is stopped by immersing the reaction mixture in an ice bath. Then 0.5 ml of inert carrier nucleic acid, consisting of a 1 : 20 dilution with H₂O of crude *E. coli* extract (Appendix L, step *ix*), is added, followed by 0.25 ml of 7% perchloric acid. The acid insoluble material is collected by centrifugation, washed twice with 1 ml portions of 1% perchloric acid, and once with 1.0 ml of 0.01 *N* HCl. The washed precipitate is dissolved in 0.4 ml of 0.05 *M* KOH. A 0.10-ml aliquot is removed and dried on a planchet, preparatory to assaying for radio-activity.

The enzyme unit defined by Littauer and Kornberg is the amount of enzyme that will catalyze the incorporation of 1 micromole of ADP into the polymer species in one hour. It is equivalent to 0.3 microunits, as defined in Chapter 4.

D. Littauer and Kornberg[36] have also used the following modification of the above method:

reaction volume:	0.25 ml
temperature:	37°
reaction mixture:	$4 \cdot 10^{-3}$ *M* ATP
	$4 \cdot 10^{-4}$ *M* ATP-8-[14]C
	(3.8 · 10⁵ c.p.m./micromole)
	0.001 *M* ADP
	$4 \cdot 10^{-3}$ *M* Mg⁺⁺
	0.08 *M* tris
	yeast adenylate kinase (1 unit)
	phosphorylase
pH:	8.0
reaction time:	10 min

The subsequent steps are the same as described in II C.

III.   PHOSPHOROLYSIS

The following procedure is that of Hendley and Beers[37] and has been used for the polynucleotide phosphorylase from *M. lysodeikticus*.

reaction volume:	2.2 ml
temperature:	37°
reaction mixture:	0.006% poly A
	$1.4 \cdot 10^{-3}$ M $MgCl_2$
	0.14 M KCl
	0.07 M tris
	$1.4 \cdot 10^{-2}$ M K_2HPO_4
	plus enzyme
pH:	8.5

The reaction is stopped by the addition of 1-ml aliquots of the reaction mixture to 0.5 ml 5% perchloric acid. After standing 10–20 min at room temperature, the mixture is clarified by centrifugation and the concentration of ADP in the supernatant determined by absorption at 260 mμ, or by the orcinol method[38]. For highly purified preparations of enzyme, 0.1 ml of 0.2% casein recently precipitated with acid is added prior to the addition of the perchloric acid.

The enzyme unit is defined as the amount of enzyme in 1 ml of reaction mixture which will catalyze the release of 1 millimole of ADP in one second. Milli- and microunits are defined as before.

IV. ^{32}P EXCHANGE

A. Grunberg-Manago *et al.*[29], have specified the following procedure for the polynucleotide phosphorylase of *A. vinelandii*.

reaction volume:	1.0 ml
temperature:	30°
reaction mixture:	$2.5 \cdot 10^{-3}$ M ADP, $3 \cdot 6 \cdot 10^{-3}$ M KH_2PO_4–K_2HPO_4
	(labeled with ^{32}P, 1–$2 \cdot 10^5$ c.p.m./micromole)
	$5 \cdot 10^{-3}$ M $MgCl_2$
	0.1 M tris
	plus enzyme
pH:	8.1
reaction time:	15 min

The reaction is stopped by the addition of 0.1 ml of 40% trichloroacetic acid and the acid-insoluble material is removed by centrifugation. The supernatant is made up to 3.0 ml with water; to which is added 0.3 ml of 10.0 M H_2SO_4, 1.5 ml of 5% ammonium molybdate, and 5.0 ml of isobutanol. The two-phase system is thoroughly mixed for one minute by the passage of a slow stream of air through the mixture. The isobutanol layer is removed and discarded. It contains the inorganic orthophosphate. The aqueous phase, which should be clear, is extracted with ether, and an aliquot (1.0 ml) removed for measurement of radioactivity. The micromoles of phosphate incorporated are determined by the equation:

$$\text{micromoles P incorporated} = \frac{\text{c.p.m. incorporated} \times (\mu\text{moles ADP} + \mu\text{moles P}_i)}{\text{c.p.m. phosphate (initial)}}$$

B. Littauer and Kornberg have used the following procedure for the nucleotide phosphorylase of *E. coli*.

reaction volume:	0.5 ml
temperature:	37°
reaction mixture:	$5 \cdot 10^{-4}$ M KH$_2$PO$_4$–K$_2$HPO$_4$, labeled with ^{32}P
	($5.2 \cdot 10^6$ c.p.m./micromole)
	$4 \cdot 10^{-3}$ M MgCl$_2$
	$8 \cdot 10^{-4}$ M nucleoside diphosphate
	0.2 M glycylglycine plus enzyme
pH:	7.4
reaction time:	20 min

The reaction is stopped by immersing the reaction mixture in an ice bath. To it are added 0.5 ml of 5% perchloric acid and 0.1 ml of acid-washed Norite A suspension (10% dry weight) to adsorb the nucleotides. The Norite is collected by centrifugation and washed three times with 2.5-ml portions of water. It is then suspended in 0.8 ml of 50% ethanol, containing 3 ml of concentrated ammonia per liter. A 0.2-ml aliquot of this suspension is placed on a planchet and its radioactivity is determined. A self-absorption factor of 1.15 is included in the calculation of the radioactivity. The number of micromoles of phosphate incorporated is computed in the following manner:

$$\frac{\text{micromoles P}}{\text{incorporated}} = \frac{\text{c. p. m. in ADP}}{\text{initial specific activity of P}_i}$$

Appendix L

The Preparation of Polynucleotide Phosphorylase from E. coli

The following procedure is that of Littauer and Kornberg[36].

(*i*) The medium for the growth of *E. coli* has the following composition:

1%	Difco dehydrated yeast extract
1%	glucose
2.18%	K$_2$HPO$_4$
1.70%	KH$_2$PO$_4$
20 mg/l	Dow-Corning Antifoam A
pH:	6.8 – 7.0

(*ii*) The medium is autoclaved, glucose being autoclaved separately and added to the cooled medium.

(*iii*) Fifteen liters of medium in a 20-l pyrex bottle are inoculated with 1.5 l of a 14–16 h culture of *E. coli* strain B.

(*iv*) The inoculated medium is incubated at 37° with vigorous forced aeration until the end of the logarithmic growth phase (3–4 h).

(*v*) The cells are harvested in a Sharples supercentrifuge. About 8 g of wet cells are obtained per liter. They are then washed with 4 volumes of cold 0.9% KCl.

(*vi*) As soon as is possible after harvesting, the washed cells (about 170 g) are suspended in a total volume of 680 ml of 0.05 M glycylglycine buffer, pH 7.4 and sonically ruptured by exposure for 10 min to a Raytheon 10 kc oscillator at 6–8°.

(*vii*) The sonically treated suspension is centrifuged for 20 min at 10,000 g in a Servall centrifuge. The supernatant solution is discarded.

(*viii*) The precipitate is resuspended in the buffer of step (*vi*) to a total volume of 680 ml and subjected to sonic oscillation, as before, for 30 min.

(*ix*) The suspension is centrifuged for 20 min at 10,000 g in a Servall centrifuge. The precipitate is discarded and the supernatant saved for further purification.

(*x*) To 615 ml of the supernatant, 31 ml of 1 M MnCl$_2$ are added with stirring at 0–3°. After 30 min stirring, the solution is clarified by centrifugation for 20 min at 10,000 g in a Servall centrifuge at 0–3°. The precipitate is discarded.

(*xi*) To the supernatant, 61 ml of 1% protamine sulfate are added, with stirring over a period of 10 min at 0–3°.

(*xii*) The precipitate is collected by centrifugation and the supernatant discarded.

(*xiii*) The precipitate is suspended in 200 ml of 0.05 M phosphate, pH 7.5, at 0–3°. It is then centrifuged for 20 min at 10,000 g in a Servall centrifuge. The supernatant is dialyzed overnight *vs* 6 l of 0.9% KCl at 0–3°.

(*xiv*) To 200 ml of the protamine eluate of step (*xiii*) are added 4 ml of 1 M potassium acetate (pH 5.5) and then 1.2 ml of 0.5 M ZnCl$_2$ (adjusted to pH 5.5 with acetic acid) at 0–3°.

(*xv*) After 10 min standing the solution is clarified by 3 min centrifugation at 10,000 g. To the supernatant, 44 ml of 50% ethanol ($-15°$) are added over a 7-min interval, during which time the temperature of the mixture is lowered to $-2°$. The precipitate is removed by centrifugation for 3 min at 10,000 g and discarded.

(*xvi*) To the supernatant 52 ml of 50% ethanol are added as before, the temperature being maintained at $-2°$ to $-4°$. The precipitate is collected by centrifugation at 10,000 g, as before.

(*xvii*) The precipitate from (*xvi*) is dissolved at 0–3° in 0.05 M tris buffer, pH 8.0, to a total volume of 67 ml. To the solution is added 0.5 M acetic acid dropwise, to pH 5.5, and then 0.40 ml of 0.5 M ZnCl$_2$. After 10 min the solution is clarified by centrifugation at 10,000 g.

(*xviii*) To the supernatant from (*xvii*) are added 13.5 ml of 50% ethanol ($-15°$) during a 7-min interval. The temperature of the mixture is lowered to $-2°$. The precipitate is collected by centrifugation at 10,000 g at 3°.

(*xix*) The precipitate is dissolved in 66 ml of 0.05 *M* tris, pH 8.0, frozen, and stored at $-10°$.

It is of crucial importance that the temperature remain low throughout steps (*ix*) to (*xix*). It is also important that step (*vi*) be commenced as soon as possible after harvesting the cells. The final product has a specific activity of the order of 7 microunits/mg or 7 milliunits/g.

Appendix M

Assays for Deoxyribonucleotide Polymerase

Polymerization

The following method is that of Lehman *et al.*[39], and was used for the polymerase from *E. coli*.

reaction volume:	0.3 ml
temperature:	37°
reaction mixture:	$1.67 \cdot 10^{-5}$ *M* ATP
	$3.33 \cdot 10^{-5}$ *M* GTP
	$1.67 \cdot 10^{-5}$ *M* CTP
	$1.67 \cdot 10^{-5}$ *M* TTP, labeled with ^{32}P
	($1.5 \cdot 10^6$ c.p.m. per micromole)
	0.067 *M* glycine
	0.0067 *M* $MgCl_2$
	0.001 *M* 2-mercaptoethanol
	0.03 mg/ml thymus DNA plus enzyme
pH:	9.2
reaction time:	30 min

Dilutions of the enzyme are made with 0.05 *M* tris buffer, pH 7.5, containing 0.1 mg thymus DNA per ml.

The reaction is stopped by immersing the reaction mixture in an ice bath. A 0.2-ml solution of thymus DNA (2.5 mg/ml) is added as a carrier. The DNA is precipitated by the addition of 0.5 ml of ice-cooled 1 *N* perchloric acid. The precipitate is homogenized with a glass pestle, 2 ml of distilled water are added and the precipitate dispersed. The precipitate is then collected by centrifugation, dissolved in 0.3 ml of 0.2 *N* NaOH, reprecipitated by the addition of 0.4 ml of cold 1 *N* perchloric acid, and redispersed after the addition of 2 ml of cold water. This process is repeated once. Finally, the DNA is dissolved in 0.2 ml of 0.1 *N* NaOH, the solution dried and the radioactivity determined.

The enzyme unit was defined by Lehman and co-workers as the amount of enzyme in the 0.3-ml reaction mixture which will catalyze the incorporation of 10 mμ-moles of the labeled deoxynucleotide into the acid-insoluble product in 30 min. It equals 0.006 microunits, as defined in Chapter 4.

Appendix N

The Preparation of the Deoxynucleotide Polymerase of E. coli

The following procedure is that of Lehman *et al.*[39].

(*i*) The medium for the growth of *E. coli* is prepared with the following composition:

$$1.1\% \text{ K}_2\text{HPO}_4$$
$$0.85\% \text{ K H}_2\text{PO}_4$$
$$0.6\% \text{ Difco yeast extract}$$
$$1\% \text{ Glucose}$$

(*ii*) The medium is autoclaved and inoculated with *E. coli* strain B. 60-l volumes were utilized by the above workers in a large Rinco growth tank. The medium is aerated vigorously.

(*iii*) The cells are chilled by the addition of ice and harvested with a Sharples supercentrifuge about 2 h after the end of the logarithmic growth phase.

(*iv*) The collected cells are suspended in 0.5% NaCl – 0.5% KCl (3 ml/g of packed cells), homogenized in a Waring Blendor, centrifuged, and stored at $-12°$. The cells are stable for several weeks under these conditions. All subsequent operations are carried out at $0°-3°$, unless otherwise specified.

(*v*) The cells are suspended in 0.05 M glycylglycine, pH 7.0 (4 ml/g cells) and disrupted by treatment for 15 min with a Raytheon 10 kc sonic oscillator.

(*vi*) The suspension is centrifuged for 15 min at 12,000 g and the supernatant collected. The protein content is measured and adjusted to a concentration of 20 mg/ml by addition of the above glycylglycine buffer.

(*vii*) 8.5-l quantities of the solution of (*vi*) are treated as follows. To a 525-ml batch are added an equal volume of 0.05 M tris buffer, pH 7.5, and then 81 ml of 5% streptomycin sulfate. After 10 min the precipitate is collected by centrifugation at 10,000 g. The precipitates from four batches are combined.

(*viii*) The combined precipitate is suspended in 0.05 M phosphate buffer, pH 7.4, to a total volume of 430 ml for the precipitate from each 2.1 l of the solution of step (*vi*). The suspension is homogenized for 30 min at low speed in a Waring Blendor.

(*ix*) The homogenate from step (*viii*) is centrifuged for 2 h at 78,000 g in a Spinco model L preparative ultracentrifuge and the supernatant collected.

(*x*) To 1.5 l of the supernatant from step (*ix*) are added 15 ml of 0.3 M MgCl$_2$ and 1.5 ml of pancreatic deoxyribonuclease (100 μg/ml). This mixture is incubated at 37° for about 5 h until 85%-90% of the ultraviolet-absorbing material is rendered acid-soluble. As a test for completion of the reaction, the optical density at 260 mμ of an aliquot is determined before and after precipitation with an equal volume of cold 1 N perchloric acid.

(*xi*) The digest is dialyzed for 16 h *vs* 24 l of 0.01 M tris, pH 7.5, and then clarified by centrifugation for 5 min at 10,000 *g*.

(*xii*) To 1.5 l of the supernatant from (*xi*) are added 195 ml of aged c γ alumina gel (15 mg dry weight per ml). The latter is prepared as specified by Willstatter and Kraut[40]. The mixture is stirred for 5 min and then centrifuged. The supernatant is discarded and the gel washed with 400 ml of 0.02 M phosphate buffer, pH 7.2.

(*xiii*) The gel is then eluted twice with 400-ml portions of 0.10 M phosphate, pH 7.4, and the eluates combined.

(*xiv*) To the combined eluates (800 ml) are added 16 ml of 5 N acetic acid and then 480 g of ammonium sulfate. After 10 min at 0° the precipitate is collected by centrifugation for 30 min at 30,000 *g* and dissolved in 90 ml of 0.02 M phosphate buffer, pH 7.2.

(*xv*) To 90 ml of the solution of step (*xiv*) are added 9 ml of 1 M phosphate, pH 6.5, 0.90 ml of 0.10 M 2-mercaptoethanol, and then 24.7 g of ammonium sulfate. After 10 min at 0°, the precipitate is removed by centrifugation for 10 min at 12,000 *g*.

(*xvi*) To the supernatant from (*xv*) 9.6 g of ammonium sulfate are added. After 10 min at 0° the precipitate is collected by centrifugation at 12,000 *g* for 10 min. The precipitate is then dissolved in 9 ml of 0.02 M phosphate, pH 7.2.

(*xvii*) A column (11 cm $\times$ 1 cm^2) of diethylaminoethyl cellulose is prepared according to the method of Peterson and Sober[20]. The column is equilibrated with 0.02 M K_2HPO_4 prior to use.

(*xviii*) 1.2 ml of the solution of (*xvi*) is diluted to 8.0 ml with 0.02 M K_2HPO_4 and passed thru the column at a rate of 12 ml/h. The column is washed with 3.0 ml of the same buffer and eluted with pH 6.5 phosphate as follows (flow rate of 9 ml/h):

> 8 ml of 0.05 M
> 10 ml of 0.10 M
> 3 ml of 0.20 M
> 4 ml of 0.20 M

The final elution contains most of the activity.

References p. 379

Appendix O

Preparation of Polynucleotide Phosphorylase from A. vinelandii [41]

(*i*) The medium for the growth of *A. vinelandii* has the following composition:

0.064%	K₂HPO₄
0.016%	KH₂PO₄
0.02%	MgSO₄.7H₂O
0.02%	NaCl
0.005%	CaSO₄.2H₂O
2%	sucrose
0.0002%	Na₂MoO₄
0.0016%	ferric citrate (3 mg Fe/l)

(*ii*) Inoculates from agar slants are transferred to 150-ml portions of the medium in 1-l Erlenmeyer flasks.

(*iii*) The culture is incubated at 32° on a rotatory shaker at top speed for 16–18 h. The yield of cells is 2.0–2.5 g/l (wet weight).

(*iv*) For large-scale production of cells, the above procedure may be stepped up in scale, either by increasing the number of shake flasks or by using larger bottles with suitable aeration systems. If large bottles are used, they should be inoculated with material from the shake flasks. The inoculum from the shake flasks should be 100 ml per 20 l of medium in the bottles. The large bottle temperature should be kept at 28°.

(*v*) The cells are harvested in a refrigerated Sharples supercentrifuge after about 20 h of growth. The yield of cells should be about 2 g/l (wet weight).

(*vi*) 15-g lots of fresh (or frozen) cells are suspended in 10 ml of distilled water and treated with a sonic oscillator (9.0 kc Raytheon oscillator) for 30 min at or near 0°.

(*vii*) The disrupted cells are extracted with 80 ml of cold water and centrifuged in a Servall angle centrifuge at 20,000 g for 1 h at, or near, 4°. From 100 g of intact cells there are obtained 500 ml of clear greenish-brown supernatant containing 20 mg protein per ml. The 280 mμ/260 mμ absorption ratio should be approximately 0.6.

(*viii*) The enzyme solution is diluted with water to a 1% protein concentration and then made 0.01 M with potassium phosphate buffer, pH 7.4, and 0.001 M with versene (EDTA). To 1 l are added 246 g solid ammonium sulfate over a period of 1 h at 0°, with the pH kept at 7.4 by the addition of 1.0 M KOH. The precipitated material is collected by centrifugation at 20,000 g for 40–60 min and then discarded.

(*ix*) The supernatant is brought from 35% to 46% saturation with an additional

78 g ammonium sulfate and centrifuged as above. The precipitate is dissolved in 9.0 ml of 0.01 M potassium phosphate buffer, pH 7.4, and dialyzed overnight against 1.5 l of 0.033 M succinate buffer, pH 6.3, containing 0.0005 M cysteine. The volume increases to approximately 30 ml. The 280 mμ/260 mμ absorption ratio is approximately 0.80.

(*x*) The dialyzed solution is diluted with the above succinate buffer to a 1% protein concentration and cooled to 0°. To 275 ml enzyme are added 50 ml of absolute ethanol, cooled to $-15°$, and 7.0 ml of 0.1 M zinc acetate over a 40-min period. The final alcohol concentration is 15% (by volume); the concentration of the zinc acetate is 0.002 M. After stirring for 30–45 min, the mixture is centrifuged at $-12°$ for 1 h at 20,000 g. The precipitate is discarded.

(*xi*) An additional 33 ml of absolute alcohol and 51.5 ml of the zinc acetate solution (0.1 M) are added to the supernatant over a period of 30–45 min. The final concentration of ethanol is 20% (by volume); that of zinc acetate is 0.014 M. The mixture is stirred for an additional 30–45 min and centrifuged at 20,000 g at $-15°$. The precipitate is immediately dissolved in 12 ml of a mixture containing 0.1 M potassium phosphate buffer, pH 7.4, 0.01 M cysteine, and 0.03 M versene, and then dialyzed against 1 l of 0.01 M potassium phosphate buffer, pH 7.4, plus 0.001 M versene, at 0° overnight. The 280 mμ/260 mμ ratio is about 1.0.

(*xii*) The ethanol–zinc preparation is diluted with 0.01 M potassium phosphate buffer, pH 7.4, to 1% protein concentration. To 46.5 ml are added 0.58 ml of 1.0 M acetate buffer, pH 4.5, to bring the pH to 5.8. Calcium phosphate gel (Sigma Chemical Company, St. Louis, Lot no. 16-240) containing 9.5% tricalcium phosphate is diluted to contain 23 mg of tricalcium phosphate per ml.

(*xiii*) To the enzyme solution are added 5.5 ml of the diluted gel at 0°, over a period of 15 min. After an additional stirring for 20 min, the mixture is centrifuged at 20,000 g for 10 min at 4°. The precipitate is discarded. To the supernatant are added 11.0 ml of the calcium phosphate gel solution. The precipitate is collected by centrifugation as above and eluted at 0° with 6.0 ml of 0.1 M potassium phosphate buffer, pH 6.0. The eluate contains the enzyme. Before use the eluate is dialyzed against 2 l of 0.01 M potassium phosphate buffer, pH 7.4. All the preparations except the initial sonic extract can be kept stored in the frozen state for several months with little or no loss in activity.

Appendix P

Preparation of Polyribonucleotide Phosphorylase from M. lysodeikticus

I. GROWTH OF CELLS

(*i*) Cultures of *M. lysodeikticus* (American Type Culture Collection, #4698) are maintained on 2% agar slants containing the following: 1% yeast extract, 2% glucose, 0.87% K_2HPO_4, and 1% of a salt solution which contains 4% $MgSO_4 \cdot 7 H_2O$, 0.2% NaCl, 0.2% $FeSO_4 \cdot 7 H_2O$, and 0.16% $MnSO_4$. The pH of the medium is brought to approximately pH 8.0 with 1 *N* KOH before the 2% agar is added. Sterilization time should be limited to fifteen minutes of autoclaving at fifteen pounds per square inch pressure. Several transfers should be made until the growth rate is maximal, *i.e.* nearly complete in 24 h at room temperature. The cells can be stored on the agar slants in the deep freeze without loss of viability or of capacity for rapid growth rate for periods up to one year.

(*ii*) The first step in the large scale production of the cells is the preparation of a 24-h submerged culture in a series of Erlenmeyer flasks, each containing 90 ml of liquid medium prepared as follows. Into each of a pair of 250 ml wide-mouth Erlenmeyer flasks are placed 45 ml of either solution A or solution B. Solution A contains 4% glucose. Solution B contains 2% yeast extract, 0.85% $NaHCO_3$, and 2% of the above salt solution of step (*i*). The flasks are cottoned, stoppered, and autoclaved for fifteen minutes at fifteen pounds pressure. After cooling, the contents of flask A are added asceptically to flask B. The cells from a 24-h agar slant are suspended in sterile water or in a portion of the above liquid media and transferred to the shake flasks (one slant for 5 flasks). The cultures are agitated on a rotatory shaker for 24 h at room temperature, at the end of which time the growth should be luxuriant.

(*iii*) Into a five gallon Pyrex carboy are added 16 l of tap water, 136 g $NaHCO_3$, 160 g yeast extract, and 160 ml of the salt solution of step (*i*). The surface of the medium is sprayed with Dow Corning antifoam A spray. A one liter beaker serves to cover the opening and neck of the bottle. The contents are sterilized, either by autoclaving at 15 pounds pressure for 1 h, or by bringing the contents to a boil on two successive days. After cooling, a sterilized solution containing 320 grams of glucose in 400 ml of water is added asceptically. The contents of approximately 6 Erlenmeyer shake flasks are added after the homogeneity of the culture in each has been checked by microscopic examination. As a general rule, however, the characteristic odor of these cultures can be used as an index of their purity.

(*iv*) The medium is then aerated vigorously with a suitable cotton-filtered aeration system for 24–48 h at room temperature. The pH of the culture should not fall below 7 and preferably not below 8.0. A low pH indicates contamination by yeast or by a spore-forming bacillus. The cells are harvested with a Sharples centrifuge or some other continuous centrifuge equipment, such as the Servall or Lourds apparatus. The yield of cells should be approximately 3.5 g/l, based on dry weight of the cells.

II. PREPARATION OF ENZYME

Freshly harvested cells or frozen cells may be used, but better control is obtained if the cells are first acetone dried. Acetone-dried cells may be stored indefinitely in the deep freeze.

(*i*) 20 g of acetone-dried cells are suspended in 200 ml of 0.5% NaCl, brought to pH 8.0 with 1 *N* NaOH and to 37° in a water bath. 50 mg crystalline lysozyme (Worthington) dissolved in 2 ml of water is added and thoroughly mixed with the cell suspension. The suspension of cells is stirred occasionally during the lysis to ascertain the texture of the preparation. During lysis the color of the cell suspension darkens and the consistency thickens slightly. At approximately 10 min (plus or minus 5) the suspension sets like rennet-treated milk and breaks into lumps of "curd" when stirred. The mixture is stirred slowly for one or two minutes until a liquid phase begins to separate from the bulk of the material, not unlike the separation of the whey from curdled milk. This stage is accompanied by a failure of the cell debris to adhere to the sides of the vessel and by the appearance of a glistening texture to the curdy material. If the suspension becomes viscous, either lysis has been allowed to progress too far, the temperature was too low, the lysozyme concentration was too high, or the pH was too low. 100 ml of saturated ammonium sulfate (4°) is added to the lysed cells and mixed briefly. The preparation is then centrifuged at 20,000 *g* for 30 min at 4°.

(*ii*) The supernatant volume of the above preparation should be in the vicinity of 200–250 ml. Small volumes indicate that the lysis was allowed to proceed too far. Larger volumes may occur if the lysis is only partially effective. The color of the supernatant should be a clear brown, with a slight yellow tinge. An equal volume of saturated ammonium sulfate is added to the supernatant to precipitate the bulk of the polynucleotide phosphorylase enzyme. The precipitate is collected by centrifugation at 20,000 *g* for 30 min at 4° and is then dissolved in 20 ml of 0.1 *M* tris buffer, pH 8.0. The material is dialyzed against distilled water for 8 h and then lyophilized for storage in the deep freeze. This preparation is suitable for the synthesis of poly A. The 280 mμ/260 mμ absorption ratio is usually in the vicinity of 0.9 to 1.1.

(*iii*) The lyophilized material is dissolved in 0.1 *M* tris buffer, pH 8.0, at a concentration of 1 g/100 ml. To the solution are added 24.4 g solid ammonium sulfate to bring the concentration to 43% of saturation. The precipitated material is spun down at 20,000 g for 30 min and discarded. To each 100 ml of the supernatant is added 8.6 g of solid ammonium sulfate to bring the concentration to 57% of saturation. The precipitate is collected as before and dissolved in a small volume of 0.1 M tris, pH 8.0. The supernatant contains the bulk of the bacterial catalase, which may be further purified separately. The solution of polynucleotide phosphorylase is dialyzed for 8 h in the cold against the same buffer and stored in the deep freeze. The 280 mμ/260 mμ absorption ratio may be as high as 1.3.

III.   FURTHER TREATMENT FOR SPECIAL PURPOSES

(*i*) Any of the above preparations may be treated with Norite A charcoal to remove the bulk of their polynucleotide material. From 2 to 5 g of charcoal is added to each 100 ml of enzyme, in 0.1 M tris, pH 8.0, at a concentration of approximately 1%. After thorough mixing, the suspension is allowed to stand for 30 min before removal of the charcoal by centrifugation at 20,000 g for 10 min. The charcoal is washed with a volume of buffer equal to that lost in the charcoal sediment and the washings are added to the supernatant. This procedure is repeated several times until the 280 mμ/260mμ ratio reaches 1.6 to 1.7. Excessive treatment with Norite A reduces the total activity and the specific activity of the enzyme.

(*ii*) An alternative method for reducing the nucleotide content as well as that of some of the competing enzymes (myokinase and phosphatase) consists of a differential denaturation step with acetone. The lyophilized material of step II-(*ii*) is dissolved in 0.1 M acetate buffer, pH 6.0, at a concentration of 1 g/100 ml. To each 100 ml are added 33 ml acetone. The mixture is incubated at 37° for 30 min. A gel precipitate forms which is collected by centrifugation at 20,000 g for 30 min. This is washed twice with an acetone–acetate buffer mixture (1 : 3) and suspended in a small volume of 0.1 M tris buffer, pH 9.0, with the aid of a glass homogenizer. The suspension is dialyzed overnight in the cold against distilled water, during which time the gel goes into solution. It is stored in the frozen state. Alternatively, the gel may be washed successively with small aliquots of 0.1 M tris buffer, pH 9.0, to elute some of the enzyme activity. By this method all, or almost all, of the myokinase activity can be separated from the enzyme. These procedures are useful for removing contaminating enzymes, but frequently result in very low yields of phosphorylase.

(*iii*) For some purposes it is desirable to carry out a further acetone fractionation. The dialyzed solution from II-(*iii*), in 0.1 M tris, pH 8.0, is chilled to 0° and fractionated by the addition of acetone precooled to $-15°$ C. The temperature of the mixture should not be allowed to rise above $-2°$ when the acetone concentration exceeds 5%.

The enzyme preparations are not sufficiently reproducible to permit exact specifications for the fractionation. It is preferable to carry it out on an empirical basis, assaying each fraction for activity. The most active fractions usually appear between 40 and 55% (by volume) acetone.

The fraction appearing between 40 and 55% acetone is more suitable for the preparation of poly U or poly C than the original enzyme preparation.

Appendix Q

The Synthesis of Polyribonucleotides

Any of the enzyme preparations described in the Appendix for *M. lysodeikticus* may be used for the synthesis of poly A and poly I. However, for the synthesis of poly U and poly C, as well as of mixed polymers, the acetone fraction of the preceding Appendix is generally preferable, as it is less likely to be contaminated with nucleases. The quantity of enzyme used in the synthesis is established approximately by a routine assay of the enzyme activity and more exactly by trial polymer synthesis runs, especially for the synthesis of large quantities of poly A.

I. ROUTINE ENZYME ASSAY

A mixture of 0.5 ml of each of the following is incubated for 20 min at 37°: 1.0 M KCl, $8 \cdot 10^{-3}$ M MgCl$_2$, 0.1 M tris, pH 9.0, 0.4% ADP, and enzyme. The reaction is stopped by the addition of 1.0 ml of 10% perchloric acid and the sediment removed by centrifugation in a clinical centrifuge. The supernatant is transferred to a Klett-Summerson tube graduated at the 5-ml mark. To it are added 0.5 ml of the molybdate reagent (2.5% ammonium molybdate in 3 N H$_2$SO$_4$), and 0.2 ml of reducing agent (0.25% 1, 2, 4-aminonaphthol sulfonic acid), and the total volume is brought to 5 ml with water. After twenty minutes the Klett units are determined. A control is determined by adding the perchloric acid before the addition of the ADP. The difference in Klett readings is recorded as a measure of the enzyme activity.

II. POLYMER SYNTHESIS

The synthesis of polymer with any given enzyme preparation should first be carried out on a small scale. A convenient trial mixture for poly A consists of the following: 3 ml of 1% ADP brought to pH 8.0 with 1 N NaOH; 0.3 ml of 0.01 M MgCl$_2$; 0.8 ml of 0.5 M tris, pH 9.5; enzyme; and water, to make a total volume of 6 ml. The quantity of enzyme added is determined roughly by the following relationship:

$$\text{ml enzyme} = 20/\text{Klett units (as determined above)}$$

The quantity of enzyme should be adjusted, if necessary, to provide completion of the synthesis in 3 h. For the synthesis of poly U approximately five times as much enzyme is required. Mixed polymers also require more enzyme.

References p. 379

The synthesis may be followed by measuring the inorganic phosphate liberated. 0.1-ml aliquots are removed and placed in a Klett-Summerson tube. The Klett readings are determined as before. When the reading reaches 300 the synthesis is usually complete and should be stopped promptly. The reaction may also be followed by measuring the viscosity in an Ostwald viscometer. The synthesis is complete when the viscosity attains a plateau and should be stopped before there is any drop in viscosity.

Upon completion of the reaction, the mixture is chilled to 0–3° and made 10^{-3} M in versene (EDTA) and 0.5 M in KCl. In the case of poly U the pH should be adjusted to 7–8 by the dropwise addition of 1 M acetic acid. Enough ethanol is added until precipitation of polymer occurs. This usually requires 50–60% ethanol (by volume).

The precipitate is collected by centrifugation and redissolved in enough distilled water to give a roughly 1% solution. 3 M KCl is then added to give a 0.5 M solution. To this is added an equal volume of chloroform. The mixture is emulsified by vigorous shaking for 10 min. The emulsion is then broken by centrifugation and the upper aqueous phase pipetted off. The denatured protein collects as a gel at the interface. This step is repeated until the chloroform–water interface is perfectly clear. In the case of poly I, H_2O-saturated phenol is used in place of chloroform.

The polymer is precipitated by the addition of ethanol, as before, and is then washed successively with 80% ethanol, absolute ethanol, and absolute ether. It is then dried *in vacuo*.

REFERENCES

1 E. Kay, N. Simmons and A. Dounce, *J. Am. Chem. Soc.*, 74 (1952) 1724.
2 S. Zamenhof, G. Griboff and N. Marullo, *Biochim. et Biophys. Acta*, 13 (1954) 459.
3 R. Hotchkiss, in S. Colowick and O. Kaplan, *Methods in Enzymology*, New York, 3 (1957) 692.
4 A. Crestfield, K. Smith and F. Allen, *J. Biol. Chem.*, 216 (1955) 185.
5 U. Littauer and H. Eisenberg, *Biochim. et Biophys. Acta*, 32 (1959) 320.
6 J. Davidson and R. Smellie, *Biochem. J.*, 52 (1952) 594.
7 E. Chargaff, B. Magasanik, E. Vischer, C. Green, R. Doniger and D. Elson, *J. Biol. Chem.*, 186 (1950) 51.
8 P. Boulanger and J. Montreuil, *Bull. soc. chim. biol.*, 33 (1951) 784.
9 H. Loring, H. Bortner, L. Levy and M. Hammell, *J. Biol. Chem.*, 196 (1952) 807.
10 A. Marshak and H. Vogel, *J. Biol. Chem.*, 189 (1951) 597.
11 R. Markham and J. Smith, *Biochem. J.*, 49 (1951) 401.
12 A. Marshak and H. Vogel, *Federation Proc.*, 9 (1950) 85.
13 E. Vischer and E. Chargaff, *J. Biol. Chem.*, 176 (1948) 715.
14 C. Tamm, M. Hodes and E. Chargaff, *J. Biol. Chem.*, 195 (1952) 49.
15 W. Cohn, *Science*, 109 (1949) 377.
16 E. Volkin and C. Carter, *J. Am. Chem. Soc.*, 73 (1951) 1516.
17 W. Cohn, *J. Am. Chem. Soc.*, 72 (1950) 1471.
18 W. Cohn, in E. Chargaff and J. Davidson, *The Nucleic Acids*, Vol. 1, New York, 1955, p. 212.
19 W. Cohn and E. Volkin, *Nature*, 167 (1951) 483.
20 E. Peterson and H. Sober, *J. Am. Chem. Soc.*, 78 (1956) 751.
21 G. Tener, H. Khorana, R. Markham and E. Pol, *J. Am. Chem. Soc.*, 80 (1958) 6223.
22 *Pabst Laboratories Circular* OR -10, Jan. 1955.
23 R. Markham and J. Smith, *Biochem. J.*, 45 (1949) 294.
24 W. Macnutt, *Biochem. J.*, 50 (1952) 384.
25 W. Cohn and C. Carter, *J. Am. Chem. Soc.*, 72 (1950) 4273.
26 G. Wyatt, in E. Chargaff and J. Davidson, *The Nucleic Acids*, Vol. 1, New York, 1955, p. 243.
27 R. Markham and J. Smith, *Biochem. J.*, 49 (1951) 401.
28 L. Heppel, P. Ortiz and S. Ochoa, *J. Biol. Chem.*, 229 (1957) 679.
29 M. Grunberg-Manago, P. Ortiz and S. Ochoa, *Biochim. et Biophys. Acta*, 20 (1956) 269.
30 K. Lohmann and L. Jendrassik, *Biochem. Z.*, 178 (1926) 419.
31 R. Beers, *Arch. Biochem. Biophys.*, 75 (1958) 497.
32 C. Fiske and Y. Subbarow, *J. Biol. Chem.*, 66 (1925) 375.
33 H. Lineweaver and D. Burk, *J. Am. Chem. Soc.*, 56 (1934) 658.
34 S. Mii and S. Ochoa, *Biochim. et Biophys. Acta*, 26 (1957) 445.
35 R. Beers, *Biochem. J.*, 66 (1957) 686.
36 U. Littauer and A. Kornberg, *J. Biol. Chem.*, 226 (1957) 1077.
37 D. Hendley and R. Beers, *J. Biol. Chem.*, in the press.
38 W. Mejbaum, *Z. Physiol. Chem.*, 258 (1939) 117.
39 I. Lehman, M. Bessman, E. Simms and A. Kornberg, *J. Biol. Chem.*, 233 (1958) 163.
40 R. Willstatter and H. Kraut, *Ber. deut. chem. Ges.*, 56 (1923) 1117.
41 S. Ochoa, personal communication.

Author Index

Subject Index

acetic anhydride, acetylation, 45
α-acetobromoglucose, 36
acridine orange, complex, effect of pH, ionic strength, temperature, 312
—, complex with poly A, effect of pretreatment with formaldehyde, 313
—, complex with polynucleotides, spectral changes, 312
—, complex I with polynucleotides, 311
—, complex I with polynucleotides, role of nearest neighbor interaction, 317
—, complex II formation, absorption spectrum, 315
—, complex II with polynucleotides, 315
—, differentiation of DNA and RNA in cells, 309
—, interaction, with poly C, 312
—, —, with poly I, 312
—, —, with thermally denatured DNA, 314
—, reaction with DNA and RNA in cells, differentiation, 318
—, spectral changes accompanying binding the poly A, 310
acridine orange–DNA complex, green fluorescence, 310
acridine orange–RNA complex, red fluorescence, 310
acriflavine binding, by DNA, 307
—, by polynucleotides, quenching of fluorescence, 307
activation of amino acids, 13
adenine, 21
—, chemical synthesis, 23
—, deamination, 24
—, hydrogen bonds, 187
—, R_F value, 360
—, solid state X-ray diffraction studies, 29
—, structure, 23, 31
—, triphosphate, see ATP
adenine–thymine pairing in DNA, 250
adenosine, amino form, 29
—, β-configuration, 36
—, deamination by nitrous acid, 34
—, diphosphate, see ADP
—, diphosphate, chemical synthesis, 49, 51, 52
—, imino form, 29
—, 2′,3′-isopropylidine derivatives, 36
—, 2′,3′-O-isopropylidine derivative, 45
—, R_F value, 360
—, synthesis, 36
—, triphosphate, chemical synthesis, 50, 51, 52
—, ultraviolet absorption spectrum, 34

adenosine-5′-benzyl phosphate, 49
—, hydrolysis by purified snake venom phosphodiesterase, 67
adenosine-5′-monophosphate, ultraviolet absorption, 155
adenosine-2′-phosphate, 40, 72
adenosine-3′-phosphate, 40, 72
adenosine-5′-phosphate, chemical synthesis, 46
adenosine-5′-phosphoramidate, 52
adenosine-5′-tribenzyl pyrophosphate, 49
adenylic a and b, 72
adenylic acid a, chemical synthesis, 40
—, synthesis, 39
adenylic acid b, synthesis, 39
adenylic acid, correlation of pK's densities, 40
—, hydrolysis of acidic form of sulfonic acid resin, 40
—, isomers, 4
2′-adenylic acid, ion exchange chromatography, 357
3′-adenylic acid, ion exchange chromatography, 357
adenylyl-5′,3′-adenylyl-5′,3′-adenosine-5′-phosphate, primer, 111
adenylyl-3′,5′-adenylyl-3′,5′-uridine-3′-phosphate, activator and polymerization of ADP and UDP, 112
adenylyl-2′,5′-uridine, chemical synthesis, 58
adenylyl-5′,3′-uridine-5′-phosphate, chemical synthesis, 58
ADP, 11
—, R_F value, 361
A. faecalis, 12
alkaline hydrolysis of RNA, mechanism of action, 42
Amberlite-120, 355
Amberlite-IRA-400, 355
Amberlite-IRC-50, 355
amino acid incorporation into microsomal protein, role of soluble RNA, 334
2-aminoacridine, spectral changes of RNA and DNA complexes, 308
3-aminoacridine, spectral changes of RNA and DNA complexes, 308
9-aminoacridine, spectral changes of RNA and DNA complexes, 308
6-amino,2,8-dichloropurine, 23
4-amino,2,6-dichloropyrimidine, 32
—, bonds, 33
—, bond angles, 33
—, σ + π bonds, 33
—, resonance structure, 33